Correlations

Proceedings of ANPA 23

K. G. Bowden, *Editor*

The Alternative Natural Philosophy Association

Correlations: Proceedings of ANPA 23/Keith G. Bowden, *Editor*

ISBN 0 9526215 8 4

published by ANPA c/o Dr. Keith G. Bowden,
139 Sandringham Rd, Barking,
Essex IG11 9AH, UK

Contents

Rafael D. Sorkin et al
General Covariance and the "Problem of Time" in a Discrete Cosmology   1

Brian D. Koberlein
Extended Causality as a Model of Discrete Gravity   18

Ioannis Raptis
Manifold Reasons against the Manifold   24

Ted Bastin and C. W. Kilmister
Algebraic Approaches to the Particle Concept   43

A. M. Deakin
Can we run Dirac's Argument backwards?   59

Clive Kilmister
The Einstein Velocity Relation, g-groups and the CH   101

B. J. Hiley
Towards a Dynamics of Moments: The Role of Algebraic Deformation and Inequivalent Vacuum States   104

Louis H. Kauffman and Samuel J. Lomonaco Jr.
Comparing Quantum Entangle ment and Topological Entanglement   135

Peter Rowlands and J. P. Cullerne
Symmetry Breaking as a Consequence of the Dirac Algebra
161

Peter Rowlands, J. P. Cullerne and Brian D. Koberlein
A Comparison between two versions of the Dirac Algebra
135

Peter Rowlands and J. P. Cullerne
Charge Accommodation and the Combinatorial Hierarchy
197

Stephen Wood
The Holographic Principle in Biological Development and Quantum Physics   200

Peter Marcer, Edgar Mitchell and Walter Schempp
Self-reference, the Dimensionality and Scale of Quantum Mechanical Effects, Critical Phenomena and Qualia   247

William M. Honig
Deriving Planck's Constant from: Its Dimensional Peculiarities, Realistic Fluid Models and Larmor's Radiation Law   269

Ted Bastin, H. Pierre Noyes, John Amson and Clive W. Kilmister
On the Physical Interpretation and the Mathematical Structure of the Combinatorial Hierarchy   302

ANPA Statement of Purpose and Organisation   346

Editorial

PI: The only part... that I really liked was the question of how many molecules are needed to make up a proton. This is a REALLY HARD QUESTION and will keep us busy for years!

SB: Actually, it depends purely on the size of the proton constructor!

PI: But you probably fail to take into account the consequence of the Dyson-Noyes phenomenon in the presence of the Schroeder-Bernstein Theorem and certain transfinite arguments of G. Cantor. These together with certain as yet undiscovered results of M(GM) Theory show that any proton constructor necessarily needs an uncountable number of molecules, thereby creating an uncertainty redeemable only through the use of hard theorems in higher Category Theory. This plugs a non-existent gap in the hypothesis of hard science.

SB: Now, now, Professor Pi. You know, I am sure, that the Genetically Modified version of M-Theory, in its undiscovered state, has no implications for the manufacture of proton constructors below the Dyson-Noyes bound of 137 molecules. Above the bound, according to Cohen forcing, and through definite Moore-Postnikov levels, the size of the proton constructor is all that counts.

PI: Yes, yes precisely. All that counts is the transfinite. You will grasp this in any forced instant of non-standard time...

Prof. Sarah Bellectomice, TPRU, Birkbeck College, London,
Prof. E. I. Pi, Professor of Ancient Renormalizations, Hard Science
University, ND, USA, July 2001

Reference

1. *Bellectomice, S,* "The Learning of Equilibrium Behavior in Cerebellectomized Lurcher Mutant Mice" in *Studies in Differential Roles of the Cerebral Cortex and Deep Cerebral Nuclei,* Imperial College, London 2001.

Thanks are due once again to David and Patrick in the Print Unit at SOAS for producing this volume

ANPA Proceedings Editorial Policy

ANPA has been criticised in the past - in particular by members of its own Advisory Board - for having no formal editorial policy for its Proceedings. This has been balanced by a feeling within ANPA that we should keep ourselves open to all viewpoints. In the last few years as editor I have tried to tighten things up in such a way as I felt would satisfy our critics whilst not compromising our own position. This has been partially successful although for some time I have felt that it is time that there was a formally stated policy. The following has been approved by the Executive Council, although it is open to feedback from all. By "the editor" is meant the Editor or (an) appropriate nominated Referee(s) (note the capital R!)

1. The paper should make a new and original contribution to the fields of ANPA's interest. Survey papers are acceptable.

2. The default use of language for submitted papers in Physics {and Philosophy of Physics}[*] should be the common language of Physics as usually understood by Physicists {and, in particular, by Philosophers of Physics}[*]. Any other use of language should be carefully explained at the start of the paper and all appropriate definitions included there.
{[*] added by KGB}

3. The editor should be satisfied that the paper is *presented* in such a way that the majority of the readership will understand the author's intentions. In particular *it should be clear* that the author has a correct understanding of the subject matter.

4. "Verbatim" reports will be accepted subject to the above three conditions only, regardless of whether the final draft is an accurate rendition of what was originally said. Other such reports are better submitted to the Newsletter.

5. Theories of any nature are acceptable material, provided they are compatible with the known facts, and provided they are deemed to be of interest to the readership. Theories of alternative, imaginary worlds are also acceptable, provided their nature is made clear.

ANPA Proceedings Notes for Authors

I would like to try to continue conformity of *style* for future issues of the Proceedings. Ideally I would like contributions to be submitted in International Journal of General Systems format (I have some copies of their Notes for Authors) or similar - **LOOK AT MY PAPER IN THE LAST ISSUE OF THE PROCEEDINGS FOR AN EXAMPLE.**

At least, Times Roman, 12 point, *single sided, two copies (HARD COPY),* is preferred. **10 point is TOO SMALL to be reduced to A5; 14 point is better for short papers.** Main heading 20 point capitalised and centred, other headings 16 point capitalised to the left. Author's name(s) capitalised and centred. Address italicised and centred. No underlining. At least a one inch bottom margin for footers; page numbers NOT top centre. *Only copy in good English will be considered, and remember, this is a formal Proceedings.* **Remember also to include your name (surprising how many people omit this!), affiliation and full address, email address and the version number (even if it is 1.0) or date of the draft, centred below the main heading.** I often get sent more than one version of a paper and invariably mix them up! Send copy **to *KEITH BOWDEN, 139 SANDRINGHAM RD, BARKING, ESSEX IG11 9AH.***

The copy date for the ANPA2002 Proceedings is January 1st 2003. The issue will go to print on April 1st 2003. This will be adhered to rigidly this year.

Keith Bowden,
Theoretical Physics Research Unit,
Birkbeck College,
Malet St,
London WC1E 7HX, UK.

k.bowden@physics.bbk.ac.uk

Tel: 0208-594-5064

FOR EDITORIAL ADDRESS SEE THE PENULTIMATE PARAGRAPH

gr-qc/yymmnnn
SU–GP–01/12–1

General Covariance and the "Problem of Time" in a Discrete Cosmology *

Graham Brightwell
Mathematics Department, London School of Economics

H. Fay Dowker
Physics Department, Queen Mary College, University of London

Raquel S. García
Physics Department, Imperial College, London

Joe Henson
Physics Department, Queen Mary College, University of London

Rafael D. Sorkin
Physics Department, Queen Mary College, University of London
and
Department of Physics, Syracuse University

Abstract

Identifying an appropriate set of "observables" is a nontrivial task for most approaches to quantum gravity. We describe how it may be accomplished in the context of a recently proposed family of stochastic (but classical) dynamical laws for causal sets. The underlying idea should work equally well in the quantum case.

1. Introduction

Perhaps I should begin by clarifying what I *don't* mean by the quoted phrase "problem of time" in my title. In the canonical quantization of gravity, as it is normally understood (and sought) the fundamental object of attention is not spacetime but space alone

---

*   To appear in the proceedings of the Alternative Natural Philosophy Association meeting, held August 16-21, 2001, Cambridge, England. This is the slightly extended text of a talk presented at the meeting by R.D.S. and based on joint work of the authors.

(corresponding to something like a Cauchy surface in spacetime) and anyone following this approach is sooner or later faced with the problem of *recovering time* from a frozen formalism (as it's sometimes called) from which time as such is absent. The problem of time *in this sense* is, I believe, insoluble and it will not be the subject of this talk. (See [1] [2].) Indeed, since I will be presupposing that the deep structure of spacetime is that of a *causal set*, temporality will be built in at the most fundamental level, and there will be no need to "recover" it, just as there would be no need to "recover time" in a continuum path integral approach to quantum gravity based on the Lorentzian manifold as the fundamental structure. *

Nevertheless, there still remain vital interpretational issues related to the generally covariant nature of gravity that sometimes are also called "problems of time", † issues that one can point to by asking (in the language of one version of quantum mechanics) "What are the observables of quantum gravity?". For my part, I'd prefer a reference to "be-ables" rather than "observe-ables", but the question I will be addressing in this talk is best posed without using either word. Rather we can simply ask "To what questions (about the causal set) can the dynamics give answers?"

Within the (stochastic but still classical) dynamical framework we will be considering, a *question* (in logicians' language a "predicate") corresponds to a collection of causal sets (the predicate's "extension") and its answer is not a simple yes or no, but the *probability* that the answer will be yes, which mathematically is the *measure* of the corresponding collection. Thus, we will be asking which classes of causal sets (the "histories" of the theory) are *measurable* in a way compatible with general covariance. I will propose a very definite answer to this question that will follow naturally from the way the dynamics will be defined as a stochastic process. Not all the resulting measurable classes (or their associated predicates) will obviously possess an accessible physical meaning, but a certain

---

* Not that, in saying this, I mean to downplay the need to explain why the dynamics tends to favor that small minority of causal sets which resemble Lorentzian manifolds over the multitude of those which don't.

† Observe in this connection that it is the diffeomorphism invariance of the gravitational Lagrangian (or rather action-integral) which is responsible for the "frozen" character of the corresponding canonical formalism

subset will (those based on "stems"). Fortunately this subset is very big, and it seems quite possible that nothing of interest — or even nothing at all — remains outside of it. After describing a precise conjecture to this effect, I will conclude by asking whether a proof of the conjecture would settle all the interpretational issues, or whether a logically independent notion of "conditional probability" is also needed. Before I can present these thoughts more fully, however, some review is needed of the causal set idea itself.

2. A Brief review of causal set theory

The causal set hypothesis states that the deep structure of spacetime is that of a discrete partial order, and that, consequently, "quantum gravity" can be realized only as a quantum theory of causal sets ("causets" for short). To say what a causet is structurally is easy: it's a locally finite partial order; but to specify fully the meaning of the words "quantum theory of causets" is much harder. It seems plausible that the dynamics of such a theory (its "laws of motion" if you will) would be specified mathematically in terms of a "decoherence functional" [3] or "quantum measure" [4] but we are only beginning to understand the principles that might lead us to the correct one. [b] On the other hand, we do have a family of *classical* dynamical laws derived from well defined general principles including a principle of "discrete general covariance" and a certain principle of "Bell causality". To the extent that these principles carry over to the quantal case, we are thus a considerable way along the road to a quantum dynamics for causets. Moreover, the projected quantum dynamics shares enough attributes with the existing classical one that it seems worthwhile to consult the latter for indications of what we can expect from its quantum generalization.

In this way, it has been possible to make some guesses and heuristic predictions which have begun to bring the theory into contact with phenomenology. The list of these must include first of all the anticipation [5] [2] [6] of time-dependent fluctuations in the cosmological constant whose predicted current magnitude of 10^{-120} in natural units has turned

---

[b] As I am using it, the term "decoherence functional" denotes no more than a certain type of mathematical object, formally defined by axioms of bi-additivity, etc. In particular, I do not mean to add any requirement that it actually "decohere" in the sense of being diagonal on any partition of the "sample space" Ω to be defined below.

out to be in good accord with recent observations. Second [7] there exists a (purely kinematical) counting of "horizon quanta" whose number is (both in order of magnitude and proportionality to horizon area) compatible with the Bekenstein-Hawking formula for both equilibrium *and* nonequilibrium examples of black holes. We also have an indication [8] of how some of the notorious large numbers of cosmology might be explained, as well as a framework [9] within which Hawking radiation can be addressed. (In the way of practical tools there also exists an extensive library [10] of Lisp functions designed for working with causets, i.e. basically with finite ordered sets or "posets".)

In the following, however, I wish to concentrate not on the phenomenological aspects of the theory but on interpretational ones, more specifically on the question already raised of which physically meaningful (i.e. generally covariant) predicates correspond to classes of causets to which the dynamics can assign a measure (probability). To this end, I will have to describe more precisely the family of stochastic dynamical laws on which these considerations will be based.

3. The classical (stochastic) dynamics of sequential growth and its formal definition as a stochastic process

As indicated by the title of this talk, we will work within a "cosmological" setting, in the sense that the probabilities in question will pertain to the causet as a whole, not just to some part of it. This seems to be necessary, as it is difficult to imagine how any generally covariant procedure could single out a definite "subregion" of the universe in an *a priori* manner. A cosmological standpoint is also appropriate formally, since the dynamical laws we will be using conceive of the "time-development" of the causet as a process of sequential growth in which elements appear ("are born") one by one; and, as formulated, these laws make sense only if there is a genuine "beginning condition" in which there are no elements at all (or at most a finite number).

The family of dynamical laws in question is described in detail in [11], where it is derived as the unique (generic) solution of certain conditions of "internal temporality", "Bell causality" and "discrete general covariance". For present purposes, it is enough to know that the resulting scheme describes a stochastic birth process which, "at stage n", yields a poset $\widetilde{C}_n$ of n elements, within which the most recently born element is maximal.

If one employs a genealogical language in which "$x \prec y$" can be read as "x is an ancestor of y", then the nth element (counting from 0) must at birth "choose" its ancestors from the elements of $\widetilde{C}_n$, and for consistency it must choose a subset S with the property that $x \prec y \in S \Rightarrow x \in S$. (Every ancestor of one of my ancestors is also my ancestor.) Such a subset S (which is necessarily finite) will be called a *stem*. The dynamics is then determined fully by giving the *transition probabilities* governing each such choice of $S \subseteq \widetilde{C}_n$. (To understand how a set of probabilities can determine a dynamics, think of a random walk. The "law of motion" of the walker is specified by giving, for each possible time and location, the probability of taking, say, a step to the right, a step to the left, or just staying put.)

We can formalize this scheme by introducing for each integer $n = 0, 1, 2, \cdots$ the set $\widetilde{\Omega}(n)$ of *labeled* causets of n elements. By definition, a member of $\widetilde{\Omega}(n)$ is thus a set $\widetilde{C}_n$ with cardinality n carrying a relation $\prec$ such that $x \prec y \prec z \Rightarrow x \prec z$ (transitivity), and $x \not\prec x$ (irreflexivity), and whose elements are labeled by integers $0, 1, \cdots, n-1$ that record their order of birth. Moreover this labeling is *natural* in the sense that $x \prec y \Rightarrow l(x) < l(y)$, $l(x)$ being the label of x. Each birth of a new element occasions one of the allowed transitions from $\widetilde{\Omega}(n)$ to $\widetilde{\Omega}(n+1)$ and occurs with a specified conditional probability τ (which turns out to depend only on a pair of simple invariants of the ancestor set $S \subseteq \widetilde{C}_n$ of the newborn).

Mathematically, however, such a set of transition probabilities τ does not yet qualify as a stochastic process, and for good reason. In the presence of fundamental randomness, no certain predictions are possible. Instead, the "laws of motion" can at best give probabilistic answers to questions about what the object under study (causet, random walker, etc.) will do, answers of the form "Yes, with probability p", where $p \in [0,1]$. For example, in the case of a random walk on the integers, one might ask "Will the walker ever return to the origin?". Since the return, if it occurs at all, might be postponed to an arbitrarily late time, its probability p can be given meaning only in terms of a limiting process. For this particular question, however, there exists an obvious definition of p as the limit of an increasing sequence of probabilities, each of which can be computed from a finite number of elementary transition probabilities τ. On the other hand, for a question like "Will the sequence of locations of the walker form an irrational decimal fraction when reduced modulo ten?", it is not immediately clear whether any meaningful probabilistic answer can be given at all on the basis of the τ.

In order to arrive at a definite theory, then, one needs to specify the set of questions that the theory can answer and for each one of them, explain how in principle, the "yes" probability can be computed. Fortunately, there exists a standard construction which will accomplish both these tasks starting from any consistent set of transition probabilities τ. The result of this construction is a triad consisting of a *sample space* Ω, a σ-*algebra* $\mathcal{R}$ on Ω, and a *probability measure* μ with domain $\mathcal{R}$. In relation to the above two tasks, each member Q of $\mathcal{R}$ corresponds to one of the answerable questions and its measure $p = \mu(Q)$ is the answer. Such a triad constitutes what one means mathematically by a "stochastic process", the transition probabilities τ serve only as raw material for its construction. (That $\mathcal{R}$ is a σ-algebra on Ω means that it is a family of subsets of Ω closed under complementation and countable intersection. That μ is a probability measure with domain $\mathcal{R}$ means that it takes members of $\mathcal{R}$ to non-negative real numbers and is σ-additive, with $\mu(\Omega) = 1$. Finally, σ-additivity means that μ assigns to the union of a countable collection of mutually disjoint sets in its domain the sum of the measures it assigns to the individual sets.)

In the case at hand, the sample space is the set $\widetilde{\Omega} = \widetilde{\Omega}(\infty)$ of *completed labeled causets* these being the infinite causets that would result if the birth process were made to "run to completion". (I'll use a tilde to indicate labeling. Notice that a completed causet, though infinite, is still locally finite. * Indeed it is past-finite in the sense that no element has more than a finite number of ancestors.) The dynamics is then given by a probability measure $\widetilde{\mu}$ constructed from the τ whose domain $\widetilde{\mathcal{R}}$ is a σ-algebra which I will specify more fully in a moment. For future use, we will need in addition to $\widetilde{\Omega}$ the corresponding space Ω of completed *unlabeled* causets, whose members can also be viewed in an obvious manner as equivalence classes within $\widetilde{\Omega}$.

(To be pedantically precise, one should perhaps speak of the members of Ω and $\widetilde{\Omega}$ not as single causets but as isomorphism equivalence classes of them — what one might call "abstract causets".)

At first hearing, calling a probability measure a dynamical law might sound strange, but in fact, once we have the measure $\widetilde{\mu}$ we can say everything of a predictive nature

---

* Local finiteness, a formal realization of the concept of discreteness, is the property that the *order interval*, $\{x | a \prec x \prec b\}$, is finite for all elements a and b.

that it is possible to say *a priori* about the behavior of the causet C. For example, one might ask "Will the universe recollapse?" (a question analogous to our earlier question of whether the random walker would return to the origin). Mathematically, this is asking whether C will develop a "post", defined as an element whose ancestors and descendants taken together exhaust the remainder of C. Let $A \subseteq \widetilde{\Omega}$ be the set of all completed labeled causets having posts.[†] Then our question is equivalent to asking whether $C \in A$, and the answer is "yes with probability $\widetilde{\mu}(A)$." It is thus $\widetilde{\mu}$ that expresses the "laws of motion" (or better "laws of growth") that constitute our stochastic dynamics: its domain $\widetilde{\mathcal{R}}$ tells us which questions the laws can answer, and its values $\widetilde{\mu}(A)$ tell us what the answers are.

Of course, this sketch of how a sequential growth model is built up is incomplete, because I haven't explained the construction that leads from the transition probabilities τ to the measure $\widetilde{\mu}$. The full details of this construction can be found in many textbooks of probability theory (e.g. [12]), but for present purposes, all we really need to know is how the domain $\widetilde{\mathcal{R}}$ of $\widetilde{\mu}$ is obtained. To each finite causet $\widetilde{S} \in \widetilde{\Omega}(n)$ one can associate the so called "cylinder set" comprising all those $\widetilde{C} \in \widetilde{\Omega}$ whose first n elements (those labeled $0 \cdots n-1$) form an isomorphic copy of $\widetilde{S}$; and $\widetilde{\mathcal{R}}$ is then the smallest σ-algebra containing all these cylinder sets. More constructively, $\widetilde{\mathcal{R}}$ is the collection of all subsets of $\widetilde{\Omega}$ which can be built up from the cylinder sets by a countable process involving union, intersection and complementation.[♭]

Finally, what about the transition probabilities τ themselves, on which the whole construction is based? Modulo certain non-generic solutions, the possibilities for the τ have been classified in [11], the main conclusion being that τ generically takes the form $\tau = \lambda(\varpi, m)/\lambda(n, 0)$ where, for the potential transition in question, ϖ is the number of ancestors of the new element, m the number of its "parents", and n the number of elements present before the birth, and where $\lambda(\varpi, m)$ is given by the formula $\sum_k \binom{\varpi - m}{k - m} t_k$ with the

---

[†] One can show that $A \in \widetilde{\mathcal{R}}$, so that $\widetilde{\mu}(A)$ is defined.

[♭] A slightly bigger σ-algebra than $\widetilde{\mathcal{R}}$ can be obtained by adjoining the sets of $\widetilde{\mu}$-measure zero, but what these sets are will depend in general on the specific dynamical law, as determined, e.g., by a choice of the parameters t_n of [11].

t_k being the free parameters or "coupling constants" of the theory. (For more details see [11] or [13].)

4. Two meanings of general covariance

It might seem strange that our growth law has been expressed in terms of *labeled* causets. After all, labels in this discrete setting are the analogs of coordinates in the continuum, and the first lesson of general relativity is precisely that such arbitrary identifiers must be regarded as physically meaningless: the elements of spacetime — or of the causet — have individuality only to the extent that they acquire it from the pattern of their relations to the other elements. It is therefore natural to introduce a principle of "discrete general covariance" according to which "the labels are physically meaningless".

But why have labels at all then? For causets, the reason is that we don't know otherwise how to formulate the idea of sequential growth, or the condition thereon of Bell causality, which plays a crucial role in deriving the dynamics [11]. Ideally perhaps, one would formulate the theory so that labels never entered, but so far, no one knows how to do this — anymore than one knows how to formulate general relativity without introducing extra gauge degrees of freedom that then have to be canceled against the diffeomorphism invariance.

Given the dynamics as we *can* formulate it, discrete general covariance plays a double role. On one hand it serves to limit the possible choices of the *transition probabilities* in such a way that the labels drop out of certain "net probabilities", a condition made precise in [11]. This is meant to be the analog of requiring the gravitational action-integral S to be invariant under diffeomorphisms (whence, in virtue of the further assumption of locality, it must be the integral of a local scalar concomitant of the metric). On the other hand, general covariance limits the *questions* one can meaningfully ask about the causet (cf. Einstein's "hole argument" [14]). It is this second limitation that is related to the "problem of time", and it is only this aspect of discrete general covariance that I am addressing in the present talk.

Just as in the continuum the demand of diffeomorphism-invariance makes it harder to formulate meaningful statements,* so also for causets the demand of discrete general

---

* Think, for example, of the statement that light slows down when passing near the sun.

covariance has the same consequence, bringing with it the risk that, even if we succeed in characterizing the covariant questions in abstract formal terms, we may never know what they mean in a physically useful way. I believe that a similar issue will arise in every approach to quantum gravity, discrete or continuous (unless of course general covariance is renounced). [†] However, it seems fair to say that both the nature of the difficulty and the manner of its proposed resolution will appear with special clarity in the context of causal sets, whose discreteness removes many of the technical difficulties that tend to obscure the underlying physical issues in the continuum.

5. What are the covariant questions?

Given the formal developments of Section 4, it is not hard to see which members of $\widetilde{\mathcal{R}}$ express covariant predicates, and from a dynamical point of view, these are the only covariant predicates of interest.

Before describing them, let me illustrate the issue we face with the question, "Which (unlabeled) causet is formed by the first n elements to be born?". In effect, we are asking for the probability distribution induced by our measure $\widetilde{\mu}$ on the space $\Omega(n)$ of unlabeled n-orders, but, although such a distribution can be computed, it has no obvious meaning because a question like "Do the first three elements of C form a 3-chain [♭]?" has in general different answers depending on what order of birth you impute to the elements of C. Thus if we were to divide the set $\widetilde{\Omega}$ into two parts, the "yes" part composed of those $\widetilde{C} \in \widetilde{\Omega}$ whose first 3 elements make up a chain, and the "no" part composed of those $\widetilde{C}$ whose first 3 elements make up one of the other four 3-orders, then some members of the "yes" set would be isomorphic to members of the "no" set.

[†] In the case of canonical quantum gravity, this issue *is* the problem of time. There, covariance means commuting with the constraints, and the problem is how to interpret quantities which do so in any recognizable spacetime language. For an attempt in string theory to grapple with similar issues see [15].

[♭] A (finite) chain is a causet whose elements can be arranged so that each is an ancestor of the next. For a 3-chain, we have three elements a, b, and c such that $a \prec b \prec c$.

We see now what it means for a subset of $A \subseteq \widetilde{\Omega}$ to be covariant: it cannot contain any labeled completed causet $\widetilde{C}$ without containing at the same time all those $\widetilde{C}'$ isomorphic to $\widetilde{C}$ (i.e. differing only in their labelings). To be measurable as well as covariant, A must also belong to $\widetilde{\mathcal{R}}$. Let $\mathcal{R}$ be the collection of all such sets: $A \in \mathcal{R} \Longleftrightarrow A \in \widetilde{\mathcal{R}}$ and $\forall \widetilde{C}_1 \simeq \widetilde{C}_2 \in \widetilde{\Omega}, \widetilde{C}_1 \in A \Rightarrow \widetilde{C}_2 \in A$. It is not hard to see that $\mathcal{R}$ is a sub-σ-algebra of $\widetilde{\mathcal{R}}$, whence the restriction of $\widetilde{\mu}$ to $\mathcal{R}$ is a measure μ on the space Ω of unlabeled completed causets. [*] It is this measure μ that provides the answers to all the covariant questions for which the dynamics has answers. [†] But what do these questions signify physically?

6. Stem sets and a conjecture

Among the questions belonging to $\mathcal{R}$ there are some which do have a clear significance. Let $S \in \Omega(n)$ be any finite unlabeled causet and let $R(S) \subseteq \Omega$ be the "stem set", $\{C \in \Omega | C \text{ admits } S \text{ as a stem}\}$. (Thus $R(S)$ comprises those unlabeled completed causets with the property that, with respect to some natural labeling, the first n elements form a causet isomorphic to S.) Since (as one can prove) $R(S)$ is measurable, it belongs to $\mathcal{R}$. For this particular element of $\mathcal{R}$, the meaning of the corresponding causet question is evident: "Does the causet possess S as a stem?". [♭] Equally evident is the significance of any question built up as a logical combination of stem-questions of this sort. To such compound stem-questions belong members of $\mathcal{R}$ built up from stem-sets $R(S)$ using union, intersection and complementation (corresponding to the logical operators 'or', 'and' and 'not'). If all the members of $\mathcal{R}$ were of this type, we would not only have succeeded in

---

[*] As just defined, an element $A \in \mathcal{R}$ is a subset of $\widetilde{\Omega}$. However, because it is re-labeling invariant, it can also be regarded as a subset of Ω, an equivalence which I will henceforth utilize without explicit mention.

[†] Notice the distinction that arises here between a subset of $\widetilde{\Omega}$ that fails to belong to $\mathcal{R}$ and one that fails even to be covariant (one that cannot be regarded as a subset of Ω). The former corresponds to a question that the dynamics can't answer, the latter to a question that is without any physical meaning at all.

[♭] Here is a simple example. Let Λ be the 3-element causet given by $a \prec c$, $b \prec c$, let V be its dual (given by $a \succ c$, $b \succ c$), and let S be the 2-chain (given by $a \prec b$). Then V possesses S as a stem, while Λ does not.

characterizing the dynamically meaningful covariant questions at a formal level, but we would have understood their physical significance as well. * The following conjecture asserts that, to all intents and purposes, this is the case.

Conjecture The "stem-sets" $R(S)$ generate [†] the σ-algebra $\mathcal{R}$ up to sets of measure zero.

Here the technical qualification about sets of measure zero complicates the statement of the conjecture but does not essentially weaken it. Some such qualification is required, unfortunately, because one can exhibit counterexamples to the unqualified conjecture. Notice, once again, that the words "measure zero" have meaning only with respect to some choice of stochastic dynamical law, since different choices correspond to different measures μ which, in general will possess different families of measure-zero sets. Thus, a more complete phrasing of the conjecture would read "For every choice of sequential growth model, the stem-sets $R(S)$ generate $\mathcal{R}$ up to sets of measure zero." Here a sequential growth model is any member of the "generic" family described briefly in Section 3 above (and at length in [11]), and more generally any solution of the conditions of Bell causality, etc. delineated in [11].

The conjecture asserts that $\mathcal{R}_S = \mathcal{R}$, where $\mathcal{R}_S$ is the subalgebra of $\mathcal{R}$ generated by the stem-sets $R(S)$. In a moment, I'll present some evidence in favor of this equality, but first I'd like to stress that, even if $\mathcal{R}_S$ fails to exhaust $\mathcal{R}$, it still supplies us with a large store of predicates whose physical significance is transparent, and this store probably suffices for practical purposes since one's experience so far indicates that all predicates of interest belong to it, either outright or up to a set of measure zero. For example, the predicate "contains a post" belongs to $\mathcal{R}_S$.

---

* This is not yet their *phenomenological* meaning, of course. To get the phenomenological significance (in cases where there is one) one must translate between the combinatorial language proper to the causet and the geometrical and field-theoretic language of macroscopic physics.

[†] A family $\mathcal{F}$ of subsets is said to *generate* a σ-algebra $\mathcal{A}$ if $\mathcal{A}$ is the smallest σ-algebra containing all the members of $\mathcal{F}$. For example, the cylinder sets introduced above generate the σ-algebra $\widetilde{\mathcal{R}}$.

Now the intuitive import of our conjecture is that everything we need to say about a causet can be phrased in terms of its stems. If this is so, then we'd expect at least that a specification of the full set of stems of a given causet $C \in \Omega$ would suffice to characterize C uniquely. As a matter of fact, not all causets enjoy this feature, but the exceptions are rare enough that the probability of one of them being produced by a sequential growth process is zero. (Employing the jargon of probability theory, we may say that a causet C produced by one of the sequential growth processes is *almost surely* characterized by its stems.) That this is so speaks in favor of the conjecture but, as far a I know, is not enough to demonstrate it fully. Its proof, in any case, can be given in three steps as follows [16].

(a) If $C \in \Omega$ *fails* to be characterized by its stems then it must contain an infinite number of copies of some stem S.

(b) If $C \in \Omega$ contains an infinite number of copies of the same stem S then it must contain an infinite antichain (indeed an infinite level).

(c) The probability is zero that a C produced by one of the classical sequential growth models will contain an infinite level, or indeed any infinite antichain.

Strictly speaking, statement (c) has been proven only for the models described above which are parameterized by the "coupling constants" $t_0, t_1, t_2, \cdots$, but these are generic in the sense that they include all solutions for which no transition probability τ vanishes [11]. Moreover (c) fails for the special case where $t_n = 0$ for all $n \geq 2$. But this exception does not affect the main conclusion, because if t_0 is the only nonzero t_n then C is almost surely an infinite antichain, while if t_0 and t_1 are both nonzero then C is almost surely an infinite number of copies of the tree in which each element has an infinite number of children; and both these causets are also characterized by their stems.

To get a feel for what these results mean, consider the causet C' consisting of an infinite number of unrelated copies of the infinite chain $e_0 \prec e_1 \prec e_2 \prec \cdots$. This causet is *not* characterized by its stems, because, e.g., the causet C'' made from C' by adjoining a single n-chain ($1 \leq n < \infty$) has precisely the same stems as C'. (A causet S is such a stem iff it is the sum of a finite number of finite chains.) The proof outlined above then tells us that C' and C'' are infinitely unlikely to "grow" in any of the models with $t_2 > 0$.

7. Conclusion and some further questions

General covariance in classical gravity is a two-edged sword. On one hand it is both philosophically satisfying (at least to those of us who favor "relational" or "dialectical" theories) and heuristically fruitful for the way in which it limits the possible equations of motion. On the other hand it forces the consequent formalism farther from experience, because it renders meaningless all statements which are not, at least implicitly, of a global character. (In this sense, the context for a generally covariant theory is always cosmological in scope.) The meaningful statements become thereby both harder to formulate and harder to interpret ("problem of time").

In the case of (classical) general relativity, these difficulties are somewhat mitigated by the theory's determinism, which means that predictions can effectively be made and verified locally. Such is not the case, however, in an indeterministic theory, where the dynamics must presumably be expressed via relations of a probabilistic character among covariant statements whose global character is much harder to circumvent. The problem of characterizing and interpreting such statements must therefore arise in virtually every approach to quantum gravity, including of course the causet approach. [b]

But the classical sequential growth models of causet dynamics are also indeterministic, and consequently the same problems arise for them. These models, which are intended primarily as a (practical and conceptual) stepping stone to the quantum theory of causets, offer a precisely defined schema within which the interpretational difficulties deriving from general covariance can be confronted. And within this setting, we have largely resolved them: the dynamically meaningful predicates have been precisely characterized in Section 5, and an interpretation for many or all of them (in terms of "stem-predicates") has been set forth in Section 6.

For an ordinary stochastic process unfolding against the background of some non-dynamical parameter time, the predicates corresponding to measurable sets of trajectories can all be built up as logical combinations of more elementary ones that acquire their full meaning in a finite time. (They don't refer to the infinite future). So it is also for the

---

[b] Among the possible exceptions would be approaches which attempt to restore strict determinism.

"cylinder set" predicates introduced in Section 3, but these predicates are unfortunately meaningless *per se* since they are not generally covariant. The nearest covariant replacements for these cylinder sets would seem to be the stem-sets $R(S)$. Unlike the cylinder sets, they do refer to the infinite future, for, although the predicate corresponding to a stem-set can become true in a finite time (after the birth of a finite number n of elements) it can only strictly speaking become false in the limit $n \to \infty$. * Nonetheless, falsehood can become certain "for all practical purposes", and in this sense, the truth or falsehood of a stem-predicate is also "verifiable in a finite time".

Moreover the physical significance of a stem-predicate is transparent, since its truth is decided simply by whether the "universe" (i.e. the actual causet) does or does not (never will) contain the stem in question. To the extent, then, that all assertions of dynamical interest can be built up from the stem predicates, we will have resolved the "problem of time" for this range of models. A proof of the conjecture of Section 6 would vouchsafe us this conclusion. It is clear, moreover, that this relatively satisfactory situation depends heavily on the discreteness of the causal set.

To what extent can we hope to repeat these same steps in the quantum case (the case of quantum gravity)? As a mathematical object, a quantum measure/decoherence functional is not that different from a classical measure like μ above, so one might hope much of the above would go through relatively unchanged. Two hurdles arise immediately, however. First, of course, the predictive meaning of a quantum measure is much less well understood than that of a classical probability measure, whence, even if we could say precisely which subsets of Ω were "measurable", we still would not know exactly how to use this information. † Second, the theorems that above led us from the transition probabilities τ to the measure $\tilde{\mu}$ (and thence to μ) break down in the quantum case because the complex amplitudes that one is constructing are no longer necessarily bounded in absolute value, unlike probabilities which are confined to the compact space $[0,1] \subseteq \mathbf{R}$. How serious these

---

* Even if a stem S has not appeared yet, we can never be absolutely certain that it won't appear later on.

† For an attempt to codify the predictive use of the quantum measure without first reducing it to a set of classical probabilities, see [17].

problems are is hard to say, but certainly the second of them means that further technical developments would need to occur before one could rigorously state a quantum analog of the conjecture of Section 6.

Finally, I want to raise — without attempting to settle it — a question about the status of conditional probability in quantum gravity, or rather in the classical analog of causet quantum gravity which has been the basis of our considerations here. Certainly, one can "relativize" the measure μ to any measurable subset of Ω and thereby lend meaning to questions of the sort "Given that S_1 occurs as a stem in C (the universe), what is the probability that S_2 also occurs as a stem?". If such questions are the only ones we need to consider, then conditional probabilities here will have the same derived status as they do in other branches of probability theory. But how clear is it that such a syntax captures what we'd really like to ask? Consider instead something like this: "Given that S_1 occurs as a stem in C what is the probability that a second stem S_2 occurs containing *this particular copy of S_1* (the S_1 that "we inhabit")?". When C contains more than one stem isomorphic to S_1, this second type of question seems different from the first, and indeed not even clearly defined on the sole basis of the "absolute" measure μ. Does this mean we need a *logically independent* concept of conditional probability and an extended formalism to express it, which would re-open the "problem of time" in a new context? Or is it enough to remark that stems of sufficient complexity are unlikely to occur more than once, whence the problem is absent in practice? As with other conceptual issues raised by quantum gravity, so also with this "this particular stem" issue, it's hard to say whether its resolution demands deep thought or just a bit of progress on the technical front.

This research was partly supported by NSF grant PHY-0098488, by a grant from the Office of Research and Computing of Syracuse University, and by an EPSRC Senior Fellowship at Queen Mary College. I would also like to express my gratitude to Goodenough College, which provided an estimable environment for life and work during my stay in London, where this paper was written.

References

[1] C.J. Isham, "Canonical Quantum Gravity and the Problem of Time", in L. A. Ibort and M. A. Rodriguez (eds.), *Integrable Systems, Quantum Groups, and Quantum Field Theories* (Kluwer Academic Publishers, London, 1993) pp. 157–288 ⟨gr-qc/9210011⟩ ; K.V. Kuchař, "Canonical Quantum Gravity" in R.J. Gleiser, C.N. Kozameh, O.M. Moreschi (eds.), *"General Relativity and Gravitation 1992 ": Proceedings of the Thirteenth Conference on General Relativity and Gravitation*, held Huerta Grande, Cordoba, 28 June-4 July, 1992 (Bristol, IOP Publishing 1993) .

[2] R.D. Sorkin, "Forks in the Road, on the Way to Quantum Gravity", talk given at the conference entitled "Directions in General Relativity", held at College Park, Maryland, May, 1993, *Int. J. Th. Phys.* **36**: 2759–2781 (1997) ⟨gr-qc/9706002⟩

[3] J.B. Hartle, "Spacetime Quantum Mechanics and the Quantum Mechanics of Spacetime", in B. Julia and J. Zinn-Justin (eds.), *Les Houches, session LVII, 1992, Gravitation and Quantizations* (Elsevier Science B.V. 1995) ⟨gr-qc/9304006⟩.

[4] R.D. Sorkin, "Quantum Mechanics as Quantum Measure Theory", Mod. Phys. Lett. A **9**:3119-3127 (No. 33) (1994) ⟨gr-qc/9401003⟩.
Roberto B. Salgado, "Some Identities for the Quantum Measure and its Generalizations", ⟨gr-qc/9903015⟩.

[5] R.D. Sorkin, "Spacetime and Causal Sets", in J.C. D'Olivo, E. Nahmad-Achar, M. Rosenbaum, M.P. Ryan, L.F. Urrutia and F. Zertuche (eds.), *Relativity and Gravitation: Classical and Quantum* (Proceedings of the *SILARG VII Conference*, held Cocoyoc, Mexico, December, 1990), pages 150-173 (World Scientific, Singapore, 1991).

[6] Y. Jack Ng and H. van Dam, "A small but nonzero cosmological constant", (Int. J. Mod. Phys D., to appear) ⟨hep-th/9911102⟩

[7] Djamel Dou, "Causal Sets, a Possible Interpretation for the Black Hole Entropy, and Related Topics", Ph. D. thesis (SISSA, Trieste, 1999)

[8] Rafael D. Sorkin, "Indications of causal set cosmology", *Int. J. Theor. Ph.* **39**(7): 1731-1736 (2000) (an issue devoted to the proceedings of the Peyresq IV conference, held June-July 1999, Peyresq France) ⟨gr-qc/0003043⟩

[9] A.R. Daughton, *The Recovery of Locality for Causal Sets and Related Topics*, Ph.D. dissertation (Syracuse University, 1993)

[10] Rafael D. Sorkin, *A library of Lisp functions for posets and other purposes*, http://www.physics.syr.edu/~sorkin (Version 1.4, December 1998, Version 2.0 to be released soon)

[11] David P. Rideout and Rafael D. Sorkin, "A Classical Sequential Growth Dynamics for Causal Sets", *Phys. Rev. D* **61**, 024002 (2000) ⟨gr-qc/9904062⟩

[12] E.B. Dynkin, *Markov Processes* (Academic Press, 1965)

[13] Xavier Martin, Denjoe O'Connor, David Rideout and Rafael D. Sorkin, "On the "renormalization" transformations induced by cycles of expansion and contraction in causal set cosmology", *Phys. Rev. D* **63**, 084026 (2001) (gr-qc/0009063)

[14] John Stachel, "Einstein's Search for General Covariance, 1912–1915", in *Einstein and the History of General Relativity*, edited by D. Howard and J. Stachel (Birkhäuser 1989)

[15] Edward Witten, "Quantum Gravity in De Sitter Space", (hep-th/0106109)

[16] H. Fay Dowker, Raquel S. García, Joe Henson and Rafael D. Sorkin (in preparation)

[17] R.D. Sorkin, "Quantum Measure Theory and its Interpretation", in *Quantum Classical Correspondence: Proceedings of the 4th Drexel Symposium on Quantum Nonintegrability*, held Philadelphia, September 8-11, 1994, edited by D.H. Feng and B-L Hu, pages 229–251 (International Press, Cambridge Mass. 1997) (gr-qc/9507057)

Extended Causality as a
Model of Discrete Gravity

Brian D. Koberlein

Department of Physics, SUNY Genseo State College,
1 College Circle, Geneseo, NY 14454

August 2001

Applying the principle of causal symmetry to the relativistic form of causality, the concept of extended causality is derived. It is shown this concept may be used to generate a discrete classical field with many quantum-like qualities. Applying extended causality to a classical point charge, a simple solution is obtained. This solution is demonstrated to have the properties of a "classical photon."

I. Introduction

Last year, an extension of general relativity was presented [1]. The basis of this extension was the application of generalized symmetry to derive an extended form of causality [2,3]. This concept was then applied to a simple scalar field to derive a "classical graviton." This paper generalizes this work to apply extended causality to a general null field. In Section II, the concept of causal symmetry is introduced and used to derive the principle of extended causality. Section III applies this principle to the derivation of a discrete field. In Section IV, the discrete field of a classical point charge is derived. The field is shown to represent a "classical photon." Finally, Section V outlines areas for further study.

II. Extended Causality

Consider a pair of points, A and B, in a Minkowski spacetime. In general these points define a 4-vector Δx, however in order for A and B to represent two observations of a free object (particle or field), Δx must satisfy the causality constraint

$$\Delta \tau^2 + \Delta x^2 = 0, \tag{2.1}$$

where τ is a real-valued parameter, known in relativity as the proper time. Equation (2.1) defines a local hypercone for the point A, which is the free object support. The object must lie on the hypercone, and B is assumed to define its path. The angle θ, given by $\tan \theta = |\Delta x| / |\Delta \tau|$, is a measure of the free object's speed. A change of θ corresponds to a change of speed and is thus an indication of interaction. For the motion of a null (massless) object, $\tan \theta = 1$.

We then apply causal symmetry to the hypercone, by assuming the hypercone is unchanged when shifted by an infinitesimal but discrete step, dx. This *extended causality* (EC) generates the finite nature of the object, introducing a second causal constraint,

$$(\Delta\tau + d\tau)^2 + (\Delta x + dx)^2 = 0. \tag{2.2}$$

By combining this with Eq. (2.1), this becomes

$$\Delta\tau + f \cdot \Delta x = 0, \tag{2.3}$$

where

$$f^\mu = \frac{dx^\mu}{d\tau^\mu}, \qquad f_\mu = -\frac{\partial\tau}{\partial x^\mu}. \tag{2.4}$$

Here the f represents a fibre in the spacetime. A line tangent to this forms the f-generator of the local hypercone. In applying extended causality to an object, one defines both its location and its immediate future.

III. Discrete Field Formalism

General Fields

To apply extended causality it is convenient to introduce a 3 + 2 flat spacetime,

$$(x^\mu, x^5) \in \mathbf{R}^5, \quad (x^5)^2 + x^2 = 0. \tag{3.5}$$

It is clear that in setting $x^5 \equiv \tau$, one imposes local causality. The EC constraint then becomes

$$(\tau - \tau_o) + f_\mu (x - x_o)^\mu = 0. \tag{3.6}$$

Applying this to the scalar field $A(x, \tau)$ constrains it to the hypercone generator, and it is designated by

$$A_f(x, \tau) \equiv A(x, \tau)|_{\text{EC}}. \tag{3.7}$$

Equation (3.6) also induces a direction to field derivatives, thus

$$\partial_\mu A_f = (\partial_\mu - f_\mu \partial_\tau) A_f \equiv \nabla_\mu A_f. \tag{3.8}$$

With Eqs. (3.7) and (3.8) it is possible to derive a discrete field equation, which becomes

$$\eta^{\mu\nu} \nabla_\mu \nabla_\nu A_f(x, \tau) = J(x, \tau), \tag{3.9}$$

where J is the source of the field, with an energy tensor

$$T_f^{\mu\nu} = \nabla^\mu A_f \nabla^\nu A_f - \frac{1}{2} \eta^{\mu\nu} \nabla^\alpha A_f \nabla_\alpha A_f. \tag{3.10}$$

In analyzing the properties of this solution, it is useful to express the solution as a Green's function. Thus

$$A_f(x, \tau) = \int d^5 y \, G_f(x - y, \tau_x - \tau_y) \, J(y, \tau_y), \tag{3.11}$$

and

$$\eta^{\mu\nu} \, \nabla_\mu \nabla_\nu \, G(x, \tau) = \delta^{(5)}(x). \tag{3.12}$$

The Green's function is then

$$G_f(x, \tau) = \frac{1}{2} \, \Theta(bf^4 \, t) \, \Theta(b\tau) \, \delta(\tau + f \cdot x), \tag{3.13}$$

where $b = \pm 1$ and Θ is the Heaviside step function. Here the $b = +1$ or $\tau > 0$ solution represents an emission at the retarded time, while the $b = -1$ or $\tau < 0$ solution is an absorption at the advanced time. Unlike the standard Green's function, Eq. (3.13) contains no singularity, therefore the discrete field propogates without changing its amplitude.

Equation (3.13) has the additional property of being independent of any transverse components of x. Specifically,

$$f \cdot x_T = 0, \quad \frac{\partial}{\partial x_T} \, G_f = 0. \tag{3.14}$$

Since the transverse dimensions are not affected by the field and do not contribute to it, the general $3 + 1$ field is reduced to a $1 + 1$ manifold.

In applying extended causality, we have created a model in which there are three general types of objects:
1. discrete, finite, point sources,
2. discrete, finite, point fields,
3. discrete, finite, point interactions.

In this way, we have introduced a unifying symmetry between fundamental objects (fermions and bosons).

Null Fields

For null fields, $\Delta\tau = 0$, and $\Delta x = x - z(\tau)$, where $z(\tau)$ is the world line of the field source. Equation (2.3) then becomes

$$f \cdot (x - z(\tau)) = 0. \tag{3.15}$$

Taking the derivative of this constraint, one finds

$$\partial_\mu f \cdot (x - z)\big|_f = 0 \tag{3.16}$$

or

$$f \cdot V|_f = -1 \tag{3.17}$$

where $V \equiv (\vec{V}, V_4) = dz/d\tau$. Taking this further, it is easily seen that

$$f \cdot a|_f = 0, \tag{3.18}$$

with $a = dV/d\tau$. This implies

$$a_4 = \left. \frac{\vec{a} \cdot \vec{f}}{f_4} \right|_f, \tag{3.19}$$

thus in the instantaneous rest frame of the charge at the point of emission (or absorption) $\vec{a}$ and $\vec{f}$ are orthogonal. While this is a well known consequence of electromagnetism, it is interesting to note that the result is true for all null fields, and therefore holds for any discrete fundamental force.

IV. The Electromagnetic Field

Consider the field of a classical, spinless point charge. The current of this charge is given by

$$J^\mu(x, t_x = t_z) = eV^\mu(\tau_z)\, \delta^{(3)}(x - z(\tau_z))\, \delta(\tau_x - \tau_z), \tag{4.20}$$

where e is the electric charge charge and $z(\tau)$ is its world line, and $V = dz/d\tau$. The solution for the emitted field is then

$$A_f(x, \tau_x) = 2\, e \int d\tau_y\, \Theta(t_x - t_y)\, \Theta(\tau_x - \tau_y)\, \delta[\tau_x - \tau_y + f \cdot (x - y)]\, V^\mu(\tau_z), \tag{4.21}$$

which can be reduced to

$$A_f^\mu(x, \tau) = eV^\mu(\tau)\, \Theta(t)\, \Theta(\tau)|_f, \tag{4.22}$$

or simply

$$A_f^\mu = eV^\mu|_f, \tag{4.23}$$

where $\tau \geq 0$, and $t > 0$.

The divergence of this field is easily obtained by noting

$$\nabla_\nu A_f^\mu = \nabla_\nu (eV^\mu)|_f = -ef_\nu\, a^\mu|_f, \tag{4.24}$$

thus

$$\nabla \cdot A_f = -ef_\nu\, a^\mu|_f = 0, \tag{4.25}$$

from which it is clear

$$\nabla \cdot J_f = 0. \tag{4.26}$$

Equation (4.25) is, of course, the Lorentz gauge, which is directly determined by Eq. (4.18). **Unlike Maxwell's equations, discrete electromagnetism has no gauge freedom.** Physically, this arises because not field "quanta" may exist without either a source or a sink. In connecting to standard electromagnetism, gauge symmetry arises from the smearing of the discrete field across the continuum.

The Maxwell tensor is easily obtained following the usual form [4]

$$F_{\mu\nu}^f = \nabla_\mu A_\nu^f - \nabla_\nu A_\mu^f = -e(f_\mu a_\nu - f_\nu a_\mu)|_f \tag{4.27}$$

from which the energy-momentum tensor becomes

$$T_f^{\mu\nu}(x, \tau_x) = F_f^{\mu\alpha} F_f^{\nu\beta} \eta_{\alpha\beta} + \frac{1}{4} \eta^{\mu\nu} F_f^{\alpha\beta} F_{\alpha\beta}^f, \tag{4.28}$$

which reduces to

$$T_f^{\mu\nu}(x, \tau_x) = -e^2 f^\mu f^\nu a^2 |_f. \tag{4.29}$$

The divergence of Eq. (4.29) vanishes,

$$\nabla_\nu T_f^{\mu\nu} = 0, \tag{4.30}$$

thus, energy-momentum is conserved.

The electric and magnetic components of the field are

$$E_f^i = F_f^{4i} = -e(f^4 a^i - f^i a^4)|_f, \tag{4.31}$$

$$B_f^i = -\epsilon_{ijk} F_f^{jk} = e\epsilon_{ijk} f^j a^k |_f. \tag{4.32}$$

From these it is clear

$$\vec{f} \cdot \vec{B}_f = \vec{f} \cdot \vec{E}_f = \vec{E}_f \cdot \vec{B}_f = 0, \tag{4.33}$$

thus, $\vec{E}_f$, $\vec{B}_f$, and $\vec{f}$ form an orthogonal triad.

From Eqs. (4.31) and (4.32) one may derive the Poynting vector as

$$\vec{S}_f = \vec{E}_f \times \vec{B}_f = e^2 f^4 a^2 \vec{f} |_f. \tag{4.34}$$

Therefore, one may conclude that A_f is *the electromagnetic field*. As such, it can be said to represent a "classical photon." The standard form may be derived by smearing the fibre, as in

$$A(x, \tau) = \frac{1}{2\pi} \int \delta(f^2) A_f(x, \tau) d^4 x \qquad (4.35)$$

where the integral is over the lightcone surface.

V. Conclusions

Comparing the discrete and continuous general forms, a shift from continuum to discrete can be summarized as

$$\{x\} \Rightarrow \{x, x^5\}, \qquad (5.36)$$

$$A(x) \Rightarrow A(x, \tau), \qquad (5.37)$$

$$\partial_\mu \Rightarrow \nabla_\mu, \qquad (5.38)$$

while the continuum can be obtained from the discrete via

$$A(x, \tau) = \frac{1}{2\pi} \int d^4 x \, \delta(f^2) A_f(x, \tau). \qquad (5.39)$$

It is clear extended causality forms the basis of a discrete and finite electromagnetic model, just as has been done for gravity [5]. A central question for extended causality is whether the process can be extended to both the strong and weak forces, forming the foundation of a fully discrete model of the universe.

REFERENCES

1. B. D. Koberlein, in *Proceedings of ANPA 22*, ed. K. G. Bowden (in press).
2. B. D. Koberlein, in *Aspects II: Proceedings of ANPA 20*, ed. K. G. Bowden (Cambridge University, 2000), p. 249.
3. H. P. Noyes and S. Starson, "Discrete Anti-gravity," in *Proc. ANPA WEST 7*, (Stanford University, 1991).
4. D. Jackson, *Classical Electrodynamics*, (Wiley, New York, 1975).
5. M. M. Souza and R. N. Silveira, "Discrete and Finite General Relativity," (gr-qc/9801040, 1998).

Manifold Reasons against the Manifold[*]

Ioannis Raptis[†]

Abstract

A brief synopsis of recent conceptions and results, the current status and future out-look of our research program of applying sheaf and topos-theoretic ideas to quantum gravity and quantum logic is presented. We center our attention on the recently proposed *quantum causal set* scenario for quantum gravity, and how it may evade, for manifold reasons, the spacetime manifold of macroscopic physics.

> *"Logics come from dynamics"*
> (D. R. Finkelstein: *'Quantum Relativity'* [29])

1 Introduction: two questions motivating our quest

The following two questions, one physical the other more mathematical, motivate essentially our general research project of applying sheaf and topos-theoretic concepts, techniques and results to quantum gravity and quantum logic:

- *Is there a fundamental connection between the quantum logical structure of the world and its dynamically variable microcausal or chronological structure at Planck scales as the latter is supposed to be determined by the until now persistently elusive quantum theory of gravity?*

and related to it:

- *How can one localize noncommutatively?*

Concerning the first question, we intuit that a sound theoretical scheme for quantum gravity should be intimately related to the logical structure of the world at quantum scales: in a strong sense, quantum causality should be unified at the dynamical level with quantum logic in the light of quantum gravity. In turn, this conjecture essentially implies our main suspicion that in the quantum spacetime deep even quantum logic should be regarded as

---

[*]A synopsis of a talk given at the 23rd Annual International Meeting of the *Alternative Natural Philosophy Association* (ANPA) in Cambridge, UK (August 15–22).

[†]EU Marie Curie Research Fellow, Theoretical Physics Group, Blackett Physics Laboratory, Imperial College of Science, Technology and Medicine, Prince Consort Road, South Kensington, London SW7 2BZ, UK; i.raptis@ic.ac.uk

a quantum 'observable' entity that is subject to dynamical changes—a *dynamical physical logic* analogous to the dynamical physical spacetime geometry of the classical theory of gravity (*ie*, general relativity) [25, 26]. That logos is somehow related to chronos at a basic level[1] has become the central theme in our quantum gravity research program over the last few years.

Our subsequent decision to implement mathematically this theme by using sheaf and topos-theoretic concepts, techniques and results is based on the by now widely established fact, at least among categorists and related 'toposophers', that *the theory of presheaves, sheaves and their topoi fuses geometry with logic at a fundamental level* [40, 31, 42]. It only appeared natural to us that if geometry could be somehow identified with 'spacetime geometry' in particular, while logic with 'quantum logic', then the long sought after unification of relativity with quantum mechanics could be possibly achieved by sheaf and topos-theoretic means. After all, the methods of sheaf and topos theory are of an essentially algebraic nature [42, 43, 44], and lately there has been a strong tendency among mathematical physicists to tackle the problem of quantum gravity entirely by categorico-algebraic means [17, 45, 46, 47, 48].

Concerning the second motivating question above which, as we will argue subsequently, is closely related to the first, our quest focuses on a possible formulation of a *noncommutative topology* and its associated *noncommutative sheaf theory* that can can be applied to the problem of the quantum structure and dynamics of spacetime. Our original motivation for looking into the possibility of a noncommutative or, ultimately, 'quantum' topology for quantum gravity relied heavily on our desire to abandon the geometric spacetime continuum on which the mathematics of general relativity (*ie*, the standard differential geometry) essentially rests for some structure of a more finitistic, algebraic and, hopefully, dynamical character [61, 47, 62, 48, 58]. This is the subject of the next section and we will use it as the *raison d'être* of our endeavor to apply sheaf and topos-theoretic ideas to quantum gravity.

Thus, the short report below commences with various physical and mathematical evidence that we have collected in the past couple of years against the classical topological (*ie*, C^0-continuous) and differential (*ie*, C^∞-smooth) manifold model of spacetime by essentially basing ourselves on quantum theory's principles of finiteness or discreteness, superposition and, as a result, algebraic noncommutativity, as well as on relativity's central principle of local causality commonly known as 'locality'. Thus, we will see how effectively sheaf and topos-theoretic ideas may be used to formulate a *locally finite, causal and quantal version of* (at least the kinematics of) *discrete Lorentzian quantum gravity* [61, 56, 57, 47, 62, 48, 58, 60], for it has been convincingly argued that capturing the 'proper' kinematical structure constitutes the first decisive step towards arriving at the notoriously elusive quantum dynamics for spacetime and gravity [73, 62].

---

[1]In fact, the opening quotation from [29] suggests that *logic derives from dynamics*!

2 The Past: manifold reasons against the spacetime manifold

A noncommutative geometry [16] has already been proposed, significantly worked out and diversely applied to the problem of the quantum structure and dynamics of spacetime (*ie*, quantum gravity). However, it seems theoretically rather *ad hoc*, lame and short sighted to think of a higher level structure such as the geometry of spacetime as being subject to some sort of quantization and as participating into, in principle measurable, dynamical variations[2] thus be soundly modelled by noncommutative mathematics, while a more basic structure such as the spacetime topology to be treated essentially as a fixed classical entity, hence be modelled after a non-varying locally Euclidean manifold equipped with algebras of commutative coordinates labelling its point events [61, 47, 58, 62]. Related to this, and from a rather general and technical perspective, while a commutative sheaf theory has been rather quickly developed, well understood and widely applied to both mathematics and physics [33, 24, 69, 43, 44, 45, 46], a noncommutative one (and the topology related to it) has been rather slow in coming and certainly not unanimously agreed on how to be applied to quantum spacetime research [69, 77, 79, 50, 51, 7, 8, 6, 47, 58][3].

At the same time, and from a physical point of view, the unreasonableness and unphysicality of the locally Euclidean topological (C^0) and differential (C^∞) manifold model M for spacetime is especially pronounced when one considers:

- (a) **Pointedness of events:** M's pathological nature in the guise of singularities that plague general relativity—the classical theory of gravity—which are mainly due to the geometric point-like character of the events that constitute it, as well as due to the algebras of C^∞-smooth functions employed to coordinatize these point events [48] (and also due to (b) next).

- (b) **Continuous infinity of events:** M's problematic nature due to the fact that one can in principle pack an uncountable infinity of the aforementioned point events in a finite spacetime volume resulting in the non-renormalizable infinities that impede any serious attempt at uniting quantum mechanics with general relativity (at least at the 'calculational' level)[4].

- (c) **Non-dynamical and non-quantal topology:** Its non-variable and non-quantal nature when one expects that at Planck scales not only the spacetime metric, but also that the spacetime topology partakes into quantum phenomena [80], that is to say, it is a dynamically variable entity whose connections engage into coherent quantum

---

[2]That is, in general relativity at least, the gravitational field, which is represented by the spacetime metric $g_{\mu\nu}$, is treated as an *observable*; in fact, the sole spacetime observable.

[3]That is to say, not all mathematicians and mathematical physicists agree on what ought to qualify as '*noncommutative topology*' proper and its related noncommutative sheaf or scheme theory. At the same time, there is no collective agreement on how such a noncommutative or quantum [34, 35, 36, 30, 29] topology may be applied to the problem of the quantum structure and dynamics of spacetime.

[4]The (a) and (b) pathological features of the manifold model above may be summarized in its character as *a geometric point set differential continuum of events* [48].

superpositions. We may distill this by saying that the manifold topology is, quantally speaking, an *unobservable* entity not manifesting quantum dynamical fluctuations or interference between its defining connections [62, 58]—a rigid substance, once and forever fixed by the theorist, that is not part of the dynamical flux of Nature at microscopic scales. Furthermore, the (algebras of) commutative C^{∞}-determinations of the manifold's point events indicate another non-quantal (classical) feature of the spacetime manifold [61, 48].

- (d) **Additional structures:** M's need of extra structures required to be introduced by hand by the theoretician and not being 'naturally' related to the topological manifold (*ie*, the C^0-continuous) one. Such structures are the differential (*ie*, the C^{∞}-smooth) and Lorentzian metric (*ie*, the smooth metric field $g_{\mu\nu}$ of absolute signature 2) ones [5], and they are implicitly postulated by the general relativist on top of M's fixed continuous topology in order to support the apparently necessary full differential geometric (*ie*, Calculus based!) panoply of general relativity. The 4-dimensional, C^{∞}-smooth Lorentzian manifold assumption for spacetime concisely summarizes the kinematics of general relativity [73, 47, 62, 48].

- (e) **Non-operationality:** M's gravely non-operational (*ie*, non-algebraic) character as a static, pre-existent background geometric structure—an inert stage on which fields propagate and interact—whose existence is postulated up-front by the theorist rather than being defined by some (algebraically modelled) physical operations of determination or localization of its point events. This seems to be in striking discord with the main tenet of the philosophy of quantum theory supporting an observer (and observation!) dependent reality [57, 47]. Furthermore, one would ultimately expect that *it is the dynamical relations between quanta that define spacetime*, that is to say, from which spacetime, with its topological, differential and Lorentzian metric properties, should be effectively derived somehow [62], so that the latter should not be regarded as an *a priori* absolute ether-like substance [22]—an unjustifiably necessary passive receptacle fixed once and forever to host dynamical fields and their interactions, but, at the same time, an entity that does not actively participate in them[5]. In any case, and in view of (b) above, we have no actual experience of a continuous infinity of events and their differential separation cannot be recorded in the laboratory; for evidently, realistic experiments are of finite duration and are carried out in laboratories of finite size. Moreover, as a matter of principle, one cannot determine the gravitational field, hence the metric separation, between infinitesimally separated events (*ie*, events whose space-time distance is smaller than Planck's—$l_p \approx 10^{-35}m$-$t_P \approx 10^{-44}s$) without creating a black hole. This seems to point to a fundamental cut-off of continuous spacetime which strongly suggests that spacetime becomes reticular or granular above a certain Planck energy ($E_P \approx 10^{-19}GeV$). The continuous commutatively coordinatized geometric manifold is experimentally (or experientially!) a non-pragmatic model of spacetime that should be replaced at a basic level by a physically more plausible, perhaps combinatorial and quantal (*ie*,

---

[5]In the words of Einstein: *"a substance that acts, but is not acted upon"* [22, 23].

noncommutative-algebraic), structure [61, 56, 47, 62, 48, 58].

- (f) **Spatiality and globalness of topology:** M's 2-way undirected, locally Euclidean topological structure, will likely prove to be inadequate for modelling the irreversible small scale connections between events, for it has been seriously proposed that the 'real' quantum theory of gravity will turn out to be 'innately' a time-asymmetric theory [54, 27, 32, 28, 58]. At the same time, the very conception of topology as a theory of reversible, spatial (or spacelike!) connections between points should be challenged, and justly so because of the prominent lack of experimental evidence for tachyons moving back and forth in spatial or spacelike directions. In any case, the general conception of topology as the study of the 'global' features of space may seem to be problematic in a fundamental theoresis of Physis where all significant dynamical variables are expected to respect some kind of locality principle (*ie*, where all observables are in effect local variables propagating in temporal or causal directions independently of whether this dynamics ultimately turns out to be time-asymmetric or not).

With these doubts about the physical soundness of the geometric spacetime continuum in the quantum deep, we are able to discuss next a finitary-algebraic model for (the kinematics of) discrete Lorentzian quantum gravity that we presently possess based on sheaf and topos-theoretic ideas, as it were, to alleviate or even evade the aforementioned (a)-(f) 'pathologies' of the classical spacetime manifold.

3 The Present: sheaves and their topoi in discrete Lorentzian quantum gravity

Pointlessness and Discreteness: Finitary substitutes for continuous spacetime topology, that is to say, when spacetime is modelled after a topological (*ie*, $\mathcal{C}^0$) manifold M, were derived in [72] from locally finite open covers of a bounded region X of M in a spirit akin to the combinatorial Čech-Alexandrov simplicial skeletonizations of continuous manifolds [1, 2, 21, 20]. These substitutes were seen to be locally finite T_0-posets and were interpreted as finitary approximations of the continuous locally Euclidean topology of M. At the heart of this approach to spacetime discretization lies the realistic or 'pragmatic' assumption [61, 62] that at a fundamental level the singular spacetime point events should be replaced (or smeared out) by something coarser or 'larger', with immediately obvious candidates being open sets (or generally, 'regions') about them [72, 73, 13]. Then, the resulting poset topological spaces that substitute M are, in fact, complete distributive lattices otherwise known as locales [42]. The pointlessness of these *finitary locales* (finlocales) should be contrasted against the pointedness of M mentioned in (a) above, while their discreteness comes to relieve M's pathology (b). Also, it should be emphasized that the continuous M, with the $\mathcal{C}^0$-manifold topology carried by its points, can be recovered at the ideal inverse limit of infinite refinement of an inverse system or net of these finlocales, so that one is able to establish a connection between these discrete topological poset substrata and the continuous manifold that they replace on the one hand, as well as to justify their qualification as sound approximations of M on the other [72, 56, 47].

Algebra over Geometry: In [57], sheaves of continuous functions on the finitary locales of the previous paragraph were studied. In the same way that the locally finite locales were interpreted as sound approximations of the continuous topology of (the bounded region X of) the spacetime manifold M, so their corresponding *finitary spacetime sheaves*[6] were viewed as reticular substitutes of the sheaf of (algebras of) C^0-functions on X which, in turn, represent the *observables of the continuous topology of the spacetime region X*. The duality of the two approaches in [72] and [56] towards discretizing the spacetime topological continuum was particularly emphasized in [56], namely that, while in the former scheme finitary locales approximate the spacetime topology *per se*, in a more *operational* (*ie, algebraic*) spirit that suits sheaf theory [43, 44], the latter approach discretizes (or 'finitizes') the sheaf structure of (the algebras of) our own observations of that continuous spacetime topology. The crucial change of emphasis in the physical semantics of the two approaches is from discretizations of a background point set geometric realm 'out there', to ones of our very own (algebraic) operations of perceiving that realm—which spacetime realm, for all we know, may not physically exist independently of these operations after all. Arguably, the finsheaf-theoretic approach comes to alleviate the shortcoming (e) of M above; while sheaves, being by definition *local homeomorphisms* [42, 43, 44, 47], certainly address M's 'globalness' problem alluded to in (f), namely, *local topological information is more important than the usual global information* about, say, handles, holes *etc* that (the 'classical' conception of) topology is concerned with [28, 47, 62].

Temporality and Causality over Spatiality and Topology: In a dramatic change of physical interpretation of the finitary topological posets involved in [72], Sorkin and coworkers insisted that the partial orders involved should not be interpreted as coarse topological or 2-way spatial relations between geometric points, but rather as directed 1-way primordial causal 'after' relations between events inhabiting so-called *causal set* substrata[7] that are supposed to fundamentally underlie the classical curved Lorentzian manifold of general relativity at Planck scales [5, 70, 71, 73, 74, 64, 75]. In contradistinction to the purely topological character of the finitary locales in [72], causets are supposed to encode information about the microcausal relations between events in the quantum spacetime deep. Moreover, as Sorkin *et al.* stress in [5], the partial order causality relation of causets encodes almost complete information not only about the topological (*ie*, C^0) structure of the classical spacetime manifold, but also about its differential (*ie*, the C^∞-smooth) and conformal Lorentzian metric structures (*ie*, the metric $g_{\mu\nu}$ of signature 2 modulo its determinant which represents the elementary spacetime volume measure) that are usually externally prescribed by the theorist on top of its continuous topology. That causality in its order-theoretic guise is a deeper, more physical[8] (and perhaps more pertinent to the problem of quantum gravity) conception than topology *per se* has already been amply noted in [83, 84, 27, 29, 74, 55, 47, 75].The upshot of the aforementioned 'semantic reversal' is that

---

[6]We will call them 'finsheaves' for short *à la* [47].

[7]Hereafter to be abbreviated as 'causets' [47].

[8]Especially due to lack of experimental evidence for tachyons. Again, see section 2.

from the causet viewpoint, locally finite partial orders should not be viewed as effective topological approximations of the classical spacetime manifold, but, on the contrary, the latter should be regarded as being of a contingent (*ie*, non-fundamental) character, and as reflecting our own ignorance about (and related 'grossness' of our model of) the very fine structure of the world. All in all, the manifold is the poor relative, ultimately, the approximation of the causet, not the other way around.

To recapitulate then, partial order as causality, not as topology: this is what is 'going on' between events in the quantum deep [75]. All this certainly presents a sound alternative to the 'additional structures' and 'spatiality' problems of the spacetime manifold mentioned above in (d) and (f), respectively.

Finitary Locales and their Corresponding Causets Quantized: In [61], an algebraic representation of Sorkin's finitary locales was given, namely, with every finitary poset substitute of a continuous spacetime manifold a complex, associative, finite dimensional and noncommutative *Rota incidence algebra* [66, 76, 53] was associated in such a way that the topological information encoded in the former was seen to be the same as that encoded in the latter [9]. Furthermore, in the new environment of the Rota algebras there is a natural linear superposition operation between the arrows (*ie*, the partial order relations) in their corresponding posets that is characteristically absent from Sorkin's formulation of discrete topological spaces [72]. In other words, and this is the main physical interpretation of the formal mathematical structures involved in [61], in the algebraic context one is able to form *coherent quantum superpositions between the topological connections defining these reticular topological substrata of the classical spacetime manifold.* Moreover, this interpretation of the incidence algebras associated with the finitary locale replacements of the classical continuum as *discrete quantum spacetime topologies* enabled us to conceive of the aforementioned inverse limit procedure by which the continuum is recovered from finitary locales in [72] as *Bohr's correspondence principle.* That is, the topological spacetime manifold arises at the classical and experientially non-pragmatic limit of infinite energy of resolution [15], and concomitant 'decoherence', of an inverse system of reticular quantum topological Rota algebraic substrata [61, 62]. Thus, in the Rota finitary-algebraic context we are able to formulate a quantum sort of spacetime topology [58] hence evade the problematic non-quantal nature of the continuum mentioned in (c) above.

In connection with this continuum classical limit, it should also be mentioned that actually not only the C^0-topological, but also the differential (*ie*, the C^∞-smooth) structure of spacetime was anticipated in [61, 62] to emerge at the classical limit from a 'foam' of such discrete quantum Rota topologies. This is so because the incidence algebras under focus in [61, 62] were seen to be *graded discrete differential manifolds* in the sense of Dimakis and Müller-Hoissen [19, 18, 3, 10][9]. Moreover, since the differential structure of the limit manifold represents the notion of *locality* in classical spacetime physics[10] [22], these algebraic discrete quantum topological substrata were coined '*alocal structures*'—as mentioned earlier,

---

[9]In a nutshell, a reticular analogue of the nilpotent Kähler-Cartan differential d (and its dual homological boundary operator d) can be defined on these incidence algebras. See [82, 48].

[10]That is, the local structure of classical spacetime is taken to be the point event and the space (graded module) of differential forms (co)tangent to it.

in a sense neither local (general relativity) nor non-local (quantum mechanics) structures [61, 62].

A couple more things should be mentioned now that we are talking about the Rota algebraic quantization of Sorkin's finitary locales. First, one should emphasize that the general method (and philosophy!), originally due to Gelfand, of extracting points from algebras as well as of assigning a fairly 'natural' topology to the latter, thus 'geometrizing', as it were, algebraic structures, was first used by Zapatrin in [81] for gathering useful geometrical information from finite dimensional incidence algebras and for establishing their topological equivalence to the finitary posets of Sorkin [9]. At the heart of this so-called 'spatialization procedure' lies the recognition that points in these algebras are precisely the (kernels of equivalence classes of) irreducible (finite dimensional Hilbert space) representations of these algebras which, in turn, may be identified with the elements of their primitive spectra (ie, the primitive ideals in the algebras) [61, 62, 58].

The second thing that should be noted here is the categorical duality (ie, a contravariant functor) between the poset category of incidence Rota algebras associated with the finitary locales of Sorkin, and the poset category of the latter when viewed as simplicial complexes à la Čech-Alexandrov[11] [61, 82, 62, 48, 58]. In [58] the latter category, consisting of finitary posets or simplicial complexes and 'refinement arrows' $\preceq$[12], was called the Alexandrov-Sorkin category[13], while the former category, consisting of finite dimensional incidence algebras and 'coarsening arrows' $\succeq$[14], was coined the Rota-Zapatrin category[15]. For the time being we note that this contravariant functor between $\mathfrak{P}$ and $\mathfrak{R}$ may be immediately recognized as defining *a presheaf of finite dimensional incidence algebras over finitary locales*.

We should also mention that in [56] an algebraic quantization procedure of the locally finite poset structures representing causets of Sorkin *et al.* [5] was suggested based on the analogous process of quantization of finlocales of Sorkin [72] proposed in [61]. In little detail, with every causet its incidence Rota algebra was associated and interpreted as a *quantum causal set*[16] in such a way that the local causal-topological information encoded in the causet[17] corresponds to the one encoded in the generating relations of the algebraic Rota topology of the qauset[18]. Another important thing to notice from [56] in the Rota algebraic environment that we have cast causets, and this is the main virtue of qausets that essentially qualifies them as the quantum analogues of causets, is that the model allows for coherent quantum superpositions between the causal arrows—a feature that was prominently absent from the purely poset categorical (arrow semigroup) structures modelling causets. Thus,

---

[11]See [1, 2, 21, 20] for this so-called 'nerve construction of simplicial complexes'.

[12]That is, injective simplicial maps or injective poset morphisms, or even, 'continuous injections' between finitary locales.

[13]Symbolized by $\mathfrak{P}$.

[14]That is epi incidence algebra homomorphisms.

[15]Symbolized by $\mathfrak{R}$.

[16]Hereafter to be referred to as '*qauset*'.

[17]That is, the info in the so-called 'covering relations'—the immediate causal arrows of the underlying poset Hasse graphs.

[18]This observation will be of crucial importance in the next paragraph where we will talk about finsheaves of qausets as local homeomorphisms between causets and qausets [47].

we have in our hands a finitary-algebraic model for quantum causal topology [58].

Curving a Noncommutative Topology for Qausality: In [47], curved finsheaves of qausets were defined as principal finsheaves of incidence Rota algebras modelling qausets having for structure group of local symmetries a finitary version of the continuous orthochronous Lorentz group and for base or localization space Sorkin *et al.*'s causets[19]. Non-trivial spin-Lorentzian (*ie*, $sl(2, \mathbb{C})$-valued) connections on these finsheaves were defined *à la* Mallios [43, 44, 48], and the resulting structures were interpreted as finitary, causal and quantal substitutes of the kinematics of Lorentzian gravity since an inverse system of these finsheaves was seen to 'converge' in the limit of infinite energy of localization to the Lorentzian manifold—the kinematical structure of general relativity [47].

Then, it has been recently speculated [47, 59, 48, 58] that as $\mathbf{Sh}(X)$—the topos of sheaves of sets over a spacetime manifold X—may be viewed as a (mathematical) universe of variable sets varying continuously over X [42], so a possible topos-organization of the curved finsheaves of qausets in [47] (call it $^{fcq}\mathbf{Sh}(X)(\vec{P})$[20]) may be regarded as a (physical) universe of dynamically variable qausets varying under the influence of a locally finite, causal and quantal version of Lorentzian gravity. In such a possible model it would be rather natural to address the question opening the present paper since the internal intuitionistic-type of logic of $^{fcq}\mathbf{Sh}(X)(\vec{P})$ should be intimately related to the intuitionistic logic that underlies quantum logic proper in its topos-theoretic guise [11, 12, 14]. This gives us significant hints for the deep connection between the quantum logical structure of the world and its dynamically variable reticular causal or chronological structure at Planck scales *vis-à-vis* quantum gravity.

The discussion above brings us to the use of presheaves and their topoi in quantum logic proper and, *in extenso*, to the logic of consistent-histories.

Presheaves and their topoi in quantum logic and consistent-histories: In [11, 12, 14], the Koch- en-Specker theorem of quantum logic was studied from a topos-theoretic perspective. In particular, it was shown that quantum logic is 'warped' or 'curved' relative to its Boolean sublogics [63]. This was achieved by showing that certain presheaves of sets over the base poset category of Boolean subalgebras of a quantum projection lattice $\mathcal{L}$ associated with the Hilbert space $\mathcal{H}$ (of dimensionality greater than 2) of a quantum system do not admit global sections, but they do so only locally. Since these sections were interpreted as valuations (on propositions represented by the projectors in $\mathcal{L}(\mathcal{H})$), and since the presheaves were organized into a topos (of so-called 'varying sets' [40]), the aforesaid warping phenomenon could be read as follows: unlike classical (Boolean) logic— which is the internal logic of the 'classical' topos **Set** of constant sets, quantum logic does not admit a global notion of truth; or equivalently: in quantum logic truth is localized on (or relativized with respect to) the Boolean logics embedded in it. Furthermore, as a result of this, and as befits the internal logic of the topos of presheaves of sets over a

---

[19]Technically speaking, finsheaves of qausets over causets are local homeomorphisms between the base causets and the qauset stalks [47]. The aforementioned local topological equivalence between finlocales and their incidence algebras comes in handy for defining such finsheaves.

[20]The topos of sheaves of (f)initary, (c)ausal and (q)uantal sets (qausets) over Sorkin *et al.*'s causets $\vec{P}$ [47].

poset category [31, 39, 67, 68, 42], Butterfield *et al.* show that quantum logic is locally intuitionistic ('neorealist'), not Boolean ('realist').

Very similar to the treatment of quantum logic by presheaf and topos-theoretic means above is Isham's assumption of a topos-theoretic perspective on the logic of the consistent-histories approach to quantum theory [38]. Briefly, Isham showed that the universal orthoalgebra $\mathcal{UP}$ of history propositions admits non-trivial localizations or 'contextualizations' (of truth) over its classical Boolean subalgebras. More technically speaking, it was shown that one cannot meaningfully assign truth or semantic values to propositions about histories globally in $\mathcal{UP}$, but that one can only do so locally, that is to say, when the propositions live in certain Boolean sublattices of $\mathcal{UP}$—the classical sites, or 'windows' [11, 12, 14], or even 'points' [58, 50, 51] within the ortholattice $\mathcal{UP}$. Moreover, the simultaneous consideration of *all* such Boolean subalgebras and *all* consistent sets of history propositions led Isham to realize that the internal logic of the consistent-histories theory is neither classical (Boolean) nor quantum proper, but intuitionistic[21]. This result befits the fact that the relevant mathematical structure involved in [38], namely, the collection of presheaves of sets varying over the poset category of Boolean sublattices of $\mathcal{UP}$, is an example of a topos [40, 4, 42], for it is a general result in category theory that every topos has an internal logic that is strongly typed and intuitionistic [31, 39, 67, 68, 42]. As in the case of quantum logic, the logic of consistent-histories is (locally) intuitionistic and 'warped' relative to its 'local' classical Boolean sublogics [63][22].

Furthermore, in [59], the base poset category of Boolean sublattices of $\mathcal{UP}$ was endowed with a suitable Vietoris-type of topology so that the presheaves of varying sets over the Boolean subalgebras of $\mathcal{UP}$ were appropriately converted to sheaves and, as a result, their respective topos was viewed as a mathematical universe of sets varying *continuously* over $\mathcal{UP}$. Moreover, the stalks of these sheaves were given further algebraic structure—that of incidence Rota algebras—together with the latter's physical interpretation as qausets [56, 47], so that we arrived at *sheaves of consistent-histories of qausets*. As a result, the topos-like organization of these sheaves—the *topos of quantum causal histories*—was anticipated to be the natural physico-mathematical universe in which 'curved quantum causality meets warped quantum logic'[23], as it were, to answer to the first question opening the present paper.

Now, the discussion about the topos of quantum causal histories brings us to speculate

---

[21]As alluded to above in the context of quantum logic proper, Isham in [38] uses the epithet 'neorealist' for the quantal logic of the consistent-histories theory in its topos-theoretic guise. Quite resonably, we feel, one could also coin this logic 'neoclassical' [57]—this name referring to the departure of the Brouwerian logic of the topos of consistent-histories in [38] from the two-valued Boolean lattice calculus obeyed by the states of a classical mechanical system which are modelled after point subsets of its phase space. Arguably then, the logic of a classical mechanical system is Boolean like that of the topos **Set** of constant 'classical' sets.

[22]This departure of quantum logic proper [11, 12, 14] and of the quantal logic underlying consistent-histories [38] from classical Boolean logic is certainly less striking than the famous 'global' difference between quantum and Boolean logic, namely that, while the latter is distributive, the former are non-distributive. Thus, properly speaking, quantum logic, although it is globally non-distributive, locally it is so; albeit, non-Boolean, but intuitionistic.

[23]See title of the talk delivered at QS5 (read first footnote in this paper).

briefly about the immediate future development of our general research project 'presheaves, sheaves and their topoi in quantum gravity and quantum logic'.

4 The Future: envisaging 'quantum sheaves' and their 'quantum topoi'

Of great interest to us for the future development of our research program, and keeping in mind the second question opening this paper, is the following project: since the incidence algebras modelling qausets are graded non-abelian Polynomial Identity (PI) rings, it would in principle be possible to develop a noncommutative sheaf or scheme type of theory [33, 24, 69] for such finitary non-abelian PI ring localizations. Rigorous mathematical results, cast in a general categorical setting, from the noncommutative algebraic geometry of similar non-abelian schematic algebras and their localizations [79, 77] are expected to deepen our physical understanding of the dynamically variable noncommutative quantum causal Rota topologies defined on the primitive spectra of qausets [61, 47, 62, 58][24]. Ultimately, the deep connection for physics is anticipated to be one between such a noncommutative conception of the causal topology of spacetime and the fundamental quantum time-asymmetry expected of the *"true quantum gravity"* [54, 27, 32]. The deep connection for mathematics is, as we briefly mentioned in the introduction, that such a general conception of a 'noncommutative topology' is supposed to be the precursor to Connes' 'noncommutative geometry'[25] [16]—a theory that in the last five years or so has become of great interest to theoretical physics, because it appears to shed more light on the persisting problem of quantum gravity. For we emphasize again: it seems unreasonable to have a full fledged noncommutative geometry and lack a noncommutative topology and its corresponding sheaf theory, especially to apply the latter to quantum gravity where even the spacetime topology is expected to be subject to quantum dynamical fluctuations and coherent superpositions [62].

This 'noncommutative quantum causal topology' project has revived this author's doctoral interests and work in topoi, their possible quantization and the application of the resulting 'quantum topoi' to the problem of the quantum structure and dynamics of spacetime [55]. In particular, but briefly, Finkelstein [29], as part of an ongoing effort to find a quantum replacement for the spacetime manifold of macroscopic physics, has developed a theory of quantum sets, which in a sense represents a quantization of ordinary 'classical' set theory. The basic idea is that spacetime at small scales should really be viewed as a 'quantum' set, not a classical one. This is supposed to be a step on the path to a 'correct' version of quantum gravity and quantum spacetime topology [30]. A question which may occur to a modern logician or 'toposopher' is: what is so special about the category **Set** of classical constant sets, since there are other logical universes just as good, and possibly better, namely 'topoi'? Perhaps it would be a better idea to try and quantize these more general categories, since the use of **Set** may be prey to classical chauvinism.

[24]I wish to thank Professor Fred Van Oystaeyen (Antwerp University, Belgium) for motivating such a study in a crucial and timely private communication, and in two research seminars—see [78].

[25]Freddy Van Oystaeyen in private correspondence.

The usual flat (*ie*, without gravity) classical and quantum field theories are conveniently formulated in **Set**, or more precisely, in **Sh**(X)-the 'classical' topos of sheaves of sets over the classical spacetime manifold X [67, 68]. However, as we said in section 2, these theories suffer from non-renormalizable infinities coming from singularities that plague the smooth spacetime manifold X. The manifold model, as an inert classical pointed geometric background continuum on which fields propagate and interact, must at least be revised in view of the pathological nature of quantum gravity when treated as another quantum field theory[26] [47]. Topoi and their topological relatives, locales, which are pointless topological spaces, are structures well-suited not to significantly commit themselves to the pathological geometric point-like character of a base spacetime manifold. As it has already been pointed out, perhaps one could arrive at the 'true' topos of Nature, on which a finite quantum theory of gravity can be founded, by considering the pointless topos of the curved finsheaves of qausets over Sorkin's causets, or even of the topos of sheaves of quantum causal histories, instead of their classical ancestor **Sh**(X). This quest for the 'right' quantum topos of Nature is also expected to shed more light on the following analogy that has puzzled mathematicians for quite some time now:

$$\frac{\text{locales}}{\text{quantales}} = \frac{\text{topoi}}{?}[27]$$

To dwell briefly on this analogy, topologically speaking any complete distributive lattice is called a locale[28] and it corresponds to a generalized (*ie*, 'pointless') topological space [42]. A quantale [6, 7, 8, 65, 49, 52, 50, 51], the noncommutative (quantum) analogue of a locale, may be represented by the lattice of closed two-sided ideals of a nonabelian (von Neumann or C^*) algebra. The primitive spectra of non-abelian qausets [61, 56, 62], when regarded as some sort of lattices[29], may also be viewed as some kind of quantales—albeit, of a finitary sort [58], hence our regarding the topos of finsheaves of qausets (or the sheaves of quantum causal histories) as a strong candidate for the elusive quantum topos.

In the same line of thought, and in connection with sheaves of qausets over consistent-histories and their possible topos-organization mentioned at the end of the previous section, we would like to mention another project that we are currently working on[30]. One may recall that in Isham's version of the quantal logic of consistent-histories [37, 38] central role is played by the tensor product '$\otimes$' structure. A sheaf $\mathfrak{H}$ of Hilbert spaces $\mathcal{H}$ over a classical spacetime manifold X was initially expected to be the appropriate mathematical structure to model Isham's scenario. However, the tensor product $\otimes$ and the 'classical' definition of a sheaf (of tensor product $\mathcal{H}$-spaces[31]) do not seem to go hand in hand for the following, at least from a physical point of view, reason: when one considers the tensor product of two distinct stalks in a vector sheaf like $\mathfrak{H}$, as when one combines two distinct quanta in the usual

---

[26]That is, 'Quantum Gravity as Quantum General Relativity'.

[27]Jim Lambek and Steve Selesnick in private communication. In this 'proportion' the missing denominator is supposed to be the elusive '*quantum topos*' structure that we are after.

[28]Logically speaking, a complete Heyting algebra [31, 42].

[29]That is, if on top of their partial order structure, $\cap$ and $\cup$-like operations are defined in them as in the case of the finlocales mentioned in the previous section.

[30]In collaboration with Chris Isham.

[31]Such sheaves may be coined 'Fock sheaves' for obvious reasons.

quantum theory[32], the two stalks 'collapse' to a tensor product stalk over a single spacetime point event of the classical base spacetime manifold X. This phenomenon is characteristic in both classical and quantum field theories (in the absence of gravity) where, when we combine or entangle systems by tensor multiplication, their spacetime coordinates combine by identification. *"This mathematical practice expresses a certain physical practice: to learn the time, we do not look at the system but at the sun (or nowdays) at the laboratory clock, both prominent parts of the episystem"* [29], and it should be emphasized that the episystem is always regarded as being classical[33] in the sense of Bohr. Thus, we expect that the formulation of some sort of *'quantum sheaf'* is required in order to be able to model non-trivially quantum entanglement; moreover, it is quite reasonable to assume that such a quantum notion of a sheaf will be accompanied by an appropriate quantum notion of spacetime topology on which such sheaves are soldered.

We conclude this paper by mentioning another potential application of sheaf and topos theory to quantum gravity that only lately we have envisaged and started to comprehend in [48]. It concerns the possible application of sheaf and topos theory towards formulating an abstract sort of differential geometry *à la* Mallios [43, 44, 45, 46] on the aforementioned curved finsheaves of qausets or their related sheaves of quantum causal histories, as it were, to transcribe most of the differential geometric apparatus of C^∞-smooth manifolds to a reticular-algebraic setting that is *ab initio* free from the former's pathological infinities and incurable diseases. For instance, we have been able to perform a finitary version of the usual C^∞-smooth Čech-de Rham cohomology, as well as initiate a finsheaf-cohomological classification of the non-trivial finitary spin-Lorentzian connections dwelling on the curved finsheaves of qausets in [47]. In this context, what we would also like to work on in the immediate future is to try to relate Mallios' Abstract Differential Geometry [43, 44] and its finitary applications in [48] with the Kock-Lawvere Synthetic Differential Geometry [41] and its promising topos-theoretic applications to quantum gravity [13]. In this respect however, the quest has just begun.

Acknowledgments

Exchanges with Chris Isham (Imperial College) on topoi and their potential application to quantum gravity, with Tasos Mallios (University of Athens) on sheaves and their possible application to quantum gravity especially via his Abstract Differential Geometry theory [43, 44, 45, 46], with Chris Mulvey (University of Sussex) on quantales and noncommutative topology, as well as a brief but timely exchange with Bob Coecke (Oxford) on a promising dynamical conception of quantum logic entirely by categorical means, are all greatly appreciated. The present work was supported by the European Union in the form of a generous Marie Curie Individual Postdoctoral Research Fellowship held at Imperial College, London (United Kingdom).

---

[32]In the sheaf $\mathfrak{H}(X)$, states of quanta are represented by its (continuous) sections.

[33]Here, the classical base spacetime manifold X.

References

[1] Alexandrov, P. S., *Combinatorial Topology*, vol. 1, Greylock, Rochester, New York (1956).

[2] Alexandrov, P. S., *Elementary Concepts of Topology*, Dover Publications, New York (1961).

[3] Baehr, H. C., Dimakis, A. and Müller-Hoissen, F., *Differential calculi on commutative algebras*, Journal of Physics A: Mathematical and General, **28**, 3197 (1995); hep-th/9412069.

[4] Bell, J. L., *Toposes and Local Set Theories: An Introduction*, Clarendon Press, Oxford (1988).

[5] Bombelli, L., Lee, J., Meyer, D. and Sorkin, R. D., *Space-Time as a Causal Set*, Physical Review Letters, **59**, 521 (1987).

[6] Borceaux, F., *Examples of Quantales in Topos Theory*, Annales de la Societe Scientifique des Bruxelles, **101** (III), 61 (1987).

[7] Borceaux, F. and Van den Bossche, G., *Quantales and their Sheaves*, Order, **3**, 61 (1986).

[8] Borceaux, F. and Van den Bossche, G., *An Essay on Noncommutative Topology*, Topology and its Applications, **31**, 203 (1989).

[9] Breslav, R. B., Parfionov, G. N. and Zapatrin, R. R., *Topology measurement within the histories approach*, Hadronic Journal, **22**, 225 (1999); quant-ph/9903011.

[10] Breslav, R. B., and Zapatrin, R. R., *Differential Structure of Greechie Logics*, International Journal of Theoretical Physics, **39**, 1027 (2000); quant-ph/9902065.

[11] Butterfield, J. and Isham, C. J., *A Topos Perspective on the Kochen-Specker Theorem: I. Quantum States as Generalized Valuations*, International Journal of Theoretical Physics, **37**, 2669 (1998).

[12] Butterfield, J. and Isham, C. J., *A Topos Perspective on the Kochen-Specker Theorem: II. Conceptual Aspects and Classical Analogues*, International Journal of Theoretical Physics, **38**, 827 (1999).

[13] Butterfield, J. and Isham, C. J., *Some Possible Roles for Topos Theory in Quantum Theory and Quantum Gravity*, Foundations of Physics, **30**, 1707 (2000); gr-qc/9910005.

[14] Butterfield, J., Hamilton, J. and Isham, C. J., *A Topos Perspective on the Kochen-Specker Theorem: III. Von Neumann Algebras as the Base Category*, International Journal of Theoretical Physics, **39**, 2667 (2000); quant-ph/9911020.

[15] Cole, E. A. B., *The Observer-dependence of Cellular Space-time Structure*, International Journal of Theoretical Physics, **5**, 3 (1972).

38

[16] Connes, A., *Noncommutative Geometry*, Academic Press, New York (1994).

[17] Crane, L., *Clock and Category: is quantum gravity algebraic?*, Journal of Mathematical Physics, **36**, 6180 (1995).

[18] Dimakis, A., and Müller-Hoissen, F., *Discrete Riemannian Geometry*, Journal of Mathematical Physics, **40**, 1518 (1999).

[19] Dimakis, A., Müller-Hoissen, F. and Vanderseypen, F., *Discrete Differential Manifolds and Dynamics of Networks*, Journal of Mathematical Physics, **36**, 3771 (1995).

[20] Dugundji, J., *Topology*, Allyn and Bacon, Inc., Boston (1966).

[21] Eilenberg, S. and Steenrod, N., *Foundations of Algebraic Topology*, Princeton University Press, Princeton, New Jersey (1952).

[22] Einstein, A., *Über den Äther, Schweizerische Naturforschende Gesellschaft Verhanflungen*, **105**, 85 (1924); English translation by Simon Saunders: *On the Ether*, in *The Philosophy of Vacuum*, Eds. Saunders, S. and Brown, H., Clarendon Press, Oxford, (1991).

[23] Einstein, A., *The Meaning of Relativity*, Princeton University Press, Princeton (1956); 3rd extended edition (1990).

[24] Eisenbud, D. and Harris, J., *Schemes: the Language of Modern Algebraic Geometry*, Wadsworth and Brooks/Cole, California (1992).

[25] Finkelstein, D., *Matter, Space and Logic*, in *Boston Studies in the Philosophy of Science*, **5**, Eds. Cohen, R. S. and Wartofsky, M. W., Dordrecht, Holland (1969); reprinted in *The Logico-Algebraic Approach to Quantum Mechanics II*, Ed. Hooker, C. A., Reidel, Dordrecht, Holland (1979).

[26] Finkelstein, D., *The Physics of Logic*, in *The Logico-Algebraic Approach to Quantum Mechanics II*, Ed. Hooker, C. A., Reidel, Dordrecht, Holland (1979).

[27] Finkelstein, D., *'Superconducting' Causal Nets*, International Journal of Theoretical Physics, **27**, 473 (1988).

[28] Finkelstein, D., *Theory of Vacuum* in *The Philosophy of Vacuum*, Eds. Saunders, S. and Brown, H., Clarendon Press, Oxford (1991).

[29] Finkelstein, D. R., *Quantum Relativity: A Synthesis of the Ideas of Einstein and Heisenberg*, Springer-Verlag, New York (1996).

[30] Finkelstein, D. and Hallidy, W. H., *Q: an Algebraic Language for Quantum-Spacetime Topology*, International Journal of Theoretical Physics, **30**, 463 (1991).

[31] Goldblatt, R., *Topoi: The Categorial Analysis of Logic*, North-Holland, Amsterdam (1984).

[32] Haag, R., *Fundamental Irreversibility and the Concept of Events*, Communications in Mathematical Physics, **132**, 245 (1990).

[33] Hartshorne, R., *Algebraic Geometry*, 3rd edition, Springer-Verlag, New York-Heidelberg-Berlin (1983).

[34] Isham, C. J., *Quantum Topology and the Quantisation on the Lattice of Topologies*, Classical and Quantum Gravity, **6**, 1509 (1989).

[35] Isham, C. J., *An introduction to general topology and quantum topology*, in *Proceedings of the NATO ASI on Physics, Geometry and Topology (August, 1989)*, 1–64, Plenum Press (1989).

[36] Isham, C. J., *Canonical Groups and the Quantization of Geometry and Topology*, in *Conceptual Problems of Quantum Gravity*, Eds. Ashtekar, A., and Stachel, J., Birkhäuser, Boston-Basel-Berlin (1991).

[37] Isham, C. J., *Quantum Logic and the Histories Approach to Quantum Theory*, Journal of Mathematical Physics, **35**, 2157 (1994).

[38] Isham, C. J., *Topos Theory and Consistent Histories: The Internal Logic of the Set of All Consistent Sets*, International Journal of Theoretical Physics, **36**, 785 (1997).

[39] Lambek, J. and Scott, P. J., *Introduction to Higher Order Categorical Logic*, Cambridge University Press, Cambridge (1986).

[40] Lawvere, F.W., *Continuously Variable Sets: Algebraic Geometry=Geometric Logic*, in *Proceedings of the Logic Colloquium in Bristol (1973)*, North-Holland, Amsterdam (1975).

[41] Lavendhomme, R., *Basic Concepts of Synthetic Differential Geometry*, Kluwer Academic Publishers, Dordrecht (1996).

[42] Mac Lane, S. and Moerdijk, I., *Sheaves in Geometry and Logic: A First Introduction to Topos Theory*, Springer-Verlag, New York (1992).

[43] Mallios, A., *Geometry of Vector Sheaves: An Axiomatic Approach to Differential Geometry*, vols. 1-2, Kluwer Academic Publishers, Dordrecht (1998).

[44] Mallios, A., *On an Axiomatic Treatment of Differential Geometry via Vector Sheaves*, International Plaza Mathematica Japonica, **48**, 93 (1998).

[45] Mallios, A., Abstract Differential Geometry, General Relativity and Singularities, invited paper in *Unresolved Problems in Mathematics for the 21st Century: a tribute to Kiyoshi Iseki's 80th birthday*, IOS Press, Amsterdam 77 (2001).

[46] Mallios, A., *Gauge Theories from the Point of View of Abstract Differential Geometry*, 2-volume continuation of book [43], in preparation (2001).

[47] Mallios, A. and Raptis, I., *Finitary Spacetime Sheaves of Quantum Causal Sets: Curving Quantum Causality*, International Journal of Theoretical Physics, **40**, 1885 (2001); gr-qc/0102097.

[48] Mallios, A. and Raptis, I., *Finitary Čech-de Rham Cohomology: much ado without C^∞-smoothness*, International Journal of Theoretical Physics (2001); gr-qc/0110033.

[49] Mulvey, C. J., '&', Supplemento ai Rendiconti del Circolo Matematico di Palermo, **II** (12), 99 (1986).

[50] Mulvey, C. and Pelletier, J. W., *On the Quantisation of Points*, Journal of Pure and Applied Algebra, **159**, 231 (2001).

[51] Mulvey, C. and Pelletier, J. W., *On the Quantisation of Spaces*, Journal of Pure and Applied Algebra, to appear (2001).

[52] Nawaz, M., *Quantales: Quantal Sets*, D.Phil. Thesis, University of Sussex, UK (1985).

[53] O'Donnell, C. J. and Spiegel, E., *Incidence Algebras*, Monographs and Textbooks in Pure and Applied Mathematics, Marcel Dekker, New York-Basel-Hong Kong (1997).

[54] Penrose, R., *Newton, Quantum Theory and Reality*, in *300 Years of Gravitation*, Eds. Hawking, S. W. and Israel, W., Cambridge University Press, Cambridge (1987).

[55] Raptis, I., *Axiomatic Quantum Timespace Structure: A Preamble to the Quantum Topos Conception of the Vacuum*, Ph.D. Thesis, University of Newcastle upon Tyne, UK (1998).

[56] Raptis, I., *Algebraic Quantization of Causal Sets*, International Journal of Theoretical Physics, **39**, 1233 (2000); gr-qc/9906103.

[57] Raptis, I., *Finitary Spacetime Sheaves*, International Journal of Theoretical Physics, **39**, 1703 (2000); gr-qc/0102108.

[58] Raptis, I., *Non-Commutative Topology for Curved Quantum Causality*, pre print (2001); gr-qc/0101082.

[59] Raptis, I., *Sheafifying Consistent Histories*, submitted to the International Journal of Theoretical Physics (2001); quant-ph/0107037.

[60] Raptis, I., *Locally Finite, Causal and Quantal Einstein Gravity*, in preparation (2001).

[61] Raptis, I. and Zapatrin, R. R., *Quantization of discretized spacetimes and the correspondence principle*, International Journal of Theoretical Physics, **39**, 1 (2000); gr-qc/9904079.

[62] Raptis, I. and Zapatrin, R. R., *Algebraic description of spacetime foam*, Classical and Quantum Gravity, **20**, 4187 (2001); gr-qc/0102048.

[63] Rawling, J. P. and Selesnick, S. A., *Orthologic and Quantum Logic. Models and Computational Elements*, Journal of the Association for Computing Machinery, **47**, 721 (2000).

[64] Rideout, D. P. and Sorkin, R. D., *A Classical Sequential Growth Dynamics for Causal Sets*, Physical Review D, **61**, 024002 (2000); gr-qc/9904062.

[65] Rosenthal, K., *Quantales and their Applications*, Longman Scientific and Technical (1990).

[66] Rota, G.-C., *On The Foundation Of Combinatorial Theory, I. The Theory Of Möbius Functions*, Zeitschrift für Wahrscheinlichkeitstheorie, **2**, 340 (1968).

[67] Selesnick, S. A., *Correspondence Principle for the Quantum Net*, International Journal of Theoretical Physics, **30**, 1273 (1991).

[68] Selesnick, S. A., *Quanta, Logic and Spacetime: Variations on Finkelstein's Quantum Relativity*, World Scientific, Singapore (1998).

[69] Shafarevich, I. R., *Basic Algebraic Geometry 2*, 2nd edition, Springer-Verlag, Berlin Heidelberg New York (1994).

[70] Sorkin, R. D., *Does a Discrete Order Underlie Spacetime and its Metric?* in *Proceedings of the Third Canadian Conference on General Relativity and Relativistic Astrophysics*, Eds. Cooperstock, F. and Tupper, B., World Scientific, Singapore (1990).

[71] Sorkin, R. D., *Spacetime and Causal Sets*, in *Proceedings of the SILARG VII Conference, Cocoyoc, Mexico*, preprint (1990).

[72] Sorkin, R. D., *Finitary Substitute for Continuous Topology*, International Journal of Theoretical Physics, **30**, 923 (1991).

[73] Sorkin, R. D., *A Specimen of Theory Construction from Quantum Gravity*, in *The Creation of Ideas in Physics*, Ed. Leplin, J., Kluwer Academic Publishers, Dordrecht (1995).

[74] Sorkin, R. D., *Forks in the Road, on the Way to Quantum Gravity*, talk given at the symposium on *Directions in General Relativity*, University of Maryland, College Park in May 1993 in honour of Dieter Brill and Charles Misner (1997); gr-qc/9706002.

[75] Sorkin, R. D., *The Causal Set as the Deep Structure of Spacetime*, draft version of a paper in preparation (5/3/2001).

[76] Stanley, R. P., *Enumerative Combinatorics*, Wadsworth and Brooks, Monterey, California (1986).

[77] Van Oystaeyen, F., *Algebraic Geometry for Associative Algebras*, Marcel Dekker, New York (2000).

[78] Van Oystaeyen, F., *Is the Topology of Nature Noncommutative ?* and *A Grothendieck-type of Scheme Theory for Schematic Algebras*, research seminars given at the Mathematics Department of the University of Pretoria, Republic of South Africa on 2-3/2/2000 (notes available).

[79] Van Oystaeyen, F. and Verschoren, A., *Non-commutative Algebraic Geometry*, Springer Lecture Notes in Mathematics, **887**, Springer-Verlag, Berlin-Heidelberg (1981).

[80] Wheeler, J. A., *Geometrodynamics*, in *Relativity, Groups and Topology*, Eds. De Witt, C. and De Witt, B. S., Gordon and Breach, London (1964).

[81] Zapatrin, R. R., *Finitary Algebraic Superspace*, International Journal of Theoretical Physics, **37**, 799 (1998); gr-qc/9704062.

[82] Zapatrin, R. R., *Incidence algebras of simplicial complexes*, Pure Mathematics and Applications, to appear (2001); math.CO/0001065.

[83] Zeeman, E. C., *Causality implies the Lorentz group*, Journal of Mathematical Physics, **5**, 490 (1964).

[84] Zeeman, E. C., *The Topology of Minkowski Space*, Topology, **6**, 161 (1967).

ALGEBRAIC APPROACHES TO THE PARTICLE CONCEPT

Ted Bastin,
Maesllwyn, Tan y Groes,
Cardigan SA43 2JF.
ted@ftech.co.uk

C.W.Kilmister,
Red Tiles Cottage,
High Street, Barcombe,
Lewes,
East Sussex BN8 5DH.

January 1, 2002

ABSTRACT

"I was, and remain, unhappy with traditional discrete mathematical approaches. I find the philosophical motivations and much of the reasoning to be contaminated with continuum ideas" (McGoveran[1]). In a like attitude we provide, within the hierarchy method, a physical picture of the quantum particle which yet is truly discrete or combinatorial in the sense that space and time have not yet been introduced. Charge and mass are defined combinatorially in connection with the basic concept of antiparticle. The algebraic structure of Rowlands and Cullerne is shown to admit similar combinatorial analysis even though those writers are far from abandoning the continuum. Strong support is provided for their suggestions for relating mass and charge.

PART I

1. Introduction

This joint paper is directed to the eternal task of getting from 'the combinatorial hierarchy' to normal physics. Its *point d'appuye* is the particles with the interaction strengths as our firm starting point and guideline and without recourse to the Newtonian little bits of matter. The dynamical concepts, too, have to appear deductively and cannot be taken over from Newtonian physics as in current quantum physics.

We are after what you might call a 'blow by blow account' of what it is to be a particle. We have an algebraic structure, the combinatorial hierarchy, to which we attach importance, and now we have to say what the algebra actually means in terms of things out there in the world. The 'program universe', years back, was the first attempt to find this meaning, but the proponents of program universe were afflicted by a sort of philosophical cold feet when asked if the world really worked like that. We shall explore certain parallels of our algebra with that used by Rowlands and Cullerne: (R&C for short). We think we can benefit from the extensive connections with detailed high energy experiment which they claim.

2. The physical argument

1. We are hoping to reach a representation of a typical elementary system, in interaction with a statistical background. In fact a high energy particle of some sort.
2. Its stability is due to the structure of discriminately closed subsets (*vide infra* P.4).
3. The stability is threatened, or perhaps we should say 'has to be maintained against', outside intervention from the statistical background.

We should like to use the hierarchy algebra like this: at every stage there is a constant flux of new elements coming into the known picture as a result of discrimination processes. The initial flux of these creates a *framework* into which the later elements can be fitted. In Parker-Rhodes'original scheme the entities were bit-strings of a certain fixed length n and the vector space over Z_2 of dimension n was such a framework. When the process view is formulated such a framework does not arise automatically but has to be postulated. In Parker-Rhodes' case, elements of the framework could be present or absent. In the process view this possibility takes the form that elements of the framework can be removed as well as created and the framework has to have a degree of independence which persists through the changes. Otherwise how can we imagine the changes with nothing to compare what is new with what has gone before? This framework is not the same as our statistical background: that we have to imagine but do not have information on except through our process. The most important use of the framework is in connection with the hierarchy levels. In general, the persistence of a framework at one level is determined by the persistence of an element at a more complex level. This persistence over a period makes it possible to speak of changes at the less complex level (although the framework as a whole persists). We can speak of changes in the *occupancy* of the level if and only if there is something which can tell us 'there is something there but there doesn't have to be'.

3. The process: what is going on?

Thus we have 1. the continual flux of discriminations, and 2. something stable enough to define a particle in the face of this flux. This stability is presumably a set of elements which persists at least for a number of steps. An element of the framework at a higher level will specify this set as a dcs. So changes are going on all the time and these are of two kinds. There are those permitted by the framework and there are those which obtrude from interactions with the statistical background. Particular interest will be attached to changes with some kind of regularity, and of these again, those which can be represented by groups will be important. So we get the picture of the groups as a sort of algebraic engine which keeps things ticking over, or indeed racing along. That is what groups are for, which otherwise is a bit of a mystery.

Parker-Rhodes' square matrices, or the linear functions of the process view, can be seen as longer bit-strings with the same interpretation in terms of yes/no properties. Even in the recent developments, to which we presently turn, where bit-strings are no longer the elements, it is still the case that the linear functions have the same sort of interpretation as the elements at the less complex level. We assume that the stable aspects of the algebra will correspond to particles, but, in addition to their stability we need to be able to identify the elements that appear in the stable subsystems with individual attributes of the particles. This idea is commonsense in current physics including quantum physics because of the tacit acceptance of the classical Newtonian particle. We however have to introduce it explicitly.

4. Can the combinatorial hierarchy fit the physical picture?

We now have the essentials of our dynamical picture for representing the geneneralized particle. We recall the steps in the hierarchy algebra construction to show that it can accommodate that picture. The occupancy or non-occupancy of sites was a principle in the earliest algebraic quadratic group work. They simply existed or did not exist. When Frederick Parker-Rhodes first set out his construction in terms of bit-strings there was a general assumption that their elements each described the possession or non-possession of certain properties -as it might be the possession or non-possession of charge by a particle. However the basis for these ideas was inadequate, so progress was slow. Deepening of the foundations has been in terms of a *process*. We recognized *equal* entities and that gave rise to a *set* of equal entities which gets a *label*. Thus entities enter the known construction at any stage and have to be *labelled*. The labels then enter the theoretical description. The essential step is then to test each new entity against an old one to verify that it is genuinely new and not another copy of one already in existence (in which latter case its label must be changed to the same as the existing one). This process is *discrimination* and if the two entities are different it yields a new entity, their discriminant. If they are the same, no new entity arises, but a *signal*, z indicates the fact. To determine the discriminant in a non-arbitrary way we took over a construction from John Conway ("On numbers and games."): label the discriminant with the least label which has not already been involved with either entity. (This assumes that the labels have been ordered in some way; one could for example use the ordinal numbers 1, 2 3, 4,....).

This construction involves the labels of the two entities symmetrically, and this assumption is needed to get the Combinatorial hierarchy in Parker-Rhodes form. In recent years we have realized that this assumption gives a special case which is allowed by the process but need not arise and should be generalized. This generalization is known by the unfortunate name "aspect", and we shall return to it.

A set of entities which has the property that every pair of entities in the set has a discriminant which is in the set is called a *discriminately closed subset* (dcs). These play an important role. The smallest non-trivial dcs has 3 members (any two entities and their discriminant) and this is called the *first level*. One can put all this in correspondence with our earlier (pre-Parker-Rhodes) work where the simplest structure was the quadratic group S. The first level also has this structure underdiscrimination if one adjoins to it the signal z and supplies values for the formal results of discriminating z and an element (or z with itself) so as to make z the identity element of S. Then it is a purely mathematical result that entities may be labelled by bit strings, and discrimination is then addition/Z_2. We have now represented S as $(1,0)$, $(0,1)$, and $(1,1)$ with z as $(0,0)$. Thus one can see the process as describing entities which have, or do not have, yes/no properties.

What has been described so far of Parker-Rhodes construction simply writes additively what we had earlier written multiplicatively. But his important contribution is what happens next. He suggested, without much explanation, that a dcs of bit strings at one level could be represented by a square matrix (over Z_2 of course) which had the elements of the dcs as its proper eigenvalues. The rationale of this "going up a level" later became clearer from the process description. If a third entity arises and is discriminated against the two already labelled, there can be an infinite regress ("can be" because of course the process can strike lucky and identify the putatively new entity first time). Thus a first level dcs with 3 independent elements and $2^3 - 1 = 7$ elements overall does not have the general application of the one with 2 independent elements. But what is possible is to "go up a level" and to ask whether the putative new element belongs to one of the dcss by representing them by linear operators and asking whether the new element is an eigenvector. And, as is well-known, the process of going up a level can be repeated, though once four levels have been formed there is a stop.

We have supposed that the stability of the particle will arise from the dcss. At first one might guess that the stability would consist in a sequence of entities all belonging to one dcs. However this is too extreme since it gives a complete stasis.The following modification seems to meet the need. Suppose that there are two dcss with no common elements and that each entity is expressible as a sum of two; one in each dcs. Moreover the element in the second dcs is always the same. This is really a slightly changed re-statement of the 'old position' using the interplay of strings: if there is a subset of places in all the strings which is not occupied then that non-occupation persists, and carries through the levels. The slight change is that the non-occupied subset is not one of the original pair of dcss but a subset of discriminants of entities which are *adjacent,* that is, come up next to each other in the process. Evidently this formulation is as general as it can be because if more dcss were involved they could be grouped with one or the other.

We sum up the process picture to show how far we have accommodated the physical requirements which we first set out. There is a constant flux of new elements coming into being, and the initial flux creates the framework into which the later elements may be fitted. This background may be such as to maintain the stability required. New elements can interact with elements of the framework at any level.

5. The world outside

This last observation about the background prompted an innovation which will seem obvious enough but which in fact represents a major change in our thinking. We had always supposed that the new elements coming from the statistical background were elementary. It followed that there was nothing in the universe of any significant structure except our own construction. A solipsist picture indeed. Through thinking more explicitly about the statistical background and the framework this picture has had to be generalized. The things 'out there' could be anything. In particular there is no reason why they should not include whole hierarchies or partly complete ones. Such things are correctly equipped to engage in discriminations with those we already have labelled. Of course all we can know about them is still only what can be discovered by the discrimination process, but we are much more in tune with commonsense in thinking of a universe having lots of things out there like the one we are constructing. The fact that, as we now see it, the flux will exhibit interference at all levels, not just the bottom one resolves a long term unease that there must always be something arbitrary, or savouring of the mathematician behind the scenes who pulls the strings, in our having to specify what level we are working at at every given moment. As things stand now this is not a decision we have to make since the background specifies it for us. I am afraid that it may seem that over a long time we have invented these last problems for ourselves and then shown great relish for finding solutions for them. Perhaps it is a bit like that.

We may be in a universe in which we have knowledge, of a sort, of things *other than* ourselves, but we must remember that this expression 'otherness' means what it says and no more. In particular it would be erroneous to infer any sort of spatial distribution whatever. It is a very bare 'not us'; it is not an 'out there'. We may hope to see a fruitful use of statistical methods being used to give meaning to notions of spatial configuration and of the dynamics resulting from changes of those configurations.

6. Aspect

'Aspect', which has already been mentioned, arose from realizing that the discriminant of a against b was not completely the same as that of b against a, because of the asymmetry in relabelling. The new element is always the one needing re-labelling. This realization necessitates some changes -minor except for one. Since discrimination is not symmetric, the addition notation introduced by Parker-Rhodes is best replaced by our old multiplication. Then one has to modify Conway's rule. There are two stages here. Firstly, one recognizes that there still remains the simpler system in which the asymmetry is ignored. Mathematically, this requires the system to have a homomorphism back to the corresponding level of the combinatorial hierarchy. This homomorphism sets up an equivalence relation on entities (two elements equivalent if they map onto the same hierarchy element). This equivalence relation requires a signal, y say, in addition to z which signals equality. Secondly, then, Conway's rule becomes: label ab with the least label which has not already been involved with   a(...)   or   (...)b, or with   ba, so long as the homomorphism is preserved.

When this procedure is carried out the first level turns out to have 6 elements instead of 3. It is possible (and allowable) to choose their relations with the two signals y, z so that the eight elements constitute the quaternion group Q. Hence the equivalence classes have two members, so that the equivalence corresponds to a duality. Now it is well known to algebraicists that this duality allows itself to be expressed in a particular way -namely by writing the pairs of entities as, say, a, -a, b, -b, c, -c. This fact is far from trivial and is a statement about the particular structure that arises. Thus aspect shows how an extra degree of freedom arises -albeit a degree of freedom of a different kind from those represented by bit-strings. It is tempting to murmur 'antiparticle', but we are not there yet (by a long way). This +/- which has arisen unbidden from the analysis refers only to the group multiplication. That is, though it does have the properties $(-a)(+b) = -ab$, there is as yet no meaning to expressions like $e + (-e)$.

Still, since R&C use a direct product of Q and a vector algebra rather like Q (and so could be rewritten in terms of QxQ), we are evidently in the same ball-park. Moreover when one goes up a level with aspect, the   +/-   structure which is just a realization of C_2 becomes $C_2 \times C_2 \times C_2$. It is generated by three quantities squaring to unity which invites comparison with the mysterious $+/-z_p$ $+/-z_t$ in R&C's "A, B, C, D, &E representations".

We have required that the framework may be extended or reduced. These changes may happen in the following way. Discriminations may be

a. between known elements, say Dkk'

b. between a known and an unknown. We mean here a new element coming in: of course it is still unknown if it is being discriminated. Call this Dku. There may also be Duu' going on but since we know nothing of it we can ignore it. Rowlands and Cullerne's rotations will be special cases of these kinds of flux.

As soon as two different elements come into play they *can* generate a whole hierarchy, but this whole hierarchy, which is the framework to fit future elements in, has to be generated gradually by the flux of discriminations. One might be tempted to say that they are all there in potentia, or else that all the elements are bit strings some of which are not there. Either of these ways of speaking seems to smuggle the mathematician in as essential to the process by the back door, and is not necessary.

Case a: Dkk'. Here k, k' are both known. A. first dispose of the case when k, k' haven't entered into discrimination before so either Dkk' = 0 (so k' = k) or Dkk' = k''. In the first situation 2 elements were in play and now only one, but there are now two instances of it. In the second, two elements were in play and at the end three are. In this second situation the hierarchy is starting to build up. B, The more general and hitherto neglected situation is: k, k' have both, at least in part, generated hirarchies. In the situation where these hierarchies are the *same*, Dkk' = 0 or k'' and so, at the end, either elements become 1 or they become 3 (so either it empties the framework or it fills it out more). In the situation where k' is *not* part of the hierarchy generated by k, k' gets added as a new element at the first level so that there are now 3 elements instead of 2.

Another way of doing it is this: k has generated a hierarchy already with, say, k, k_1 at lowest level. Then dkk' will provide the possibility of another hierarchy with k, k_1 at lowest level: so the hierarchies are not disjoint. Perhaps they have to have a common member to be in the same universe.

Case(b) Dku. Here, if Dku = 0 nothing changes (i.e. u has come in but it turns out is simply k). If Dku = k' then *either* k' fills out the existing frame or it extends the frame further.
How is all this changed where the possibility of aspect is recognized? Not all that much. However there are now two signals, y and z. If Dpq = z then p = q; if Dpq = y, then p, q are dual elements. So the Dkk' case is like this:

	= z	empties frame by 1
Dkk'	= y	k,k' duality
	≠ y, z	fills out frame by 1

with similar changes for Dku.

7. Antiparticles and antiproperties

The connection between antiness and 'aspect' has been pointed out though the connection falls short of provision of the charge concept in terms of the 0/1 principle, and we must therefore push that principle a bit farther. If we cannot refer implicitly to continuum particle classical physics to import all the dynamical concepts such as charge, then they have also to be brought under the 0/1 banner. But how? The answer depends on the antiparticle principle. To introduce that we need to be able to use the framework, and particularly to work with two adjacent levels together.

We want to make a different configuration without changing the occupancy of the vectors, so we need a new kind of operation. The antiness operation satisfies the requirement of not changing the occupancy (i.e. the distribution of 0's and 1's) and there is only one change it can make and that is to produce antiness. Part of the meaning of this is that it is a change which restores the status quo when repeated. There can then be a discussion as to how far this operation or combination of operations warrants the designation +/- which is conveyed by the idea that anti-particles are what result from changeing the sign of one or more attributes.

To get from antiness to sign of charge we need to understand the mechanism by which the antiness displays itself. There has to be some element of something (one might call it a 'property' if there were already something defined for it to be a property of) which can be changed to 0 or non-existence or 'no'. Call the change together with what changes it Z. Now use Y to denote the reverse change together with what changes it. Then add that the combination of X and Y produces no change. Then X and Y will be antiness operations defined in terms of existence/non-existence. As I see things antiness must be so reducible.This definition is what requires the background even if it has not been required by the earlier steps, because there has to be something for each of X and Y to fit into and exist independently of them both. In the background there are dcss produced by the discrimination process on the elements which continually enter. These are constantly changing their composition but there is no mechanism defined to say anything about anything that involves individuality for them until we have a new level.

PART II

In the first part of this paper we gave an outline of what is supposed to be going on out there in the world that accords with our Combinatorial Hierarchy. In particular this outline considered the nature and stability and partial stability of the particles. In doing this it was necessary to give a meaning, additional to the stability, to the idea that a particle was an association of physical attributes like charge and mass. Of course these ideas do not seem necessary in current thinking since it all comes with the tacit acceptance of the classical Newtonian particle, and this has never been replaced in quantum physics.

Currently the whole concept of a stable or unstable particle is procured by throwing in *yet more particles*.

8. Comparison with the algebraic structure of Rowlands and Cullerne

We shall use work of Rowlands and Cullerne (hence forward "R&C") in our effort to find a bridge from our radical construction of the particle concept, and my references will be to their paper "The Dirac Algebra and SU5 symmetry"[2]. R&C by no means follow our radical approach and in fact they arrived at their theory using the usual particle concept of naive realism. Nevertheless they have introduced certain pieces of mathematics which appear to make the best sense when viewed as part of a free-standing combinatorial scheme, as we shall see. What is more, their basic structure of group algebra bears strong correspondences with ours. Therefore we ask your indulgence, and theirs, in treating the combinatorial structure which we see in R&C as something separable from the usual dynamical ideas and standing in its own right as a starting point.. We think that we can reach a useful clarity that way. Moreover that way of working might put R&C in a position to work backwards and *derive* results in conventional theory which otherwise they have to assume. We shall come to an important case of this later.

The beginning point of our connexion with R&C is their use of quarks and quark colours, and this is encapsulated in a 3 x 3 array in which the quark colours are plotted against the three interaction strengths (not including the gravitational interaction). i, j, k are the quaternion designations. Also coefficients 0 and 1 are always assigned to each of the quaternion designations which means that at any given time some of the assignments exist and some do not.

	B	G	R
+/- e	j	i	k
+/- s	I	k	j
+/- w	k	j	i

Array 1

We now wish to take over from R&C the use of quark colours as the vital intermediary or 'interlingua' between particle identification and the structure which represents the dynamics. (I say 'quark colours' rather than 'quarks' so as to avoid unsubstantiated assumptions.) Thus we seek to the degree of correspondence of the classificatory table, 1, with the second level of the hierarchy. Here are a few comments on the correspondence which we are trying to establish:

1. The interaction strengths which are vertical in the array 1. are regarded by R&C as 'charges', thus extending that term from electric charge to the other two. It must be remembered that the experimentally defined thing is the interaction strength.

2. The +/- assigned by convention to the three charges have no equivalent in the hierarchy algebra but it will be an essential step later to show how the +/- introduced by aspect relates to this..

3. The array 1. is regarded by R&C as essentially dynamic in the sense that transformations among the elements are supposed to go on in accordance with two quaternion group structures. Thus the existence or non-existence of all the elements singly in the array continually changes in accordance with the transformations specified by the quaternions. These transformations are regarded as rotations as though the rows and columns in 1. play the part of spatial axes. I have assumed that the rotations go on all the time, though this is not much discussed by R&C. Presumably we are looking to describe a particle as a stable configuration of rotations. Of course one gets no help from current theory in which there is no account given of what a particle is. I suppose that by default it is a little bit of Newtonian matter cut up as small as possible with some funny non-Newtonian quantum restraints.

4. R&C follow the usual custom of quantum theorists in that having once used the spatial ideas to define their transformations they proceed to exploit the algebraic possibilities without regard to the original meaning. Thus these rotations seem to be able to go on in the restricted space of these quantum systems being studied while the rest of the universe goes on unperturbed. In our approach everything depends on introducing algebra without spatial connotations being presumed at the outset.

5. Rotations, for us, are a special case of the transformations which go on all the time in response to the background flux and the resulting discriminations. The invariants under these rotationsprobably arise as dcss since these are the only way of getting a set of elements which has stability against the effects from outside. In the   0/1 string representation this stability works for discriminations within the created elements but the interpretation for unknown things from outside needs ad hoc specification. For the group representation, which is more fundamental, discriminations only take place with structures from

outside which are a counterpart, sizewise, with those existing, so they are on a par with those from inside.

6. In the combinatorial hierachy the 3x3 structure derived from the dcss and which we use in our comparison with R&C is not the source of the 3-dimensonality of space. That comes from the 3-level structure, and is comprehensible as something which is omnipresent in the detailed mechanics because interactions with the background can take place at any level. We used to have trouble in understanding this because of our obsession with starting at the bottom level which made the dimensions seem irreducibly asymmetrical. In fact any attempt to identify the components of the full dcs at level with -say- 3-momentum and extending that to 4-momentum is wrong. This means that we have serious work to do before getting to a representation of position or momentum vectors, and that our attempt to link with R&C is threatened. On this last point we note that R&C have a very unnatural step to sustain in making the jump from their array to a spatial interpretation. This is shown by the totally disparate character of the charges, and this apparent anomaly leads them into a very complex representation which they call the accommodation of charges which we must study separately if we wish to use their array as a stepping-stone into current theory.

7. First, for completeness, I mention a later step taken by R&C to make the spatial interpretation of the array more natural. They interpret m, p, and E as a separate dimensional scheme associated with their second quaternion group.

9. Accommodation of charges

R&C use the seeming clash between the symmetry of the quaternion groups and the diversity of the charges, to get towards the symmetries envisaged in the Standard Model. They have to establish a departure from symmetry of application of the colours to s, e, w. At any given time in array 1. existence symbols 0/1 are put as coefficients of each term. It is a fundamental requirement of R&C that "unit assignments should be indistinguishable from zero assignments". (P.17, top paragraph).I think this has to mean that there is no restriction on the assignment during the rotations due to the quaternion groups. In the hierarchy this simply means that we are not operating on level 2 so that the transformations are not available. They attach particular importance to configurations of the table in which one charge may take take unit value (i.e.exist) in one colour only whereas the other charges have freedom to change colour.

B   G   R

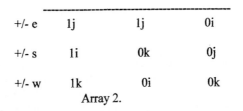

+/- e	1j	1j	0i
+/- s	1i	0k	0j
+/- w	1k	0i	0k

Array 2.

Thus, in the particular shown in array 2., s has this property alone. This combinatorial principle is the base for further identification. R&C say "We find that in every conceivable arrangement of any workable scheme involving three 'colour' states there is always at least one charge that is confined to a unit value in only one of the colours." This statement is plays an important role but needs clarification. One would say that R&C are here stating the combinatorial principle which they will use: justification needs separate discussion. It is not clear what is meant by 'conceivable' or by 'workable'.

R&C say they are free to make the choice of the strong interaction first, and they choose s because it makes the best physical sense. Identification of e and w follow in that order and require the use of antiparticle status in the case of e, and of the +/- designation in the case of w. For us the identification is much more definitive. The order cannot be other than that adopted by R&C. It follows from our identification of the whole scheme of coupling constants.

They argue that rotations are altering the unit charges the whole time but that this is undetectable if and only if their tables of colours and therefore quarks forbid the rotations to affect e and w.

R&C (article 14) say that the interactions at the s level are, or give rise to, exchange forces. I think this is unexeptionable and will not lead to trouble later on. It is less clear what it is that is interchanged. From the fact that each is a dcs it follows that any change in an element will give another element so that the term exchange is not inappropriate. Now there are charges which are the elements which change, and there are the associations of them which are the nearest thing to quarks and could be so-called.

R&C give schemes A, B, C which are said to be equivalent to a transfer of the unit s component between the B,R,G quarks without change in the e and w.

10. Charge exclusion

R&C introduce a new principle which they sometimes call *charge exclusion*. This term occurs in a different paper of R&C -"An investigation of the Higgs mechanism" [2], *P.10.* It does not appear in the SU5 symmetry paper to which we have mainly referred. Instead, the expression "charge obscuring" is used at the beginning of section 15, P.28 ; also in section 17 middle of P. 31 "the mechanism for obscuring charge designations is not so strict now". R&C hold that charges are constraind to be zero one by one. They argue that rotations are altering the unit charges the whole time but that this is undetectable if and only if their tables of colours and therefore quarks forbid the rotations to affect e and w. In another way of looking at it (P.27) they say "Consequently it is the effective exchange of a single strong charge between the three bound quarks which prevents the identification of any one quark by its colour." In effect, at any given stage there is a subset of the available charge sites that is constrained to be zero, and from the building up of this number the idea of a scale of magnitude appears for the first time. R&C note this, but do not give it special prominence because physics is not normally thought of without that logical possibility. For us the situation is very different, and we should like to emphasize this as a vital step in the logical progression toward a theory in which measurement of a range of possible magnitudes can be given a place. This emphasis makes the contrast between the approaches much stronger.

11. Quantization of charge/mass

The principle of charge exclusion leads R&C to a tentative theory about the *mutual* build up of numerical measures of electric charge and mass. Thus at the bottom of P.2 of their "Higgs mechanism" paper, R&C remark "These tables (ABCDE) are the ultimate product of taking the parameter charge to be composed of three individually conserved units, s, e, w, represented by quaternion operators, i, j, k, which are not individually conserved but are rotation symmetric."

At a risk of being repetitive I quote further from R&C because I need to reassure myself that their words do back up my glosses. My confused way of working requires the excuse that whereas I am picking out the combinatorial elements in their thinking in their own right, they have a presupposed dynamical language for which the combinatorial elements are seen as providing additional support.

In explaining the need for charge exclusion R&C speak of "mass-energies of the composite baryons and leptons based on the number of zero units of charges". For R&C it all starts from the invariance of the strong charges. This is for them an empirical requirement since they single out the strong charge (bottom of P.16 in D A and SU5) saying that the choice is arbitrary but fits with experiment. This invariance consists in all the places being designated 1 so that no change under the rotations is possible. (I shall speak of 'rotations' for convenience since they do that. They refer to the 'vector' one of the quaternion groups). The invariance of the strong charge is discussed in the first paragraph of section 14 (loc. cit). Their view seems to be that by having all the charge values as 1 in the three colours the necessary rotations do not make any difference to anything. This is why they keep on talking about the need to preserve the symmetry of the group rotations while having to let the charges change. "Thus the charge component e could be associated with i or k as easily as it could be associated with j."

The next step involves +/-. R&C maintain that they are precluded by the above argument from accommodating the e charges if they start with s 'stabilized' (as we will call it for convenience). They do not pursue precisely what restrictions are imposed because they are not arguing from this point of view. However clearly there is restricted choice. They think of it with the e charges having the possibility of + and - with s being constrained to + (say). The argument is complicated because they in effect reinterpret stabilization as charge identity in s and compel introduction of +/- starting from the 0/1 occupation symbols. This step is only possible if +/- are regarded as uninterpreted symbols, and at that point they identify them with antiness in the quarks. Hence antimatter is how you get electric charge with sign.

Now follows a bit of reasoning which we tentatively ascribe to them. Since some numbers representing the occupancy of charge are there we presume that we can construct all values or rather all (integral) numbers. This assumption can be connected with R&C's argument about the combined introduction of charge and mass which is very important. We may quote from the first two paragraphs of P.10 of "Investigation of the Higgs mechanism". "The Higgs mechanism was introduced earlier to account for the spectrum of particle masses. We have previously shown [R&C 200a] that the breaking of symmetry which produces mass is largely a result of the production of zero states of charge, mass and charge acting as an invariant in the same manner as space and time. Zero charges represent complete coupling to the Higgs field, non-zero charges represent a reduction of the vacuum state to less vacuum. The complete coupling to a zero charge may be equivalent in energy to one unit of m_e/α."

Here we have a very strong tie-up with the hierarchy picture which may be conveyed in a few points:

1. The electromagnetic level provides a discrete scale of magnitudes which has the (uncorrected) reciprocal of the fine-structure constant as its maximum -137. This progression should be identifiable with R&C;s charge exclusion.

2. Since both e and m appear in the dimensionless form of this constant ('m' via h) we are committed to a mutual generation of m and e. We do not get one without the other. This accords with the position of R&C.

3. The correspondence between the two theories at this point is more evident if we recall that in both cases the mechanism comes from the group transformations directly.

4. For us, this is the first appearance of a quantized magnitude with physical interpretation, and everything proceeds from here. For R&C the situation is more complicated since they take ove the concepts of mass and charge from continuum physics

5. R&C would seem to have a basis for quantization itself starting here. Here 'quantization' means associating integers, and subsequently perhaps rationals with the numbers derived from the algebra of the two-group picture. Such a construction is already entailed when we impose some finite and fixed value to Planck's constant. You could say that they are greatly underplaying their hand.

We stop at this exciting point because we have not got any further. R&C say they have suggested ways of counting up the zero charges in the multiplets, and their thoughts on these matters should guide us in extending the interpretation of our combinatorial algebra.

References

1. D. McGoveran, "Comment on 'Our joint work'" in Noyes "Bit string physics" World Scientific 2001, P.299.

2. Peter Rowlands and J.P.Cullerne, "The Dirac algebra and SU5 symmetry". Website of IQ Group, Liverpool, www.liv.ac.uk/~iqg .

3. Peter Rowlands and J.P.Cullerne, "An investigation of the Higgs mechanism". Implications Proc. XXII ANPA Conference, Cambridge 2001, Ed. K.Bowden.

CAN WE RUN DIRAC'S ARGUMENT BACKWARDS?

A RESEARCH REPORT

A. M. Deakin, 75 Clatterford Rd, Newport, Isle of Wight, PO30 1NZ
E-Mail: amdeak.deakin@virgin.net

ABSTRACT

This report summarises the results of an ongoing study of the implications of a previous paper [1]. In that paper we consider the quantizations of an hierarchy of differential identities involving particle coordinates. The quantizations of the two lowest level identities, when taken together, predict/ describe the motion of a particle to better accuracy than the lower level alone. The quantizations are identities only if the Hamiltonian operator takes certain forms. An Hamiltonian that satisfies both levels must be linear in the momenta; an Hamiltonian that is quadratic satisfies only the first level quantization. So the linear Hamiltonian is more exact. We suppose that the two Hamiltonians describe the motion of the same particle but, necessarily, with different precision. We cannot approximate the Hamiltonians themselves; but we can approximate measurements (averages) of the velocities of a free particle under each Hamiltonian. The conditions necessary for the approximation are that:- the momentum/ speed is low; the coefficients in the linear Hamiltonian satisfy an extension of the Dirac algebra (the mass is represented by an operator not a scalar); the measurement epoch is long. In consequence all the formulae of SR free-particle kinetics are reproduced as relations between the eigenvalues of commuting operators. The eigenvalue of the quadratic Hamiltonian is the low speed, Newtonian approximation. The $h/2$ spin appears, more or less, as in Dirac's theory; thus the particle is a fermion.

1. PRELIMINARIES

1.1 Preface

The investigations reported in this paper and its predecessor [1] have the following design: (i) Start with the bare bones of the formalism

1

traditionally used to describe the quantum dynamics of particles (scalar time; unitary evolution of the state $\psi(q)$ generated by the Hermitian operator $H(\underline{P}, \underline{Q})$; coordinates $\underline{Q}$ with continuous spectra q; conjugate variables $\underline{p}$, resulting from the FT of the normed function $\psi(q)$, which correspond to operators $\underline{P}$ on the Hilbert space of the $\psi(q)$; H identified as the Hamiltonian operator with Hamilton's equations as identities that follow from the definitions of rate operators). (ii) Impose criteria of smoothness, predictability and statistical stability that are assumed to be the hallmark of classical systems. (iii) Look for resulting structure that is recognisably classical (e.g., in the form of the Hamiltonian) and without ambiguity.

If this project were successful it would explain why part of the world behaves classically although all of the world is believed, at bottom, to be quantum mechanical. It would also explain why some classical models are successful in Quantum Mechanics (QM); but there would be the inference that it may be dangerous to 'quantize' classical models (including field equations) as a matter of course.

1.2   The Differential Identities

We adopt the notation and conventions of [1]. Suppose that $q \equiv \{q_1, q_2, \ldots q_n\}$ is a set of Cartesian coordinates of one or more point particles. The q are assumed to be continuous differential functions of the time t. The system of particles may, therefore, be said to be *classical*.

Let $\theta(q)$ be *any* real, continuous, differentiable function that does not depend explicitly on t. Suppose that $\theta(q)$ is a characteristic of the system (e.g., a curvilinear coordinate, a potential, a field strength). Then, by successive differentiations of $\theta(q)$, we produce an hierarchy of differential identities (using the Einstein summation convention)

(1) $\dot{\theta} = \dot{q}^j \theta_{,j}; \quad \theta_{,j} \equiv \dfrac{\partial \theta}{\partial q^j}; \quad j = 1, 2, \ldots n$

(2) $\ddot{\theta} = \ddot{q}^j \theta_{,j} + \dot{q}^j \dot{q}^k \theta_{,j,k}$

(3) $\dddot{\theta} = \dddot{q}^j \theta_{,j} + 3\ddot{q}^j \dot{q}^k \theta_{,j,k} + \dot{q}^j \dot{q}^k \dot{q}^l \theta_{,j,k,l}$

and so on. Here, as usual, a dot indicates differentiation with respect to time and suffices on the coordinates have been raised to implement the summation convention.

1.3   Quantizations

We interpret these differential identities as if they were equations of motion in Classical Mechanics (CM); and we *quantize* them according to the rules set out in [1].

Identity (1) yields the *first level condition* [1]

$$(4) \qquad \dot{\Theta} = \frac{i}{h}(H\Theta - \Theta H) = \tfrac{1}{2}(H^{\cdot j}\Theta_{,j} + \Theta_{,j}H^{\cdot j}); \quad \Theta \equiv \Theta(\underline{Q})$$

where the $\underline{P}$ are the momentum operators conjugate to the coordinate operators $\underline{Q}$ and $H(\underline{P},\underline{Q})$ is the Hamiltonian operator. The continuous scalars $\underline{q}$ are the spectra of the operators $\underline{Q}$ and $\theta(\underline{q})$ is the spectrum of $\Theta(\underline{Q})$. The notations

$$(4a) \qquad (.)_{,j} \equiv \frac{i}{h}[P_j(.) - (.)P_j] \equiv \frac{\partial(.)}{\partial Q^j}; \quad (.)^{\cdot j} \equiv \frac{i}{h}[(.)Q^j - Q^j(.)] \equiv \frac{\partial(.)}{\partial P_j};$$

are short for commutators with the $\underline{P}$ and the $\underline{Q}$. The PD notation indicates how the commutators may be calculated; but, in this calculation, the order of non-commuting terms must be retained. See Section 1.5 for more detail.

Identity (2) yields, similarly, the *second level condition* [1]

$$
\begin{aligned}
\ddot{\Theta} = & \frac{-1}{h^2}[H(H\Theta - \Theta H) - (H\Theta - \Theta H)H] \\
(5) \qquad = & \frac{i}{2h}[(HH^{\cdot j} - H^{\cdot j}H)\Theta_{,j} + \Theta_{,j}(HH^{\cdot j} - H^{\cdot j}H)] \\
& + [(H^{\cdot j}H^{\cdot k} + H^{\cdot k}H^{\cdot j})\Theta_{,j,k} + \Theta_{,j,k}(H^{\cdot j}H^{\cdot k} + H^{\cdot k}H^{\cdot j})]/4
\end{aligned}
$$

with the same notation. It is possible also to quantize the differential identity (3); some remarks concerning this quantization are to be found in [1]. The results of higher level quantizations are, however, very complicated. Here we concentrate on the implications of (4) and (5) only.

1.4   (4) And (5) Are Not Identities

Examples are given in [1] to show that although (1) and (2) are identities for arbitrary $\theta(\underline{q})$ their quantizations, (4) and (5), are not identities for arbitrary $\Theta(\underline{Q})$ and/ or arbitrary H.

1.4.1 Only Quadratic and Linear Forms Permitted Given Arbitrary $\Theta(\underline{Q})$

It can be shown that, if $\theta(\underline{q})$ (and hence $\Theta(\underline{Q})$) is to be arbitrary then, the linear form

$$H \equiv H_D \equiv \sigma^j P_j + \sigma; \quad \sigma^j \text{ and } \sigma \text{ are Hermitian operators}$$

(6) $$\Rightarrow \dot{P}_j \equiv \frac{i}{h}(HP_j - P_j H) = -H_{D,j} = O;$$

$$\dot{Q}^j \equiv \frac{i}{h}(HQ^j - Q^j H) = H_D^{\cdot j} = \sigma^j; \quad O \equiv \text{the null operator}$$

does satisfy both (4) and (5); but the quadratic form

(7)
$$H_N \equiv W \sum_{j=1}^{n} P_j^2 + U; \quad W \text{ and } U \text{ are Hermitian operators}$$

$$\Rightarrow \dot{P}_j = -H_{N,j} = O; \quad \dot{Q}^j = H_N^{\cdot j} = 2WP_j$$

satisfies only (4). Here the coefficient operators $\underline{\sigma}$ and W and the 'constant' terms σ and U are assumed to commute with the $\underline{P}$ and the $\underline{Q}$ but not necessarily to commute with each other; they are also assumed to be representable by Hermitian matrices of finite order. These restrictions are required in order to make contact with conventional physics.

With $n = 3$ the form (7) is that of the Hamiltonian of a single, low speed, free particle provided that W and U are suitably interpreted: the eigenvalues of W are taken to be $1/(2m)$ where m is one of the possible masses of the particle; and, the eigenvalues of U are taken to be the possible values of mc^2 where c is the speed of light. This last specification ensures that (7) can be regarded as a Newtonian approximation. The form (6), on the other hand, is the corresponding relativistic Hamiltonian assumed by Dirac; see, for example, [2], p. 265. Dirac arrived at this form by taking the square root of the SR (Special Relativity) energy/ momentum/ mass relation for a free particle. He then extended (6) to cover EM phenomena by analogy with classical cases.

In Appendix A we show that forms more elaborate than (6) or (7) also satisfy (4) and (5) given arbitrary $\Theta(\underline{Q})$; but these forms are still either linear or quadratic in the $\underline{P}$. The linear forms, like (6), satisfy both (4) and (5); the quadratic forms, like (7), satisfy only (4). The elaborated forms are all recognisable as the Hamiltonians of known systems; nevertheless, because the expressions are operators (as opposed to scalars), they may, upon study, lead to new physics.

1.4.2 Permitted $\theta(\underline{q})$ Given Arbitrary H

It is worthy of note that if

(8a) $\Theta \equiv Q^I$

Then both (4) and (5) are identities for arbitrary H. So, there are ancillary questions: for what operator functions $\Theta(\underline{Q})$ is (4) an identity for arbitrary H?; and, for what operator functions $\Theta(\underline{Q})$ are both (4) and (5) identities for arbitrary H? For example, if

(8b) $\Theta \equiv (Q^I)^2$

then (4) is an identity but (5) is not; and neither (4) nor (5) are identities when, for example,

(8c) $\Theta \equiv (Q^I)^3$

Because (4) and (5) are linear in Θ, $\Theta_{,j}$ and $\Theta_{,j,k}$ linear combinations of the $\underline{Q}$, with coefficients that commute with both the $\underline{P}$ and the $\underline{Q}$, also satisfy (4) and (5) for arbitrary H.

1.5 Operator Differentiation

In what follows we refer to the commutations (4a) as *operator differentiation*; they are analogous to partial differentiation as indicated. This statement is based on the usual definitions

(9)
$$P_j P_k = P_k P_j; \quad Q^j Q^k = Q^k Q^j; \quad Q^j P_k - P_k Q^j = ih\delta_k^j I;$$
$$j,k = 1,2,....n$$

and the identities

(10a) $(\alpha A + \beta B)' = \alpha A' + \beta B'; \quad (AB)' = A'B + AB';$ preserve order

(10b) $[A^r]' \equiv \sum_{j=1}^{r} A^{(j-1)} A' A^{(r-j)}; \quad r = 1,2,...; \quad j = 1,2,...n;$ preserve order

where A, B are operators, $\alpha' = O, \beta' = O$ and

(10c) $A' \equiv A^{,k} \ or \ A_{,k}; \quad k = 1,2,...n$

Notice that (10b) reduces to the familiar

(10d) $[A^r]' = rA^{(r-1)}A'$

if it happens that A' commutes with A. A consequence of the need to preserve order is that we can use the familiar 'function of a function' rule to evaluate, say, $[F(A)]'$ only if A' commutes with A; (here $F(A)$ is a power series or polynomial in A). If A' does not commute with A the evaluation may be complicated.

Notice that we have defined A' at (10c), as being one of the commutators (4a), only because these are the commutators that particularly interest us. (10a) and (10b) are identities when A' is defined as a commutator of A with *any* operator.

The above rules are used throughout this paper. For example, they are used at (6) and (7) to express the operators $\dot{P}_j$ and $\dot{Q}^j$ and also to show which of the forms (6) and (7) satisfy (4) and (5) for arbitrary $\Theta(\underline{Q})$; see Appendix A.

2.   THE MEANING OF THE QUANTIZATIONS

2.1   The Use Of Measurements For Prediction

What does it mean if both H and Θ satisfy the first level condition (4)? The first level identity (1) is contingent on the conditions that the functions $\theta(\underline{q})$ and $\underline{q}(t)$ should be continuous and should possess at least first derivatives. These restrictions are, surely, conditions of predictability. For, given knowledge of the function $\theta(\underline{q})$ and measurements of the $\underline{q}$ and the $\underline{\dot{q}}$ at time t, we are able to make a short term prediction

(11) $\theta(t+\delta t) \approx \theta(t) + \dot{\theta}(t)\delta t; \quad \theta(t) \equiv \theta(\underline{q}); \quad \dot{\theta}(t) = \dot{q}^j \theta_{,j}(\underline{q})$

Here our knowledge of the function $\theta(\underline{q})$ constitutes a predictive theory. So, it appears, the condition (4) ensures that if we make measurements subject to the laws of QM then we will, in principle, be able to use those measurements for the short term prediction of θ.

What of the second level condition (5)? One might say that, when combined with (4), it allows either more precise short term prediction or prediction over a longer epoch. The second level identity (2) is contingent on the conditions that the functions $\theta(\underline{q})$ and $\underline{q}(t)$ should be continuous and should possess derivatives to at least second order. These conditions of predictability are more refined than those associated with the identity (1); and if they hold then both identities follow. We may then make a more accurate short term prediction.

(12)
$$\theta(t+\delta t) \approx \theta(t) + \dot{\theta}(t)\delta t + \ddot{\theta}(t)\frac{\delta t^2}{2}$$
$$\theta(t) \equiv \theta(\underline{q}); \quad \dot{\theta}(t) = \dot{q}^j \theta_{,j}(\underline{q}); \quad \ddot{\theta}(t) = \ddot{q}^j \theta_{,j} + \dot{q}^j \dot{q}^k \theta_{,j,k}$$

Notice, however, that, in order to use (12), we must measure not only the $\underline{q}$ and the $\underline{\dot{q}}$, at time t, but also the $\underline{\ddot{q}}$. This seems to raise a difficulty. In order to make better and better predictions we need to measure higher and higher derivatives of $\underline{q}$. There is, however, another possibility. If we have a DE expressing $\underline{\ddot{q}}$ in terms of $\underline{q}$ and $\underline{\dot{q}}$ we need, again, only measure $\underline{q}$ and $\underline{\dot{q}}$; the DE merely constitutes another element in our predictive theory. If we wish to take the prediction further we need only differentiate the DE to express higher derivatives of $\underline{q}$ in terms of $\underline{q}$ and $\underline{\dot{q}}$.

Given H such a DE is provided, in classical mechanics, by Hamilton's equations:

(13a) $\quad \dot{p}_j = -\dfrac{\partial H}{\partial q^j}; \quad \dot{q}^j = \dfrac{\partial H}{\partial p_j}; \quad CM$

that correspond to the operator equations

(13b) $\quad \dot{P}_j = \dfrac{i}{h}(HP_j - P_j H); \quad \dot{Q}^j = \dfrac{i}{h}(HQ^j - Q^j H); \quad QM$

in QM. These operator equations can be thought of as identities that follow from definitions [1].

We conclude that (4) and (5) are conditions that must be satisfied to ensure that, given the forms of $\theta(\underline{q})$ and H, we may us the calculus to predict future values of $\theta(\underline{q})$ using measurements of $\underline{q}$ and $\underline{\dot{q}}$ as initial conditions. It is also clear that if H satisfies only (4), e.g., it has the quadratic form (7), then the predictions will be less accurate than if H satisfies both (4) and (5), e.g., it has the linear form (6).

2.2 Some Functions $\theta(\underline{q})$ Are More 'Classical' Than Others

It is shown in [1] that, given the usual form

(14) $\quad W \equiv I/(2m); \quad I$ is the unit operator

the quadratic (7) satisfies (4) unconditionally; but it satisfies (5) only if

(15) $\quad -\dfrac{h^2}{4m^2}\sum_{j,k}\Theta_{,j,j,k,k} = O$

the LHS of (15) being the imbalance in (5) given (7); the greater the mass m the smaller the imbalance. When $n = 3$, and the $\underline{q}$ are the Cartesian coordinates of a single particle, the operator equation (15) corresponds to the scalar PDE

$$(16) \quad \nabla^2(\nabla^2\theta(\underline{q})) = 0$$

A number of the solutions of (16) (the Poisson equation with a density that is a solution of the Laplace equation) are functions of importance in CM. For example: the Cartesian coordinates, the radius, its square and its reciprocal, the azimuth (but not the polar angle) and the potential $V(\underline{q})$, in empty space, given that $\nabla^2 V = 0$. For these functions, then, (5) is an identity given (7); and, as explained above, (7) must therefore represent the dynamical behaviour of these observables more accurately than that of other functions of the coordinates. A function $\theta(\underline{q})$, that satisfies (16), can be said to be *more classical* than an arbitrary function!

3. CAN H_D AND H_N REPRESENT THE SAME SYSTEM?

3.1 The Need For H_D And H_N To Represent The Same System

These considerations raise another question in regard to (6) and (7): can these Hamiltonians represent the *same system*? This is, surely, a requirement if the interpretation given to (4) and (5), in the previous section, is to make sense. We might suppose that, to meet this requirement, (7) must be an approximation, in some sense, to (6) because it is the less accurate descriptor. The operators $\underline{\sigma}$ and σ are at our disposal for the purpose of such an approximation.

Even in CM the question, as to whether two Hamiltonians (or their corresponding Lagrangians [5]) represent the same system, is tricky. This question has been investigated, thoroughly, in respect of Lagrangians. For example, two Lagrangians that render the same equations of motion can differ by a factor that is a constant of that motion; see [6], Art. 6.4.

In what follows we show that H_D and H_N cannot approximate; and, worse still, the respective instantaneous velocities and accelerations, under these Hamiltonians, cannot approximate. But, as it turns out, measurements of these quantities can approximate; and this allows us to reverse Dirac's argument in the manner described in the Abstract.

3.2   Representations And A Commutation Condition

From now on we adopt the representation in which the $\underline{P}$ are scalar (see (9))

(17) $P_j \equiv p_j I; \quad Q^j \equiv ih\dfrac{\partial}{\partial p_j}; \quad p_j \ scalar; \quad -\infty < p_j < \infty$

We observe that Hermitian operator U, that commutes with both the $\underline{P}$ and the $\underline{Q}$, can be added to the RHS of (7) without altering Hamilton's equations and without affecting the condition (4). In order to make contact with conventional physics it is necessary to assume that W and U commute. They are then constants of the motion under H_N because

(18) $H_N U = U H_N; \quad H_N W = W H_N$

3.3   The Hamiltonian Operators H_D And H_N Cannot Approximate Well

Suppose that we assume that, if H_D and H_N are to represent the same system then, they must approximate in some sense; (see Section 3.1). We require that

(19a) $H_N = W\displaystyle\sum_{j=1}^{n} p_j^2 + U \approx H_D = \sigma^j p_j + \sigma$; see (6) and (7)

This condition is satisfied, and then only roughly, if

(19b) $p_j \to 0$ and $U \equiv \sigma$

Because the $\underline{\sigma}$ commute with both the $\underline{P}$ and the $\underline{Q}$ there is, evidently, no choice of these operators that improves the approximation of the Hamiltonians (6) and (7).

3.4   Can The Observed Motions Approximate?

3.4.1 Measurements of Velocity are Averages

There may be, however, choices that approximate the observed motions of the particle as described by the two sets of Hamilton's equations

(20a) $\dot{Q}_D^j = \sigma^j$; $\dot{Q}_N^j = 2Wp_j$; see (6) and (7)

(20b) $\dot{P}_{jD} = \dot{P}_{jN} = O$

where the suffices refer to motions under H_D and H_N respectively. It is clear that (20b) need concern us no further because the $\underline{P}$ are constants of the motion under either Hamiltonian. We concentrate on (20a). For the reason already given,

(21a) $\sigma^j \neq 2Wp_j$

so the approximation

(21b) $\dot{Q}_D^j \approx \dot{Q}_N^j$

seems impossible.

But, measurements take time. What we actually observe are not the instantaneous velocity components $\underline{\dot{q}}_D$ or $\underline{\dot{q}}_N$ but their mean values (in some sense) over the epoch of measurement. If the velocity components fluctuate then the mean values must, in general, differ from the instantaneous values; and, the mean values will then be represented by operators that differ from the operators that represent instantaneous values. The criterion is whether or not the observables $\underline{\dot{q}}_D$ and $\underline{\dot{q}}_N$ are constants of the motion. If an observable is a constant of the motion its Schrödinger representation equals its Heisenberg representation and there is no fluctuation. The contrary case, however, offers the possibility that operators that represent the mean values may approximate even when operators that represent instantaneous values cannot.

3.4.2 Which Velocities are Constants of the Motion?

The $\dot{Q}_N^j = 2Wp_j$ commute with H_N and are, therefore, constants of the motion under H_N; their Schrödinger and Heisenberg representations are equal under H_N. If, however, the $\underline{\sigma}$ and σ do not mutually commute then the $\dot{Q}_D^j = \sigma^j$ are not, necessarily, constants of the motion under H_D; their Heisenberg representations will thus fluctuate; and, for example, the mean values of the Heisenberg representations need not equal the Schrödinger representations. This allows at least the possibility for the *mean values* of the Heisenberg representations of $\dot{Q}_D^j$ and $\dot{Q}_N^j$ to approximate.

3.4.3 Definition of an Operator that Represents the Average of an Observable

We can define the Schrödinger operator $\overline{A}$, that represents the mean value $\overline{a}$ of an observable a represented by Schrödinger operator A, as follows: *the expectation of $\overline{A}$ at the centre of the epoch of measurement is equal to the mean of the expectation of A over that epoch.*

Different ways of calculating the mean must lead to different results. For simplicity, we define the 'mean value' as the output of a moving window smoothing filter; the window is taken to be of finite duration $2T$ and the weighting is assumed uniform. Thus $\overline{A}$ is defined by

(22a) $\quad <t|\overline{A}|t> \equiv \dfrac{1}{2T} \int\limits_{t-T}^{t+T} < \tau|A|\tau > d\tau$

where t is the centre time. Now denote the Heisenberg representation of A by

(22b) $\quad A(\tau) \equiv \exp(iH\tau/h)A\exp(-iH\tau/h)$

If we assume that the state at the centre time is arbitrary then (22a) is equivalent to the operator equation (take the expectation brackets on the RHS of (22a) outside the integral)

(22c) $\overline{A}(t) \equiv \dfrac{1}{2T} \displaystyle\int\limits_{-T+t}^{T+t} A(\tau)d\tau \Rightarrow \overline{A} \equiv \dfrac{1}{2T} \displaystyle\int\limits_{-T}^{T} A(\tau)d\tau$

Thus Schrödinger $\overline{A}$ turns out to be the mean of the Heisenberg representation of A.

3.4.4 Rapid Fluctuation of the Heisenberg Operators About a Fixed Mean and a Long Measurement Epoch Assumed

We now simplify (22c) by assuming that $A(\tau)$ has a particular form: the fluctuation of $A(\tau)$ is a bounded and very rapid oscillation about a fixed mean; the number of fluctuations during the epoch of measurement is then large. In consequence we may take the limit $T \to \infty$ giving

$$\overline{A} \equiv \underset{T \to \infty}{Lt}\, \frac{1}{2T} \int\limits_{-T}^{T} A(\tau)d\tau; \quad A(\tau) \equiv \exp(iH\tau/h)A\exp(-iH\tau/h)$$

(22d)

$$= \underset{T \to \infty}{Lt}\, \frac{1}{2T} \int\limits_{-T}^{T} [\cos(Ht/h)A\cos(Ht/h) + \sin(Ht/h)A\sin(Ht/h)]dt$$

3.4.5 An Explicit Expression for the Mean Rate Operator

We can deduce from the definition (22d) that

(23)
$$\overline{\dot{A}} \equiv \underset{T \to \infty}{Lt}\, \frac{1}{2T} \int\limits_{-T}^{T} [\cos(Ht/h)\dot{A}\cos(Ht/h) + \sin(Ht/h)\dot{A}\sin(Ht/h)]dt$$

$$= \underset{T \to \infty}{Lt}\, \frac{i}{T}[\sin(HT/h)A\cos(HT/h) - \cos(HT/h)A\sin(HT/h)]$$

and, in particular, that

(24a) $\overline{\dot{Q}_D^{\,j}} = \overline{\sigma^{\,j}} = -\underset{T \to \infty}{Lt}\, \dfrac{h}{T}[\sin(Y)\{\cot(Y)\}^{\cdot j}\sin(Y)]; \quad$ see (4a)

where

(24b) $Y \equiv H_D T/h; \quad$ see Appendix B for details

The formulae (23) and (24) turn out to be difficult to handle; more useful, for our present purpose, are some special cases evaluated directly from (22d).

3.4.6 Special Cases

Observe that if A is a constant of the motion then

(25) $\quad AH = HA \Rightarrow \overline{A} = A$

as is to be expected. This result depends on

(26) $\quad \cos^2(Ht/h) + \sin^2(Ht/h) = I$

If, instead,

(27) $\quad AH^2 = H^2A$ and H^{-1} exists

then

(28) $\quad \overline{A} = AC + HAH^{-1}S = (A + HAH^{-1})/2 \neq A$ if $HA \neq AH$

where

(29) $\quad C \equiv \underset{T \to \infty}{Lt} \frac{1}{2T} \int\limits_{-T}^{T} [\cos^2(Ht/h)]dt = \frac{I}{2} = S \equiv \underset{T \to \infty}{Lt} \frac{1}{2T} \int\limits_{-T}^{T} [\sin^2(Ht/h)]dt$

These last formulae show the importance of the limit in the definition (22d). If, instead, we use the definition (22c), with T finite, the factors C and S differ; they are complicated functions of T and H that only approximate $I/2$. In Appendix C we deduce an important result concerning the smoothing filter that represents the average $\overline{A}$. When the weights are non-uniform, but slowly varying with time and the number of oscillations of $A(\tau)$ within the measurement epoch is large, both the averages (25) and (28) are multiplied by the *same factor*.

The proofs of (26) and (29) depend on the notion that H can be represented by a matrix of finite order. Consider the representation in which H is diagonal. Then for every non-zero element of the matrix there are relations, of the forms (26) and (29), where H is replaced by one of its eigenvalues and, I is replaced by unity. (26) then follows directly; and (29) is easily verified by integration.

3.5   Approximation Of The Average Velocities

3.5.1   A solution Exists Independent of the Filter Weighting

We hope to find conditions under which

(30) $\overline{Q_N^j} \approx \overline{Q_D^j} \Rightarrow 2Wp^j \approx \overline{\sigma^j}$

These conditions must involve the $\underline{\sigma}$ and σ; so, in order to make use of (28), we make the assumptions (27) that

(31) $\sigma^j H_D^2 = H_D^2 \sigma^j; \quad H_D^{-1} \text{ exists}$

These assumptions must be consistent with the eventual results. (28) and (29) then give

$$(32) \quad \begin{aligned} 2Wp^j &\approx \overline{\sigma^j} = (\sigma^j + H_D \sigma^j H_D^{-1})/2 \\ &\Rightarrow 2Wp^j H_D \approx (\sigma^j H_D + H_D \sigma^j)/2 \end{aligned}$$

The LHS of (32) is quadratic in the $\underline{p}$ whereas the RHS is linear in the $\underline{p}$; see (6). We now invoke (19b). Neglect the terms on the LHS that are of second order in the $\underline{p}$ and equate constant and linear terms on both sides:

(33) $\sigma\sigma^j + \sigma^j\sigma = O; \quad \sigma^j\sigma^k + \sigma^k\sigma^j = O; \quad j \ne k; \quad 2W\sigma = (\sigma^j)^2$

These results must be consistent with (31). We have (see (6))

(34) $H_D^2 = \sigma^j p_j \sigma^k p_k + \sigma^j p_j \sigma + \sigma\sigma^k p_k + \sigma^2 = \sum_j (\sigma^j)^2 p_j^2 + \sigma^2$

from which it is obvious (again employing (33)) that (31) holds.

Notice that because $(\sigma^j)^2$ is Hermitian we have

(35) $W\sigma = \sigma W$

Also because we may set

(36) $\quad p_j = 0 \ \forall j \Rightarrow H_D \equiv \sigma$

a necessary condition for H_D^{-1} to exist is that σ^{-1} should exist. That it is also a sufficient condition can be argued as follows. From (33) we see that the two terms on the RHS of (34) commute; they therefore share a common diagonal representation. If σ^{-1} exists then the eigenvalues of σ^2 are non-zero and positive. The eigenvalues of H_D^2, being the sum of a positive term with a non-negative term, are, therefore, non-zero; H_D^{-1} exists.

Notice that, because the LHS of (30) is a constant of the motion, we have used both (25) and (28); and, as is shown in Appendix C, when the filter weighting is non-uniform both these expressions are multiplied by the same factor. This factor cancels from (30). So, the results (33) are independent of the weighting.

3.5.2 The Average of the Coordinate Accelerations and all Higher Derivatives, Under H_D, are Zero

These ideas should apply to the coordinate accelerations

(37) $\quad \ddot{Q}^j \equiv \dfrac{i}{h}(H\dot{Q}^j - \dot{Q}^j H);$

(5) is, after all, a condition about accelerations. Assume then that we require

(38) $\quad \overline{\ddot{Q}_N^j} \approx \overline{\ddot{Q}_D^j}$

where

(39) $\quad \ddot{Q}_D^j = \dfrac{i}{h}(H_D\sigma^j - \sigma^j H_D); \quad \ddot{Q}_N^j = \dfrac{2Wi}{h}(H_N p^j - p^j H_N) = 0$

So, we require $\overline{\ddot{Q}_D^j}$ to vanish. Now, by virtue of (31), the relations

$$H_D^2 \frac{i}{h}(H_D\sigma^j - \sigma^j H_D) = \frac{i}{h}(H_D\sigma^j - \sigma^j H_D)H_D^2$$
$$\Rightarrow H_D^2\ddot{Q}_D^j = \ddot{Q}_D^j H_D^2 ;$$

(40)

$$H_D \frac{i}{h}(H_D\sigma^j - \sigma^j H_D) + \frac{i}{h}(H_D\sigma^j - \sigma^j H_D)H_D = O$$
$$\Rightarrow H_D\ddot{Q}_D^j + \ddot{Q}_D^j H_D = O$$

are identities. (28) can, therefore, be applied to give

(41) $\overline{\ddot{Q}_D^j} = O$

The requirement (39) is thus met without placing any further constraints on the $\underline{\sigma}$ and σ. Finally, observe that identities like (40) can be constructed for higher time derivatives of the coordinates. It follows that the mean values of the Heisenberg representations of *all* the higher derivatives of the coordinates vanish under H_D; this is desirable because all these derivatives also vanish under H_N.

3.6 Is The Solution That Approximates The Motions Unique?

3.6.1 Explicit Expressions for the Average Velocities Under H_D are Hard to Derive

A set of rules like (19b) allied with (33) can be described as a joint solution of the approximate equations (30) and (38). It is indeed remarkable that the assumption of the commutation rule (31) leads to (33) which turns out to be consistent with (31). The question arises: is this joint solution unique? This question is difficult to answer because it requires us to find *explicit expressions* for the means of the Heisenberg coordinate velocities $\sigma^j(t)$; and, as (24a) shows, this entails expressing $\{\cot(Y)\}^{.j}$ in closed form (in order to be able to evaluate the limit $T \to \infty$). Such a closed form can be found by making simplifying assumptions like (31); but, so far and without assumptions, I have found only series expressions for $\{\cot(Y)\}^{.j}$. This matter is discussed in Appendix D. It looks highly likely that the solution (33) is unique; but I have not proved it so!

3.6.2 The Problem has Been Partly Solved

The remainder of the conditions (33) can be derived from (24) on the assumption that

(42) $\quad \sigma\sigma^j + \sigma^j\sigma = O$

without making further assumptions; see Appendix D.

4. VERSIONS OF THE MEASURED COORDINATE

4.1 Apparent Coordinates

The average velocity (see (28) and (33))

(43) $\quad \overline{\dot{Q}^j} = \overline{\sigma^j} = (\sigma^j + H_D\sigma^j H_D^{-1})/2 = (\sigma^j)^2 p_j H_D^{-1}$

can be thought of as the rate of some coordinate $\widetilde{Q}^j$ defined by the relation

(44) $\quad \dfrac{i}{h}(H_D\widetilde{Q}^j - \widetilde{Q}^j H_D) \equiv (\sigma^j)^2 p_j H_D^{-1}$

This definition is not unique because any expression that commutes with H_D may be added to $\widetilde{Q}^j$ without affecting (44). It is easy to show, for example, that

(45) $\quad \widetilde{Q}^j \equiv (H_D Q^j II_D^{-1} + Q^j)/2 = Q^j + \dfrac{h}{2i}\sigma^j H_D^{-1}$

is a solution of (44). This expression differs slightly, but crucially, from the instantaneous coordinate Q^j; we call it *an apparent coordinate*. We can get an idea of the size of the difference term

(46a) $\quad \widetilde{Q}^j - Q^j = \dfrac{h}{2i}\sigma^j H_D^{-1}$

by evaluating its eigenvalues, for simplicity, in the case $\underline{p} = \underline{0}$. Then

(46b) $\tilde{Q}^j - Q^j = \dfrac{h}{2i}\sigma^j\sigma^{-1}; \quad \underline{p} = \underline{0}$

which can be shown to have eigenvalues $\dfrac{\pm 1}{4\pi} \times$ Compton Wavelength; see item (n) in Table 1 below.

4.2. The Mean Coordinate Is An Apparent Coordinate

Although the particle is in motion it makes sense to calculate the mean value of Q^j over a large window centred at the instant $t = 0$. The appropriate definition is (see (22d))

(47) $\quad \overline{Q^j} \equiv \underset{T\to\infty}{Lt}\ \dfrac{1}{2T}\displaystyle\int_{-T}^{T}[\cos(Y)Q^j\cos(Y) + \sin(Y)Q^j\sin(Y)]dt;$

$\quad\quad Y \equiv H_D t / h$

To evaluate the RHS of (47) we make use of (4a) together with the redefinition of Y at (47)

(47a) $(.)^j \equiv \dfrac{i}{h}[(.)Q^j - Q^j(.)] \equiv \dfrac{\partial(.)}{\partial P_j}; \quad Y \equiv H_D t / h$

We then have from (31)

(47b) $XY^j = Y^j X; \quad Y^{-1}\ exists; \quad X \equiv Y^2$

and it follows, from the product rule, that

(47c) $\quad X^j = YY^j + Y^j Y = (t/h)^2 (H_D\sigma^j + \sigma^j H_D);$

$\quad\quad YX^j = X^j Y; \quad XX^j = X^j X$

By expressing $\cos(Y)$ as a series in X we deduce that

(48a) $\quad [\cos(Y)]^j = \displaystyle\sum_{r=0}^{\infty}(-1)^r [X^r]^j /(2r)!$

$\quad\quad = -Y^{-1}\sin(Y)X^j$

from term by term differentiation. Similarly

$$(48b) \quad [Y\sin(Y)]^{\cdot j} = \sum_{r=0}^{\infty}(-1)^r[X^{(r+1)}]^{\cdot j}/(2r+1)!$$

$$= [\cos(Y)+Y^{-1}\sin(Y)]X^{\cdot j}$$

from which

$$\cos(Y)Q^j\cos(Y)+\sin(Y)Q^j\sin(Y)$$

$$= Q^j\cos^2(Y)+Y^{-1}Q^jY\sin^2(Y)+$$

$$(48c) \quad \frac{h}{i}\left([\cos(Y)]^{\cdot j}\cos(Y)+Y^{-1}[Y\sin(Y)]^{\cdot j}\sin(Y)\right)$$

$$= Q^j\cos^2(Y)+Y^{-1}Q^jY\sin^2(Y)+\frac{h}{i}\left(Y^{-2}\sin(Y)\right)X^{\cdot j}$$

We can now calculate

$$(49) \quad \overline{Q^j} \equiv \underset{T\to\infty}{Lt}\frac{1}{2T}\int_{-T}^{T}[\cos(Y)Q^j\cos(Y)+\sin(Y)Q^j\sin(Y)]dt \quad ; \text{ see (25a)}$$

$$= (Q^j+H_D^{-1}Q^jH_D)/2 = H_D^{-1}\widetilde{Q}^jH_D$$

This result depends on the recognition that both $Y^{-1}Q^jY$ and $Y^{-2}X^{\cdot j}$ are independent of t.

So, it appears, $\overline{Q^j}$ and $\widetilde{Q}^j$ differ; such a conclusion is counter intuitive. But the difference turns out to be only a question of definition. We find that (compare with (45))

$$(50) \quad \widetilde{Q}^j \equiv (Q^j+H_D^{-1}Q^jH_D)/2 = \overline{Q^j} = Q^j-\frac{h}{2i}H_D^{-1}\sigma^j$$

is also a solution of (44); that is, the mean coordinate is an apparent coordinate; (the difference between the two definitions commutes with H_D).

Notice that

$$(51) \quad \widetilde{Q}^jP_k - P_k\widetilde{Q}^j = ih\delta_k^j I; \text{ see (9)}$$

20

It can be proved [4] that if

(52) $AB - BA = iI$

then both A and B have continuous spectra. It follows that the spectra of the apparent coordinates $\underset{\sim}{\widetilde{Q}}$ are continuous.

5.   RELATION OF THE RESULTS TO STANDARD PHYSICS

5.1   Special Relativity (SR) Kinetics Of A Single Free Particle

5.1.1 The System of Particles

The Hamiltonians (6) and (7) are taken to describe the motion of a system of particles. Both Hamiltonians contain a term for each coordinate together with a single extra term. There is, ostensibly, no interaction between the particles; they are free.

The Hamiltonians (A.20) and (A.19), see Appendix A, satisfy (4) and (5) in the same way as (6) and (7) respectively. But these Hamiltonians contain field terms in addition to the kinetic terms that appear in (6) and (7). There is one component of vector potential, per coordinate, together with a single scalar potential; these potentials can be functions of all the coordinates. The particles associated with (A.19) and (A.20) are, therefore, not free. Their motions may be said to interact through the potentials. Similar remarks apply to the other Hamiltonian forms, such as (A.17), that can be interpreted as containing field terms.

There is nothing in the theory that tells us how many coordinates there are per particle (i.e., the dimensionality of the coordinate space); but a particular richness of structure appears when $n = 3$ or a multiple of 3. Although there are hints, in the Hamiltonian forms, the theory does not specify a metric.

It may be possible to extend the above theory to cover pairs of linear and quadratic Hamiltonians that contain field terms (e.g. (A.19) and (A.20)); similar ideas of approximation and averaging might be used to yield structure (e.g., operator field equations); but such a theory would be much more complicated and is quite outside the scope of this paper. We are concerned here only with the first part of Dirac's theory of the electron in which he considers a single, free, relativistic particle with a linear Hamiltonian of the form (6); see Section 5.2.

5.1.2 A Single Particle

Because, within the set

(53) $\{H_D, \sigma^2, P_j, (\sigma^j)^2 = 2W\sigma = 2\sigma W, (\sigma^k)^2, \overline{\sigma^j}, W = (\sigma^j)^2 / (2\sigma)\}$,

the elements mutually commute we may write relations governing their eigenvalues; see Table 1. To connect these formulae with conventional physics we interpret

- c as the velocity of light,
- m as the rest mass,
- s as the rest energy,
- λ_D as the total energy (i.e., the relativistic mass $\times c^2$),
- λ_N as the total energy in the Newtonian approximation,
- p_j as the jth Cartesian component of (measured) momentum (with $n = 3$),
- $\overline{\dot{q}^j}$ as the jth Cartesian component of (measured) velocity (with $n = 3$),
- t as the time measured by a clock at rest at the origin.

The formulae in Table 1 are then recognisable as those that govern the SR kinetics of a single free particle. The conditions (18) and (19b) seem to be essential to ensure the approximation $\lambda_N \approx \lambda_D$; see item (l) of the table. There is nothing obvious, in the present theory, that requires c to be a universal constant; but, because they are identical, the $(\sigma^j)^2 = 2W\sigma$ all have common eigenstates and common eigenvalues c^2; see Section 5.5 for a naïve explanation of the universality of $|c|$. Note, also, that for the particle or particles for which $\sigma \to O \Rightarrow m \to 0$ we have $v^2 \to c^2$; see item (i) of Table 1. We also have the correct relation between momentum and energy for low mass particles; see item (n) of Table 1. But, if $(\sigma^j)^2$ has more than one eigenvalue (i.e., is not scalar) then, these low mass particles can have states in which the values of $|c|$ differ. NB the theory applies only to particles for which $\sigma \neq O$ because this condition guarantees that H_D^{-1} exists; see (31) and (36).

Of the operators listed in the second column of the table, all but σ and σ^j represent constants of the motion under H_D.

No.	Operator	Eigenvalue	Formula	Reference
(a)	P_j	p_j	Definition	
(b)	H_D	λ_D	Definition	
(c)	$(\sigma^j)^2 = 2W\sigma = 2\sigma W$	c^2	Definition	(33), (35)
(d)	$\dot{Q}^j = \sigma^j$	$\dot{q}^j$	$\dot{q}^j = \pm c; \quad c > 0$	(24a),(c)
(e)	W	$1/(2m)$	Definition $m \neq 0$	
(f)	$\sigma^2 = (\sigma^j)^4 /(2W)^2$	s^2	$s^2 = c^4 m^2$	(33),(c),(e)
(g)	σ	s	$s = \pm c^2 m$	
(h)	$\overline{\dot{Q}^j} = \overline{\sigma^j}$ $= (\sigma^j + H_D \sigma^j H_D^{-1})/2$ $= (\sigma^j)^2 p_j H_D^{-1}$	$\overline{\dot{q}^j}$	$\overline{\dot{q}^j} = c^2 p_j \lambda_D^{-1}$	(28),(32), (33),(b)
(i)	$V^2 \equiv \sum_j (\overline{\dot{Q}^j})^2$ $= 2\sigma W(1 - \sigma^2 H_D^{-2})$	v^2	$v^2 = \sum_j (\overline{\dot{q}^j})^2$ $= c^2(1 - c^4 m^2 \lambda_D^{-2})$	(c),(h),(j)
(j)	$V^2 \vert \sigma \to O = 2\sigma W = (\sigma^j)^2$	$v^2 \vert m \to 0$	$v^2 \vert m \to 0 = c^2$	(c),(i)
(k)	$H_D^2 = \sum_j (\sigma^j)^2 p_j^2 + \sigma^2$	λ_D^2	$\lambda_D^2 = \sum_j c^2 p_j^2 + c^4 m^2$ $= (mc^2)^2 /(1 - v^2 / c^2)$	(34),(33), (h),(i)
(l)	$H_N; \quad p_k \to 0$	λ_N	$\lambda_N = \pm\left(\sum_j p_j^2 /(2m) + c^2 m\right)$ $\approx \pm\sqrt{\lambda_D^2}$	(7),(19b), (g),(k)
(m)	$P^2 \equiv \sum_j (\overline{\dot{P}^j})^2$	p^2	$p^2 = \sum_j p_j^2$ $= (mv)^2 /(1 - v^2 / c^2) = \dfrac{\lambda_D^2}{c^2} - c^2 m^2$	(h),(i),(k)
(n)	$P^2 \vert \sigma \to O$	$p^2 \vert m \to 0$	$p^2 \vert m \to 0 = \dfrac{\lambda_D^2 \vert m \to 0}{c^2}$	(m)
(o)	$(\widetilde{Q}^j - Q^j)^2 \vert p_k = 0$ $= \left(\dfrac{h}{2i}\sigma^j \sigma^{-1}\right)^2 = \dfrac{h^2}{4}(\sigma^j)^2 \sigma^{-2}$	$\left(\dfrac{h}{2mc}\right)^2$	$\left(\dfrac{l_0}{4\pi}\right)^2; \quad l_0 \equiv Compton\ Wavelength$ $\equiv \dfrac{2\pi h}{mc}$	(33),(50), (c),(f)
(p)	$\widetilde{Q}^j - Q^j \vert p_k = 0$	$\dfrac{\pm h}{2mc}$	$\dfrac{\pm l_0}{4\pi}$	(50),(o)
(q)	$(i\sigma^j \sigma^k)^2 = (\sigma^j)^2 (\sigma^k)^2$	c^4	$c^2 \times c^2$	
(r)	$i\sigma^j \sigma^k$	$\pm c^2$	$\sqrt{c^4}$	

Table 1: Operator and Eigenvalue Relations for a Single Free Particle

5.2   Relation To The Dirac Theory [2]

The Dirac theory of the electron (Art 66, et seq.) recognises the relation, between the energy of a free particle E the momenta p the mass m and the velocity of light c,

$$(54) \quad E^2 = c^2 \sum_{j=1}^{j=3} (p_j)^2 + c^4 m^2 I$$

as either an empirical fact or a deduction from the postulates of SR. Dirac insists that the DE of motion of a particle should be linear in the operator

$$(55) \quad E \equiv ih \frac{\partial}{\partial t}$$

and also linear in the momenta. He therefore, in effect, makes the identification

$$(56) \quad E \equiv H_D \equiv \sigma^j p_j + \sigma$$

So, squaring (56), substituting into (54) and equating coefficients of the powers of the p, he gets (compare with (33))

$$(57) \quad \sigma^j \sigma^k + \sigma^k \sigma^j = O; \quad \sigma^j \sigma + \sigma \sigma^j = O; \quad (\sigma^j)^2 = c^2 I; \quad \sigma^2 = c^4 m^2 I$$

In the present theory there is nothing that requires σ and all the σ^j to square to scalars; but, as pointed out above, the $(\sigma^j)^2$ are equal in the present theory. Otherwise our $\sigma's$ correspond to Dirac's $\alpha's$.

Dirac did not have (4) and (5) with respective solutions of the type (7) and (6). He therefore had no justification to reverse his argument (on the basis of the approximation and rapid fluctuation postulates) so to deduce (33) together with the other formulae given in Table 1.

Because the σ and σ do not square to a scalar it is slightly more difficult, in the present theory, to demonstrate the existence of spin angular momentum; but it can be done. When $n = 3$ an angular momentum operator vector can be defined by analogy with the classical case (Dirac, p. 140):

$$M_1 = Q^2 P_3 - Q^3 P_2$$
$$(58) \quad \underline{M} \equiv \underline{Q} \times \underline{P} \Rightarrow M_2 = Q^3 P_1 - Q^1 P_3$$
$$M_3 = Q^1 P_2 - Q^2 P_1$$

from which follow commutation relations (see (2a))

$$M_1 = \frac{i}{h}(M_3 M_2 - M_2 M_3)$$
$$(58a) \quad M_2 = \frac{i}{h}(M_1 M_3 - M_3 M_1)$$
$$M_3 = \frac{i}{h}(M_2 M_1 - M_1 M_2)$$

It follows from (58) that, for motion under H_D,

$$(59) \quad \dot{M}_1 = \frac{i}{h}(H_D M_1 - M_1 H_D) = \sigma^2 P_3 - \sigma^3 P_2$$

So, M_1 is not a constant of the motion.

Now define

$$(60) \quad \beta_1 = i\sigma^2\sigma^3(2W\sigma)^{-1}; \quad \beta_2 = i\sigma^1\sigma^3(2W\sigma)^{-1}; \quad \beta_3 = i\sigma^1\sigma^2(2W\sigma)^{-1}$$

from which (see (33))

$$(61) \quad \begin{aligned} &\beta_k^2 = I; \quad \beta_k\sigma = \sigma\beta_k; \quad \beta_j\beta_k + \beta_k\beta_j = O; \\ &\beta_1 = i\beta_3\beta_2; \quad \beta_2 = i\beta_1\beta_3; \quad \beta_3 = i\beta_2\beta_1; \quad \beta_1\beta_2\beta_3 = i \end{aligned}$$

being the properties assigned to the Pauli spin operators ($\sigma's$ in Dirac's notation, p. 149). These operators satisfy commutation rules analogous to (58a)

$$\beta_1 = \frac{i}{2}(\beta_3\beta_2 - \beta_2\beta_3)$$
$$(61a) \quad \beta_2 = \frac{i}{2}(\beta_1\beta_3 - \beta_3\beta)$$
$$\beta_3 = \frac{i}{2}(\beta_2\beta_1 - \beta_1\beta_2)$$

so $\underline{\beta}$ has the commutation properties of an angular momentum vector

(61b) $\underline{M} = \dfrac{h}{2}\underline{\beta}$; see (58a)

By using the identities

(61c) $\sigma^1 \beta_1 = \beta_1 \sigma^1$; $\quad \sigma^2 \beta_1 = -\beta_1 \sigma^2 = \sigma^3$; $\quad \sigma^3 \beta_1 = -\beta_1 \sigma^3 = -\sigma^2$

we find that

(62) $\quad \dot{\beta_1} = \dfrac{i}{h}(H_D \beta_1 - \beta_1 H_D) = \dfrac{2}{h}(\sigma^3 P_2 - \sigma^2 P_3)$

so β_1 is not a constant of the motion. But (see (59))

(63) $\quad \dot{M_1} + \dfrac{h}{2}\dot{\beta_1} = O$

showing that it is necessary to add $h\underline{\beta}/2$ to the classical angular momentum $\underline{M}$ in order to produce constants of the motion under H_D. In view of (61a) and (61b), and because β_1 has eigenvalues ± 1, the term $h\beta_1/2$ is identified as a spin angular momentum with magnitude $h/2$; (recall that, under H_N, the components of $\underline{M}$ are each constants of the motion with differing eigenstates). Our particle, characterised by (6) and (33) is, therefore, a fermion.

The theory given here differs from that of Dirac only in the way the $\beta's$ are defined; see (60). Here they are defined, directly, in terms of the $\sigma's$. In the Dirac theory the procedure is reversed. The Pauli spin operators are given, ab initio, and the Dirac $\alpha's$ are defined in terms of them.

5.3   Note On Fermions And Bosons

Fermions: particles of half integer spin ($h/2, 3h/2, 5h/2.....$). They include leptons (e.g., electron, muon, neutrino), baryons (e.g., neutron, proton, lambda particle) and nuclei of odd mass number. The

Exclusion Principle states that no two fermions may occupy exactly the same position/ spin eigenstate.

Bosons: particles of zero or integer spin (0, h, $2h$,.....). They include mesons (e.g., pion, kaon), the exchange particles of fields (e.g., photon, gluon) and nuclei of even mass number. Bosons are not subject to the Exclusion Principle.

5.4   The Rapid Fluctuation Postulate

The suitability of (22d), as a definition of $\overline{A}$, depends on the postulate that $A(t)$ fluctuates many times during the period of measurement of A. Now the modal angular frequencies of fluctuation of (see (22b))

(64) $A(t) \equiv \exp(iY)A\exp(-iY); \quad Y \equiv H_D t / h$

depend on the eigenvalues of H_D. That is, they are made up of the angular frequencies λ_D / h together, possibly, with sums and differences; see item (k) of Table 1; (these angular frequencies are large provided that the relativistic mass is sufficiently large). This point can be underlined by calculating (see (33) and (43))

(65)
$$\sigma^j(t) \equiv \exp(iY)\sigma^j \exp(-iY)$$
$$= \frac{1}{2}(\sigma^j - Y\sigma^j Y^{-1})\exp(-2iY) + \frac{1}{2}(\sigma^j + Y\sigma^j Y^{-1})$$
$$= \frac{ih}{2}\dot{\sigma}^j H_D^{-1} \exp(-2iY) + \overline{\sigma^j}$$
$$= (\overline{\sigma^j} - \sigma^j)\exp(-2iY) + \overline{\sigma^j}$$

which shows $\sigma^j(t)$ to be made up of an oscillating term added to the mean value. The second to last expression, on the RHS, is given by Dirac, p. 263. Dirac uses this result to explain the discrepancy between the classical SR velocity $c^2 p_j / \lambda_D$ and the instantaneous velocity σ^j (eigenvalues $\pm c$); he asserts that we measure not σ^j but the mean value of $\sigma^j(t)$.

Now suppose that the position (coordinate) is determined by collision with a photon; velocity can, at least notionally, be determined by

successive such collisions. Let this photon have angular frequency ω.
Unless (see Table 1, item (k))

$$(66) \quad \omega h << \lambda_D \Rightarrow \omega << \left(\frac{mc^2}{h}\right)(1 - v^2/c^2)^{-1/2},$$

so that the energy of the photon is small compared with the total energy
of the particle, the measurements of position and velocity must be
disturbed; indeed the scattering may prove inelastic so that the identity of
the particle is lost. More exactly, although we cannot measure both
velocity and position with indefinitely high precision, we can get
reasonable precision for both provided that (compare with (66))

$$(67) \quad \frac{\omega h}{c} << mv(1 - v^2/c^2)^{-1/2} \Rightarrow \omega << \left(\frac{mvc}{h}\right)(1 - v^2/c^2)^{-1/2}$$

This condition ensures that the momentum of the photon is small
compared with that of the particle. The first collision cannot then impart
appreciable momentum to the particle and thus spoil the velocity
measurement. The best precision of the position measurement, on the
other hand, is of the order of the wavelength $2\pi c/\omega$ of the photon.

The epoch of measurement $2T$ must be of the order of the duration
of the photon wave-group and will, therefore, contain a number of wave-
periods $2\pi/\omega$. Condition (67) ensures that the wave period $2\pi/\omega$ is
many times larger than the SR Compton period $\lambda_D/(2\pi h)$. The rapid
fluctuation postulate applies, therefore, to reasonable observations of the
position and/ or velocity of the particle that do not destroy its identity.

For the low mass particle the Compton wavelength tends to
infinity. The argument seems, therefore, to break down; but, to achieve an
optimum measurement of position and velocity, the wavelength of the
colliding photon must still greatly exceed the Compton wavelength;
condition (67) must still hold. If we can *never* achieve optimum
measurements of position and velocity it is inappropriate to refer to the
subject of the measurement as a particle. Neutrinos, being fermions, are
candidate 'low mass' particles in the present theory. Photons are not
candidates; they are *bosons* with *zero* mass.

5.5   The Universality of $|c|$

Suppose that we interpret (6) as governing the motions of a *system* of N particles. Then $n = 3N$ and, evidently, the particles interact only through their spins. The $(\sigma^j)^2 = 2W\sigma$ are identical and they commute with all the operators that characterise a particle. It follows that there will be eigenstates of the system which are eigenstates of $2W\sigma$ with eigenvalue c^2; see Table 1. In a given eigenstate of the system, therefore, the value c^2 will be common to *all* the particles.

Our system of particles is much too simple to constitute a universe! But if, for the moment, we entertain this conceit then the above argument suggests that all the denizens of such a universe would perceive the same value of c^2. Presumably they would be unaware that, in a different eigenstate, their universe could exhibit a different value.

6. CONCLUSIONS

Confine attention to Hamiltonians that are polynomial in the Cartesian components of the momenta of a system of particles. Then only those that are linear satisfy *both* the conditions (4) and (5) when $\Theta(\underline{Q})$ is arbitrary; but, condition (4) is also satisfied by quadratic Hamiltonians; (6) and (7) are the forms appropriate to free particles. See Appendix A.

An Hamiltonian that satisfies (4) and (5) provides a more accurate description of the motion (of a particle or system of particles) than an Hamiltonian that only satisfies (4). This suggests that the linear form (6) should, in some sense, approximate the quadratic form (7).

The Hamiltonians themselves cannot be approximated; but the operators that represent measurements of the Cartesian components of velocity can approximate. Here measurement is conceived as performing an average over a finite epoch. This process is here represented by a moving window filter.

The conditions under which the measured motions approximate are that: (a) the mean speed is low; (b) the coefficient operators in (6) satisfy an algebra slightly more general than that of Dirac (the mass is represented by an operator not a scalar); (c) the measurement epoch is long. The formulae for the SR kinetics of a single free particle are thereby derived, from the formalism of non-relativistic QM, without recourse to classical ideas.

These results are independent of the weights assumed for the averaging filter provided that the weights vary slowly as a function of time. See Appendix C.

The eigenvalue of the quadratic Hamiltonian is the low speed Newtonian approximation. See Table 1. The $h/2$ spin appears, more or less, as in Dirac's theory; thus the particle is a fermion.

I have not been able to prove that the Dirac algebra is the only algebra that satisfies; but it seems likely. See Appendix D.

Mean coordinates are *apparent coordinates*; (these are alternative definitions of Cartesian coordinates measured over a finite epoch). An apparent coordinate differs from the corresponding instantaneous coordinate by an increment of the order of (Compton Wavelength)/(2π). Apparent coordinates have continuous spectra. They do not commute either with the instantaneous coordinates or with each other.

There is, at least, a naïve argument, within the theory, that explains why the speed of light is universal.

7.   REFERENCES

[1]	Deakin, A. M.	'Where Does Schrödinger Equation Really Come From?', The Proceedings of ANPA 20- Aspects II- p. 277, May 1999
[2]	Dirac, P. A. M.	'The Principles of Quantum Mechanics', Ed. 4, O.U.P., 1958
[3]	Abramowitz, M Stegun, I. A.	'Handbook of Mathematical Functions', Dover, 1972
[4]	Newing , R. A. Cunningham, J.	'Quantum Mechanics', Oliver & Boyd, 1967
[5]	Kilmister, C. W.	'Hamiltonian Dynamics', Longmans, 1964
[6]	Kilmister, C. W.	'Lagrangian Dynamics', Logos Press, 1967

APPENDIX A

FORMS OF $H(\underline{P},\underline{Q})$ THAT SATISFY (4) AND/ OR (5) GIVEN THAT $\Theta(\underline{Q})$ IS ARBITRARY

A.1   No General Method Found

I cannot find a systematic method to obtain general solutions $H(\underline{P},\underline{Q})$, of (4) and (5), given that $\Theta(\underline{Q})$ is arbitrary. But, particular solutions may be arrived at by restricting the form of H. Our main restriction, here, is that H is assumed to be a polynomial in the $\underline{P}$ with coefficients that may or may not be operators. The reader is reminded that a pure operator function of the $\underline{P}$ is a polynomial or series in the $\underline{P}$ with numerical coefficients. The function is Hermitian only if the coefficients are real. Pure functions of the $\underline{Q}$ are defined similarly.

A.2   Polynomial Solutions Of (4) Can Take Various Linear Forms

Firstly, consider (4) in the cases where the coefficients in H are numerical. When

(A.1) $H \equiv U$; see (7)

commutes with both the $\underline{P}$ and the $\underline{Q}$ then both sides of (4) vanish. With the choice

(A.2) $H \equiv P_l$; $l = 1,2,...n$

both sides of (4) reduce to Θ_l. So, (A.2) is a solution of (4). But (4) is linear in H; thus, any linear compound of the $\underline{P}$, with numerical coefficients, is also a solution. Further, substitution of

(A.3) $H \equiv P_l F(\underline{Q}) + F(\underline{Q})P_l + U + V(\underline{Q})$

(F and V are pure functions of the $\underline{Q}$) gives $2\Theta_l F$ on either side of (4). So the coefficients in the linear form may also be pure functions of the

$\underline{Q}$. Notice that H is given symmetrical form, at (A.3), to ensure that it has the Hermitian property. Substitution of (6) into (4) gives $\sigma^j \Theta_{,j}$ on both sides. So, a linear form in which the coefficients commute with *both* the $\underline{P}$ and the $\underline{Q}$, but not necessarily with each other, also satisfies (4).

A.3 The Order of Polynomial Solutions Of (4) Does Not Exceed 2

Now suppose that $A(\underline{P})$ and $B(\underline{P})$ are pure functions of the $\underline{P}$, and that both A and

(A.4) $H \equiv AB \Rightarrow H^{,j} = A^{,j}B + AB^{,j}$; see (4a)

are solutions of (4). Then

(A.5) $\dfrac{i}{h}(A\Theta - \Theta A) = \tfrac{1}{2}(A^{,j}\Theta_{,j} + \Theta_{,j}A^{,j});\quad \Theta \equiv \Theta(\underline{Q})$; see (4)

and

(A.6) $\dfrac{i}{h}(H\Theta - \Theta H) = \dfrac{i}{h}[(A\Theta - \Theta A)B + A(B\Theta - \Theta B)]$

Substitute (A.4) and (A.6) into (4) and subtract (A.5)$\times B$ to give

(A.7) $\dfrac{i}{h}A(B\Theta - \Theta B) = \tfrac{1}{2}[A^{,j}(B\Theta_{,j} - \Theta_{,j}B) + AB^{,j}\Theta_{,j} + \Theta_{,j}AB^{,j}]$

If B is scalar then both sides of (A.7) vanish as is to be expected. If

(A.8) $B \equiv P_l$

then

(A.9) $\dfrac{i}{h}(A\Theta_{,l} - \Theta_{,l}A) = A^{,j}\Theta_{,j}$

The LHS of (A.9) is Hermitian; so, the RHS must be likewise. Thus $A^{,j}$ commutes with an arbitrary function of the $\underline{Q}$; and, because, by definition, it is not a function of the $\underline{Q}$, it must be a scalar. It follows that A is linear in the $\underline{P}$ and H is quadratic in the $\underline{P}$. Now suppose that

(A.10) $B \equiv P_l^2$

then

(A.11) $\dfrac{i}{h}(A\Theta_{,j} - \Theta_{,j}A)P_l = A^{,j}(P_l\Theta_{,j,l} + \Theta_{,j,l}P_l)$

Form $P_l \times A(11)$. The LHS of the resulting equation is Hermitian showing that $P_l A^{,j}$ must commute with $(P_l\Theta_{,j,l} + \Theta_{,j,l}P_l)$. This is an Hermitian function of the $\underline{P}$ and the $\underline{Q}$ which is arbitrary in the $\underline{Q}$. $P_l A^{,j}$ is, therefore, scalar. But, P_l^{-1} does not exist and A is, in any case, defined in terms of non-negative powers of the $\underline{P}$. So, $A^{,j}$ vanishes. It follows that A is scalar confirming that H is, at most, of second order in the $\underline{P}$. If we define B, as a polynomial of order higher than 2, then we always get equations for A that cannot be satisfied for arbitrary Θ.

A.4   Quadratic Forms That Are Solutions of (4)

A further generalisation, that follows from the linearity of (4), is that if the W^{jk} are Hermitian operators that commute with both the $\underline{P}$ and the $\underline{Q}$, but not necessarily with each other, then (see(A.3))

(A.12) $H \equiv W^{jk}P_jP_k + P_jF^{J}(\underline{Q}) + F^{J}(\underline{Q})P_j + V(\underline{Q}); \quad W^{jk} = W^{kj}$

is a solution of (4); the $F^{J}(\underline{Q})$ and $V(\underline{Q})$ are pure functions. In other words, we may replace the numerical coefficients in the quadratic form by operators such as the W^{jk}. A particular case is of special interest. Suppose that

(A.13) $W^{jk} \equiv g^{jk}W; \quad g^{jk} = g^{kj}$

where the g^{jk} are scalars and W commutes with both the $\underline{P}$ and the $\underline{Q}$. Suppose also that the $n \times n$ matrix G, with elements g^{jk}, has positive eigenvalues. Then G can be expressed as

(A.14) $G = L^{T}L$; L is a real matrix and τ denotes transpose and it can be shown that the transformations

(A.15) $\qquad \underline{P}' \equiv L\underline{P}; \quad \underline{Q}' \equiv (L^T)^{-1}$

leave the form of (9) unchanged. We then have

(A.16) $\qquad W^{jk} P_j P_k = W \underline{P}^T G \underline{P} = W \underline{P}'^T \underline{P}' = W \sum_{j=1}^{n} (P_j')^2$

which is the first term in (7) with $\underline{P}$ replaced by $\underline{P}'$. It can be shown that the transformations (A.15) are equivalent to rotation (orthogonal transformation) followed by scaling; so the $\underline{P}'$ and the $\underline{Q}'$ are still Cartesian. There is a further generalisation related to (A.13). It is easy to show that if

(A.17) $\qquad H \equiv W[g^{ij}(\underline{Q})P_j P_k + P_j P_k g^{ij}(\underline{Q})]; \quad g^{jk} = g^{kj}$

(where $g^{ij}(\underline{Q})$ is a pure function of the $\underline{Q}$) then both sides of (4) reduce to

(A.17a) $\qquad W[g^{jk}(P_j \Theta_{,k} + \Theta_{,k} P_j) + (P_j \Theta_{,k} + \Theta_{,k} P_j) g^{kj}]$.

So, (A.17) is yet another quadratic form permitted for H.

A.5 The Polynomial Solutions Common to (4) and (5) Are Linear

For reasons which are explained in Section 2.1 we are only interested in operators H that satisfy (4) *and* (5) for arbitrary $\Theta(\underline{Q})$. Substitute (A.1) into (5) and both sides vanish. Substitute (A.2) into (5) and we get $\Theta_{,JJ}$ on both sides. We can substitute (6) into (5) to show that the linear form (6) is a solution of (5) irrespective of the commutation rules that govern the $\underline{\sigma}$ and σ; but, the algebra is tedious. Because (6) satisfies (4) it is easier to proceed as follows. Form the commutator $\frac{i}{h}[H(.) - (.)H]$ with (4) and subtract the result from (5) to yield

$$(A.18) \quad \frac{i}{2h}[\Theta_{,j}HH^{,j} - H^{,j}H\Theta_{,j} + H^{,j}\Theta_{,j}H - H\Theta_{,j}H^{,j}]$$

$$+ [(H^{,j}H^{,k} + H^{,k}H^{,j})\Theta_{,j,k} + \Theta_{,j,k}(H^{,j}H^{,k} + H^{,k}H^{,j})]/4 = O$$

If (6) is to satisfy (5) then it must satisfy this equation for arbitrary Θ. Substitute (6) into (A.18) and we find that the LHS vanishes identically.

The quadratic forms of H do not satisfy (5); and higher order forms fail to satisfy either (4) or (5); see [1] and Section (2.2). So, only linear forms satisfy both conditions.

A.6   Recognisable Forms

The generalisation of (6)

$$(A.19) \quad H_D \equiv \sigma^j \Pi_{Dj} + A_{D0} + \sigma; \quad \Pi_{Dj} \equiv P_j - A_{Dj}$$

$$\Rightarrow \dot{P}_j = -H_{D,j} = +\sigma^k A_{Dk,j} - A_{D0,j}; \quad \dot{Q}^j = H_D^{,j} = \sigma^j$$

where the A_D and A_{D0} are pure functions of the Q, can be shown to satisfy (4) and (5). The generalisation of (7)

$$H_N \equiv \left(W \sum_{j=1}^{n} \Pi_{Nj}^2 \right) + A_{N0} + U$$

$$(A.20) \quad \Rightarrow \dot{P}_j = -H_{N,j} = W \sum_{k=1}^{n} (\Pi_k A_{Nk,j} + A_{Nk,j} \Pi_k) - A_{N0,j};$$

$$\dot{Q}^j = H_N^{,j} = 2W\Pi_{Nj}$$

where the A_N and A_{N0} are pure functions of the Q, is of the form (A.12) and, therefore, satisfies (4). The form (A.20) will be recognised as that of the Hamiltonian of a single, low speed, charged particle moving in an EM field; the A_N are proportional to the components of the vector potential and A_{N0} is proportional to the scalar potential. The forms (A.19), on the other hand, is that of the corresponding relativistic Hamiltonian assumed by Dirac; see, for example, [2], p. 265. Dirac arrived at this form by analogy with the classical cases. We reject classical analogy. The suffices N and D refer, of course, to Newton and Dirac respectively.

APPENDIX B

AN EXPLICIT EXPRESSION FOR THE MEAN RATE OPERATOR

Observe that

$$
i\frac{d[\sin(Y)A\cos(Y) - \cos(Y)A\sin(Y)]}{dt}; \quad Y \equiv Ht/h
$$

$$
(B.1) \quad = \cos(Y)\frac{i}{h}(HA - AH)\cos(Y) + \sin(Y)\frac{i}{h}(HA - AH)\sin(Y)
$$

$$
= \cos(Y)\dot{A}\cos(Y) + \sin(Y)\dot{A}\sin(Y)
$$

It follows (see (22d)) that

$$
\overline{\dot{A}} \equiv \underset{T\to\infty}{Lt}\frac{1}{2T}\int_{-T}^{T}[\cos(Y)\dot{A}\cos(Y) + \sin(Y)\dot{A}\sin(Y)]dt
$$

$$
(B.2)
$$

$$
= \underset{T\to\infty}{Lt}\frac{i}{T}[\sin(HT/h)A\cos(HT/h) - \cos(HT/h)A\sin(HT/h)]
$$

APPENDIX C

WHEN THE WEIGHTS ARE NON-UNIFORM THE AVERAGES (22) AND (25a) ARE MULTIPLIED BY ALMOST THE SAME FACTOR

Redefine $\overline{A}$ according to (21c) with non-uniform weights

$$
(C.1) \quad \overline{A} \equiv \frac{1}{2T}\int_{-T}^{T}f(t)A(\tau)d\tau
$$

where $f(t)$ is a smooth scalar function, representing the weights, which varies slowly over the data window (i.e., the measurement epoch). This redefinition modifies (25) to

(C.2) $\overline{A} = \overline{f}A; \quad \overline{f} \equiv \dfrac{1}{2T}\int\limits_{-T}^{T}f(t)d\tau$

and it redefines the operators C and S (see (29) as

(C.3) $C \equiv \dfrac{1}{2T}\int\limits_{-T}^{T}[\cos^2(Bt)]f(t)dt; \quad S \equiv \dfrac{1}{2T}\int\limits_{-T}^{T}[\sin^2(Bt)]f(t)dt; \quad B \equiv H/h$

We will now show that, providing the number of oscillations of $A(\tau)$ within the measurement epoch is large,

(C.4) $C \approx S \approx \overline{f}I/2$

In consequence (28) becomes

(C.5) $\overline{A} = AC + HAH^{-1}S \approx \overline{f}(A + HAH^{-1})/2$

It will be sufficient to evaluate S. Assume the diagonal representation of H so that $\sin(Bt)$ and S are also diagonal. Consider a single row of the second matrix equation (C.3) corresponding to the eigenvalues b of B and s of S

(C.6) $s = \dfrac{1}{2T}\int\limits_{-T}^{T}[\sin^2(bt)]f(t)dt = \dfrac{1}{2N}\int\limits_{-N}^{N}[\sin^2(\pi x)]f(\pi x/b)dx$

where

(C.7) $x \equiv tb/\pi; \quad N \equiv T|b|/\pi$

Assume that N is an integer. Then, according to (C.6),

(C.8) $\begin{aligned} s &\approx \dfrac{1}{2N}\sum_{j=1}^{N}f[(2j-N-1)\pi/b]\int_{2j-N-2)}^{(2j-N)}\sin^2(\pi x)dx \\ &= \dfrac{1}{2N}\sum_{j=1}^{N}f[(2j-N-1)\pi/b] \approx \dfrac{1}{2N}\int\limits_{-N}^{N}\dfrac{f(\pi x/b)}{2}dx \\ &= \dfrac{1}{4T}\int\limits_{-T}^{T}f(t)dt = \overline{f}/2 \end{aligned}$

The first approximation at (C.8) divides the range of integration into N segments each of width 2 and replaces f by its value at the centre of a segment; the result is a sum of N central values. The second approximation replaces the sum by an integral keeping in mind that each segment is of width 2. The conditions N large, $f(t)$ smooth and slowly varying are essential to these approximations.

A similar argument can be applied to the calculation of C; the formulae (C.4) follow. When N is not an integer these calculations are in error by a fraction of order $1/N$.

APPENDIX D

IS THE KNOWN SOLUTION UNIQUE?

D.1 Conditions On σ And The $\underline{\sigma}$

With the aid of (24) equation (30) can be written in full as

(D.1)
$$2Wp_j \approx - \underset{T \to \infty}{Lt} \frac{h}{T}[\sin(Y)\{\cot(Y)\}^{\cdot j} \sin(Y)];$$
$$Y \equiv TH_D/h; \quad Y^{\cdot j} = T\sigma^j/h$$

Set

(D.2) $$p_j = 0 \ \forall j \Rightarrow H_D \equiv \sigma$$

in (D.1) to get

(D.3) $$\underset{T \to \infty}{Lt} \frac{h}{T}[\sin(Z)\{\cot(Y)\}^{\cdot j}\big|_{p_j=0} \sin(Z)] = O; \quad Z \equiv \sigma T/h$$

This condition appears to connect σ and σ^j.

To make the condition explicit we need an expression for $\cot(Y)$; we will also need to express $\cos ec^2(Y)$. To this end we employ the analogue of the scalar series [3]

$$\cot(\varphi) \equiv \frac{1}{\varphi} + 2\varphi \sum_{k=1}^{\infty} \frac{1}{\varphi^2 - k^2\pi^2} = \sum_{k=-\infty}^{\infty} \frac{1}{\varphi + k\pi};$$

(D.4) $$\cosec^2(\varphi) \equiv \sum_{k=-\infty}^{\infty} \frac{1}{(\varphi + k\pi)^2};$$

$$\varphi \neq 0, \pm\pi, \pm 2\pi, \ldots\ldots$$

which are valid for large arguments. Thus

(D.5) $$\cot(Y) \equiv Y^{-1} + 2Y \sum_{k=1}^{\infty} (Y^2 - k^2\pi^2 I)^{-1} = \sum_{k=-\infty}^{\infty} (Y + k\pi I)^{-1}$$

from which, by forming the commutator of Q^j with both sides of (D.5),

(D.6) $$[\cot(Y)]^{\cdot j} = -\sum_{k=-\infty}^{\infty} (Y + k\pi I)^{-1} Y^{\cdot j} (Y + k\pi I)^{-1}$$

giving

(D.7) $$[\cot(Y)]^{\cdot j}\Big|_{p_j=0} = -\sum_{k=-\infty}^{\infty} (Z + k\pi I)^{-1} Y^{\cdot j} (Z + k\pi I)^{-1};$$

$$Z \equiv T\sigma / h; \quad Y^{\cdot j} = T\sigma^j / h$$

from which

(D.8) $$\underset{T \to \infty}{Lt} \frac{h}{T} [\sin(Z)\{\cot(Y)\}^{\cdot j}\Big|_{p_j=0} \sin(Z)]$$

$$= -\underset{T \to \infty}{Lt} [\sin(Z)\{\sum_{k=-\infty}^{\infty} (Z + k\pi I)^{-1}\sigma^j (Z + k\pi I)^{-1}\}\sin(Z)]$$

According to (D.3) the RHS of (D.8) must vanish. We expect this to happen when the first of the conditions (33) is satisfied

(D.9) $\sigma\sigma^j + \sigma^j\sigma = O \Rightarrow \sigma^j (Z + k\pi I)^{-1} = (-Z + k\pi I)^{-1}\sigma^j$

so that (D.8) becomes

$$Lt_{T \to \infty} \frac{h}{T} [\sin(Z)\{\cot(Y)\}^{\cdot j}|_{p_j=0} \sin(Z)]$$

(D.10)
$$= \sigma^j \; Lt_{T \to \infty} [\sin(Z)\{\sum_{k=-\infty}^{\infty}(Z^2 - k^2\pi^2 I)^{-2}\}\sin(Z)]$$; see(D.4)

$$= \sigma^j \; Lt_{T \to \infty} \sin(Z)\{Z^{-1}\cot(Z)\}\sin(Z)$$

$$= \sigma^j \; Lt_{T \to \infty} Z^{-1}\frac{\sin(2Z)}{2} = O$$

Our expectation is realized. On the other hand, if

(D.11) $\sigma\sigma^j = \sigma^j\sigma$

then, we expect

$$- Lt_{T \to \infty} \frac{h}{T}[\sin(Z)\{\cot(Y)\}^{\cdot j}|_{p_j=0} \sin(Z)]$$

(D.12)
$$= \sigma^j \; Lt_{T \to \infty} [\sin(Z)\{\sum_{k=-\infty}^{\infty}(Z + k\pi I)^{-2}\}\sin(Z)]$$; see (D.4)

$$= \sigma^j \; Lt_{T \to \infty} [\sin(Z)\{\cos ec^2(Z)\}\sin(Z)] = \sigma^j$$

which is not null by hypothesis; we conclude that σ^j and σ cannot commute.

But, is (D.9) the only relation between σ^j and σ that causes the RHS of (D.9) to vanish? This seems to be a difficult question to answer. There are two branches to the question. Firstly, given σ, are there matrices σ^j that cause the series on the RHS of (D.8) to diverge? Secondly, given σ and given that the series converges, what matrices σ^j cause the function to vanish in the limit $T \to \infty$?

D.2   The Remainder of The Conditions (33) Follow From (D.9)

Under the conditions (19b) we can use (D.9) to approximate (D.1) so to deduce the remainder of the conditions (33). Define

(D.13) $\Delta \equiv \sigma^j p_j$; summed

then, making use of (D.9)

$$(D.14) \quad \begin{aligned} H_D &= \sigma + \Delta; \quad \Delta\sigma = -\sigma\Delta; \quad \Delta^2\sigma = \sigma\Delta^2; \\ H_D^2 &= \sigma^2 + \Delta^2; \quad H_D^2\Delta = \Delta H_D^2 \end{aligned}$$

It follows that, for an even pure operator function of H_D,

$$(D.15a) \quad F(H_D^2) \approx F(\sigma^2) + \Delta^2 \frac{dF(\varphi)}{d\varphi}\bigg|\varphi \equiv \sigma^2; \quad p_k \to 0$$

and that, for an odd pure operator function of H_D,

$$(D.15b) \quad H_D^{-1}G(H_D^2) \approx H_D^{-1}\left(G(\sigma^2) + \Delta^2 \frac{dG(\varphi)}{d\varphi}\bigg|\varphi \equiv \sigma^2\right); \quad p_k \to 0$$

because Δ commutes with H_D^2. These results can be used to evaluate

$$(D.16a) \quad \sin(Y) \approx H_D^{-1}\sigma \sin(Z); \quad \text{neglecting } \Delta^2 \text{ and higher powers}$$

and

$$(D.16b) \quad \cot(Y) \approx H_D^{-1}\left(\sigma \cot(Z) + \Delta^2[\sigma^{-1}\cot(Z) - \frac{T}{h}\cos ec^2(Z)]/2\right)$$

When T is large, therefore,

$$(D.17) \quad \begin{aligned} -\frac{h}{T}\cot(Y) &\to H_D^{-1}\left(\Delta^2 \cos ec^2(Z)\right)/2 \\ &\approx \sigma^{-1}\frac{\Delta^2}{2}\cos ec^2(Z); \quad T \to \infty \end{aligned}$$

The last step at (D.17) follows because

$$(D.18) \quad H_D^{-1}\Delta^2 = \sigma^{-1}\Delta^2 + order(\Delta^3); \quad p_k \to 0$$

From (D.17)

$$-\frac{h}{T}[\cot(Y)]^{\prime j} \to \sigma^{-1}\frac{[\Delta^2]^{\prime j}}{2}\cos ec^2(Z); \quad T \to \infty$$

(D.19) $\qquad = \sigma^{-1}\frac{(\Delta\sigma^j + \sigma^j\Delta)}{2}\cos ec^2(Z)$

$$= \sigma^{-1}\cos ec(Z)\frac{(\Delta\sigma^j + \sigma^j\Delta)}{2}\cos ec(Z)$$

The last step at (D.19) follows because Z commutes with $(\Delta\sigma^j + \sigma^j\Delta)$. Now substitute the results (D.16a) and (D.17) into (D.1)

$$2Wp_j \approx$$

(D.20)
$$\underset{T\to\infty}{Lt}\ H_D^{-1}\frac{(\Delta\sigma^j + \sigma^j\Delta)}{2}\cos ec(Z)[H_D^{-1}\sigma\sin(Z)]; \quad p_k \to 0$$

Each of the terms in $(\Delta\sigma^j + \sigma^j\Delta)$ is proportional to one of the p_k; and the LHS of (D.20) is proportional to p_j. It follows that we should neglect terms of order Δ^2 and higher powers on the RHS of (D.20). We may, therefore, set

(D.21) $\qquad H_D = \sigma$

on the RHS to get

(D.22) $\qquad 2Wp_j \approx \sigma^{-1}\frac{(\Delta\sigma^j + \sigma^j\Delta)}{2}; \quad p_k \to 0$

Equate the coefficients of the p_k on either side of (D.22) and we get the remainder of the conditions (33)

(D.23) $\qquad \sigma^j\sigma^k + \sigma^k\sigma^j = O; \quad j \neq k; \quad 2W\sigma = (\sigma^j)^2; \quad W\sigma = \sigma W$

A. M. Deakin   19/12/2001

The Einstein velocity relation, g-groups and the CH.

Clive Kilmister
Red Tiles Cottage
High Street
Barcombe
Lewes
BN8 5DH, UK

This paper does not claim to show any new results but only to report on a problem in progress. You are welcome to share in the labour. Recall that last ANPA meeting I raised the spectre of non-associative algebras. This came about in this way: in the original Combinatorial Hierarchy (CH) the first level is $G_{12} \simeq S \simeq C_2 \times C_2$. Here G_{12} is Arleta's notation for systems with one signal and two generators, S is Klein's quadratic group. For Parker-Rhodes the next step was to go up a level to get $G_{13} \simeq C_2 \times C_2 \times C_2$. But even if the system does not go up a level, the next step is again G_{13} which is important for Parker-Rhodes because he can then argue that the second level is "much the same" as the first and so the process of going up a level can be repeated. In our process view of this, once we had realised that "aspect" was important – that is, it makes a difference whether you discriminate a against b or b against a – then the first level is not S but the quaternion group, $G_{22} \simeq Q$. Then the question arises, is the next level isomorphic to G_{23} ? Alas, no, since no G_{23} can exist; an attempt to get it leads to non-associativity.

Now one could argue, but I shall not, that it does not matter all that much because even in the original CH, whereas it is easy and direct to construct G_{12}, G_{13} may take an infinity of steps (because each unsuccessful discrimination produces new elements) and indeed the expectation value of the number of steps is infinite. I shall not take this way out because, none the less, G_{13} may form.

Three remarks, then: (i) If a, b, c all anti-commute, then assuming associativity, abc is in the centre of the algebra. commutes with everything, and if "everything" anticommutes, this is ruled out. So there must be some non-associativity.

(ii) Moreover, as I argued last year, taking the signal z (for equality) as −1 and the symbol y (for equivalence) as 1 so as to give Q is allowed but perverse. z = 1 would be more natural so that even at the first level we do not have the associative G_{22} but the non-associative L_{22}.

(iii) So: general panic. How should we proceed ?

A possible White Knight rides onto the scene in the form of a book by Ungar (2001). He begins by pointing out, what is often not noticed, that the Einstein velocity relation shows that addition of velocities in SR is not commutative. This is not noticed because attention is concentrated on the one-dimensional form which _is_ commutative. But as you know this has to be accompanied by beta-factors on the transverse velocities which destroys the commutativity, except approximately, as in Newtonian mechanics. Indeed, the same can be said for the associativity as well. Now what Ungar does is, very cleverly, to abstract just enough properties of the velocity addition to characterise the structure abstractly. In my notation, which is not his, he looks at a set closed under multiplication with the properties: 1. There is a left identity, 1_L, such that $1_L x = x$ (all x)

2. For any x there is an x' such that $x'x = 1_L$

3. $u(vw) = (uv)\phi_{uv}(w)$, where the ϕ_{uv} are functions (which may be automorphisms or involutions (anti-automorphisms)).

4. $\phi_{uv} = \phi_{uv,v}$ for any u, v.

He then constructs a finite example of such a system (which he calls a gyro-group because he has got it from those features of the Einstein velocity relation which give rise to the Thomas precession). His finite one has 16 elements, which is what made me sit up. Having done this, he goes on to show how such a system can be embedded in a group.

The first question is: do we have a gyro-group ? The first 3 conditions are easily verified but the fourth fails to hold. To see this consider, not the whole of L_{23}, but the two sub-systems Q* (which is, briefly, Q with the squares all made +1) and Q** (which is Q with two of the elements saddled

with a $\sqrt{-1}$ but all the squares forced to be 1 none the less). The values
of the functions ϕ for these two cases are:

ϕ	i	j	k
i	A_1	I_2	I_3
Q*: j	I_1	A_2	I_3
k	I_1	I_2	A_3

ϕ	i	j	k
i	A_1	I_3	I_2
Q**: j	I_1	I	I_1
k	I_1	I_1	I

where I is the identity, A_1 is the automorphism

A_1: i,j,k $\rightarrow$ i,-j,-k

and I_1 is the involution

I_1: i,j,k $\rightarrow$ -i,j,k.

In each of these cases 4 does not hold. So we do not have a structure of
Ungar's type, and so I have called my structures g-groups.

It may be just as well that we do not have exactly Ungar's system, for
his book contains three pages in italics of an irascible kind, directed against
those who had, he alleged, plagiarised his ideas. But he has been very clever
in abstracting properties which, amongst other things, allow for group
embedding. My problem is to find similar such abstract characterisations
in L_{23} with some hope of embedding. So far my progress has been very small.
For my systems, $\phi_{ab}(a) = a$ follows from the fact that a(ba) = -(ba)a = (ab)a.
You are welcome to try for more!

REFERENCES

Ungar, A. 2001. Beyond the Einstein Addition Law and its Gyroscopic Thomas
Precession. Dordrecht, Kluwer.

Towards a Dynamics of Moments: The Role of Algebraic Deformation and Inequivalent Vacuum States.

B. J. Hiley

Theoretical Physics Research Unit, Birkbeck College,
Malet Street, London WC1E 7HX.

b.hiley@bbk.ac.uk

Abstract.

We continue our investigations of the algebra of process by discussing a general evolution in terms of 'moments', $[T_1, T_2]$, a notion that arises naturally in our approach. Firstly we show how our work is related to the iterant algebra of Kauffman and a possible connection to the incidence algebra of Raptis and Zapatrin. Then by considering the limit as the duration of the moment approaches the infinitesimal, we obtain a pair of dynamical equations, one expressed in terms of a commutator and the other which is expressed in terms of an anti-commutator. These two real equations are equivalent to the Schrödinger equation. If these moments are then described in purely algebraic terms we make contact with the quantum field approach of Umezawa. This enables us to discuss quantum processes at finite temperatures within one formalism. This in turn enables us to express our dynamical evolution in a way that is equivalent to a movement between inequivalent vacuum states. Thus we are able to make contact with the discussion on the thermodynamic origin of time.

Introduction.

I want to start by facing directly a very basic question "What is a quantum object?" That's easy surely? An electron is a quantum object! Those simple words hide a perplexing riddle that takes us far from the comfort of our classical world. Let us venture into a quantum world with a simple analogy, originally proposed by Weyl. Take 'shape' and 'colour' as quantum operators that do not commute. To make this world simple suppose there are only two shapes that are the 'eigenvalues' of the 'shape' operator and only two colours that are 'eigenvalues' of the 'colour' operator—sphere, cube, red, and blue.

I want to collect together an ensemble of red spheres. In this world I have to use an instrument to measure colour and another incompatible instrument to measure shape. I decide first to collect together spheres and discard all the cubes. I then decide to collect together those spheres that the colour-measuring device classifies as red. I am done. I have an ensemble of red spheres. So what is the problem? Just recheck that the objects in the ensemble are in fact spheres. We check and find that half are now cubes! No *either/or* in this world. No *and/and* either!

Let us look closer at this world and follow a suggestion of Eddington (1958) that the elements of existence can be described by idempotents. The eigenvalues of an idempotent is 1 or 0, existence or non-existence. In symbols

$$E^2 = E, \qquad \text{with} \quad \lambda_e = 1 \text{ or } 0.$$

This is fine if all idempotents commute. Existence is absolute. However in quantum theory, idempotents (projection operators) do not commute.

$$[E_a, E_b] \neq 0$$

What then of existence?

$$\text{Either } e_a \text{ or } e_b, \qquad \text{never} \qquad e_a \text{ and } e_b$$

Existence, non-existence and in between? Clearly no world of classical objects.

What now is the position of reductionism? It won't work because we cannot start with some set of basic building blocks. We cannot separate objects into ensembles with well-defined properties. How can we build stable structures if we can't do that? And when cube is blue, can we rely on it still being a cube as we try to build a structure of blue cubes?

No structures at all? How can this be? Quantum mechanics was introduced to explain stable structures. Without quantum mechanics there is no stability of matter! Without quantum mechanics there would be no atom as we know it. No crystalline structures, no DNA, and no classical world. But our observations start from the classical world. We are the DNA unfolded! We probe the quantum world from our classical world, so naturally we insist on reductionism. We strive to find the elementary objects, the quarks, the strings, the loops and the M-branes from which we try to reconstruct the world.

Surely we are starting from the wrong premise. Parker-Rhodes (1981) must be right, so too is Lou Kauffman (1982)! We should start with the *whole* and then make distinctions. Within these distinctions we can make finer distinctions and so on. These provide us with an order in the world, but an order that starts with us looking *out*. We are not God-like looking *in*. Should we think of these distinctions as passive marks or are we going to allow for the fact that we are part of the process of making these distinctions? Are we participators? Wholeness implies that we and our instruments are inside the whole process, yet our current theories start with the assumption that we and our instruments are outside our cosmos and we are struggling to get back in!

At this stage we must pause. The mere thought of "putting ourselves back into it" traps us into thinking that there is something independent and separate to be put back in. We should never be *out of it* in the first place! Now I hear alarm bells ringing. "He is going to suggest that we must put subjectivity back into our science whereas we know that the whole success of science has been to keep the subject out!" That is true of classical physics, but quantum physics says we must at least put our measuring instruments back into the system.

As Bohr constantly reminds us there is no separation between the system and its means of observation. He emphasises that this fundamental inseparability arises as a direct consequence of what he called "the indivisibility of the quantum of action". After warning us of the dangers of using phrases like 'disturbing the phenomena by observation' and 'creating physical attributes to atomic objects by measurements' he gives an even clearer statement of his position. He writes, "I advocate the application of the word phenomenon exclusively to refer to the observations obtained under specified circumstances, *including an account of the whole experimental arrangement*." Because of the meaning Bohr attaches to the word 'phenomenon', he insists that analysis into parts is *in principle* excluded.

However Bohr (1961) himself as the observer, is still outside. He claims to be a *detached* observer. No pandering to subjectivity here. But the question that fascinates me is "How did he become detached?" Let me spell out problem. I am assuming that the universe did come into being from some form of quantum fluctuation along the lines that is currently assumed. The exact details as to whether this takes the form of a unique occurrence or in the form of a multiverse, or yet something else is of no significance for my argument here. Any quantum birth must have evolved into our classical world and the question is what are the essential properties of this evolution for the emergence of a classical world to take place.

Bohm and I have already given a description of how this could happen in the context of the Bohm approach (Bohm and Hiley 1993), but there we already start half-way along the road when we single out the particle. In this paper I want to look at the problem from a very different perspective. This perspective does not allow me to start with particles. It does not let me use the popular story of decoherence. That is fine if a classical world already exists. There decoherence plays a vital role. But I see no way of making sense of classical ideas starting from the notion of an indivisible unity that is the baby universe.

Activity and Process.

I want to start from the flow of experiences we encounter from the time we leave our collective intellectual womb. As Lou Kauffman (1982) stresses, the primitive perception is *distinction*. We perceive differences, make distinctions and build an order. We do this through relationships. We relate different differences. We perceive similarities in these differences and then look for the differences in these similarities and so on. In this way we construct a hierarchy of order and structure in the manner detailed by Bohm (1965) in his long forgotten paper *Space, Time and the Quantum Theory understood in Terms of Discrete structure Process.*

But the differences of what? Just difference! We experience a flux of sensations, which we must order if we are to make sense of our world. We focus on the invariant features in that flux. What is inside, what is outside, what is left, what is right and so on. More generally what is A, what is not-A. But the distinction A/not-A is not necessarily absolute in a world of process. In a different flux of perceptions, B and not-B may become a distinction. In this context it may not be possible to make the distinction between A and not-A. The processes are ontologically and epistemologically incompatible so that even distinction becomes a relative concept. Ultimately we could reach some domain when the distinction becomes absolute in that domain. Thus emerges the classical world with its absolute and stable distinctions. But note that this ordering does not only apply to the material world. It also applies to the world of thought. Here it is quite clear that the observer, the I of my mind, is part and parcel of the overall structure of the same mind. It is here that we have direct experience with the notion of wholeness. It is also here that we have direct experience of flux, activity and process philosophically highlighted by Fichte and Schelling.

But even here it is easy to slip back into the categories of objects being the primary, forgetting that these objects take their form from the very activity that is thinking. I cannot capture this point better than Eddington (1958) did when he wrote,

> Causation bridges the gap in space and time, but the physical event at the seat of sensation
> (provisionally identified with an electrical disturbance of a neural terminal) is not the *cause*

4

of the sensation; it *is* the sensation. More precisely, the physical event is the structural concept of that which the sensation is the general concept.

Or perhaps we should use the school of continental philosophers like Fichte (1994) who wrote,

> For the same reason, no real being, *no subsistence or continuing existence*, pertains to the intellect; for such being is the result of a process of interaction, and nothing yet exists or is assumed to be present with which the intellect could be posited to interact. Idealism considers the intellect to be a kind of doing and absolutely nothing more. One should not even call it an *active subject*, for such an appellation suggests the presence of something that continues to exist and in which an activity inheres.

Idealism? Probably much too far for physicists, but the emphasis on activity *per se* and *not* the activity of a thing is the message to take. Neither idealism nor scientific materialism, but something new.

How can we hope to begin a description of such a general scheme? Start with Grassmannn (1995). In the process of thought we ask the question "Is the new thought distinct from the old thought, or is it one continuous and developing activity? We find it easier to 'hold' onto our description as the old, T_1, and the new, T_2. But are they separate? Clearly not! The old thought has the potentiality of the new thought, while the new thought has the trace of the old thought. They are aspects of one continuing process. They take their form from the underlying process that *is* thought. Each has a complex structure of yet more distinctions, so that each T can be thought of as the tip of an 'iceberg' of activity.

In order to symbolise this basic indivisibility, we follow Grassmann (1995) and Kauffman (1980, 1987) who enclose the relationship in a square bracket, $[T_1, T_2]$[1]. Relationship is a start but not enough in itself. Our task then is to order these relationships into a multiplex of structure. To do that we need some set of rules on how to put these relationships together.

In my paper on *The Algebra of Process* (Hiley 1995) I tentatively suggested two rules of combination. Firstly a multiplication rule that I am told defines a Brandt groupoid. Secondly I introduce a rule for addition. These two binary relations, of course, define an algebra. Our defining relations are

---

[1] NB this is not a Lie bracket.

(1) $[kA,kB] = k[A,B]$ Strength of process.

(2) $[A,B] = -[B,A]$ Process directed.

(3) $[A,B][B,C] = [A,C]$ Order of succession.

(4) $[A,B] + [C,D] = [A+C,B+D]$ Order of coexistence.

(5) $[A,[B,C]] = [A,B,C] = [[A,B],C]$ Associativity.

Notice $[A,B][C,D]$ is NOT defined.

From these rules I showed how the quaternions and indeed how a general orthogonal Clifford algebra emerges from this structure (Hiley 1995, 2002a). These ideas have been put on a firmer mathematical footing and indeed have been taken much further by the excellent and detailed work of Arleta Griffor (2000, 2001) reported in earlier conferences. I can recommend these papers for those interested in the beautiful mathematical structure implicit in these ideas.

I don't want to develop these ideas here as I have done this elsewhere (Hiley 1995). Rather I want to relate them to a structure introduced by Lou Kauffman (1980), which he called the iterant algebra. To explain the ideas lying behind his work I will start with the plane and divide it into two, the 'inside' and the 'outside'. Now introduce the activity of 'crossing the boundary' and denote the activity of crossing from inside to outside by $[I, O]$, while the crossing from outside to inside is denoted by $[O, I]$. Here I and O are simply symbols denoting 'inside' and 'outside'. This is the primary distinction.

Kauffman then introduces a product defined by

$$[A, B]^*[C, D] = [AC, BD] \qquad (1)$$

and shows that one can also use this relationship to generate the quaternions. Thus we have two structures with two different products producing the same algebra. But are they so different? When $B = C$ we have

$$[A, B]^*[B, D] = [AB, BD] = B[A, D] \qquad (2)$$

Thus the products can be brought closer together. In fact product (3) above is simply an equivalence class of the Kauffman product. But notice product (3) is undefined when

$B \neq C$ which is what makes it a Brandt groupoid.

To see how the quaternions arise in Kauffman's approach we need to introduce a transformation T defined by

$$T([A, B]) = W*[A, B] \tag{3}$$

where W can be some suitable pair C, D. We then need to introduce three transformations, p, q and r defined by

$$p*[A, B] = [A,-B]$$
$$q*[A ,B] = [-A, B]$$
$$r*[A, B] = [B, A]$$

Then it is not difficult to show that

$$ir \Leftrightarrow \mathbf{i} \quad ip \Leftrightarrow \mathbf{j} \quad pr \Leftrightarrow \mathbf{k} \tag{4}$$

where $\mathbf{i}$, $\mathbf{j}$, $\mathbf{k}$ are the quaternions and $i = \sqrt{-1}$ (See Kauffman 1982). If we use the physicist's language these can be written in the form

$$r \Leftrightarrow \sigma_x \quad p \Leftrightarrow \sigma_z \quad ipr \Leftrightarrow \sigma_y. \tag{5}$$

where σ are the Pauli spin operators.

Now I want to go deeper into the general structure of Clifford algebras. Schönberg (1958) and Fernandes (1996) have shown us how to build any orthogonal Clifford algebra from a pair of dual Grassmann algebras whose generators satisfy the relationship

$$\left[a_i, a_j^\dagger\right] = g_{ij} \quad \left[a_i, a_j\right] = 0 = \left[a_i^\dagger, a_j^\dagger\right] \tag{6}$$

These will be recognised as vector fermionic 'annihilation' and 'creation' operators[2]. Notice these are *vector* operators and not the *spinor* operators used in particle physics. Using these we find

$$\sigma_x = a + a^\dagger \quad \text{and} \quad \sigma_y = a - a^\dagger \tag{7}$$

---

[2] I have suggested that these operators create and annihilate extensions.

Now it is interesting to ask what these operators do when they operate on an iterant pair. In fact it is straightforward to show

$$a*[A,B] = [B,0]$$

$$a^\dagger*[A,B] = [0,A]$$

Thus we see that here the annihilation operator a destroys the inside and puts the outside inside. While the creation operator $a^\dagger$ destroys the outside and puts the inside outside!

We can actually carry this further and ask what action the algebraic spinors (minimal left ideals) have on an iterant pair. It is not difficult to show that we have two algebraic spinors given by

$$\psi_{L1} = aa^\dagger + a^\dagger \quad \text{and} \quad \psi_{L2} = a + a^\dagger a. \tag{8}$$

This is in contrast to the spinor used by physicists who have only one spinor in this case. One can show that this single spinor is an equivalence class of the algebraic spinor when it is projected onto a Hilbert space (see Bratteli and Robinson 1979). The projection means that we have lost the possibility of exploiting the additional structure offered by the algebraic spinors. Notice that these spinors are themselves part of the algebra. The whole thrust of my argument is that we must exploit the properties of the algebra and not confine ourselves to Hilbert space. When we do this we can continue with our idea that the elements of our algebra describe activity or process. Then in the case of the iterant algebra the spinor itself must produce some change in $[A, B]$. What is this change? Again this is easy to answer because

$$\psi_{L1}*[A, B] = (aa^\dagger+a^\dagger)*[A,B] = [A, A] \tag{9}$$

$$\psi_{L2}*[A, B] = (a+a^\dagger a)*[A, B] = [B, B] \tag{10}$$

This means that one type of spinor, ψ_{L1}, destroys the outside and puts a copy of the inside outside, while the other spinor, ψ_{L2}, destroys the inside and puts a copy of the outside inside! In other words these operators remove the original distinction, but in different ways. More importantly from the point of view that we are exploring here is that we see how the algebraic spinor itself is active in producing a specific change in the overall process.

8

Lets take this a little further. Consider the following relationship

$$a*[A, 0] = [0, 0] \qquad (11)$$

This should be compared with the physicist's definition of a vacuum state,

$$a|0\rangle = a\Downarrow = 0 \qquad (12)$$

where we have introduced the notation used by Finkelstein (1997). Thus equation (12) shows that $[A, 0]$ acts like the vacuum state in physics. Furthermore

$$a^{\dagger}*[0,B] = [0,0] \qquad \text{should be compared with} \qquad a^{\dagger}\Uparrow = 0$$

Finkelstein calls, $\Uparrow$, the plenum. Thus we see that $[0, B]$ acts like the plenum. Thus we see that here the vacuum state is not empty. Internally it has content but externally it is empty. For the plenum it is the other way round, so unlike Parmenides we can have 'movement' from outside to inside!

We can take this a bit further by recalling that we can write the projector onto the vacuum as $V = |0\rangle\langle 0|$, then we have $aV = 0$. If the projector onto the plenum is $P = |\infty\rangle\langle\infty|$ we find $a^{\dagger}P = 0$.

All of this suggests that we could write $[A, B]$ as $|A\rangle\langle B|$. By making this identification we can bring out the relationship of our work to that of Zapatrin (2000) and of Raptis and Zapatrin (2001) who developed an approach through the incident algebra. In this structure the product rule is written in the form

$$|A\rangle\langle B| . |C\rangle\langle D| = |A\rangle\langle B| C\rangle\langle D| = \delta_{BC}|A\rangle\langle D| \qquad (13)$$

Again this multiplication rule is essentially rule (3), the order of succession above. But there is a major difference. When $B \neq C$ the product to zero, whereas we leave it undefined at this level. Since there is a close similarity between these three different structures it would be worth studying this relationship in some detail. However I will not discuss this relationship here as I want to take the rest of my time exploiting the ideas that are open to us when we look at process in terms I have been trying to develop above.

The Intersection of the Past with the Future.

I want to look more deeply into the structure based on relationships like $[T_1, T_2]$ by, as it were, 'getting inside' the connection between T_1 and T_2. Remember I am focusing on process or flux and I am symbolising *becoming* by $[T_1, T_2]$. Ultimately I want to think of these relationships as ordered structure defining what we have previously called 'pre-space'. (See Bohm 1986 and Hiley 1991.) In other words these relationships are not to be thought of as occurring in space-time, but rather space-time is to eventually be abstracted from this pre-space. This is a radical suggestion so let me try to develop my thinking more slowly.

Conventionally physics is always assumed to unfold in space-time, and furthermore the evolution is always assumed to be from point to point. In other words physics always tries to talk about time development *at an instant*. Any change always involves the limiting process $Lim_{\Delta t \to 0} \dfrac{\Delta x}{\Delta t}$. But before taking the limit it looks as if we were taking a point in the past (x_1, t_1) and relating it to a point in the future (x_2, t_2), that is relating what *was* to what *will be*. But we try to hide the significance of that by going to the limit $t_2 - t_1 \to 0$ when we interpret the change to take place at an instant, t. Yet curiously the instant is a set of measure zero sandwiched between the infinity of that which has passed and the infinity of that which is not yet. This is fine for evolution of point-like entities but not for the evolution of structures.

When we come to quantum mechanics it is not positions that develop in time but wave functions and wave functions like the Pauli spinor can be treated as an ideal in the algebra (See Hiley 2002b) which, as we have seen above, are actions involving 'separate' regions. Recall Heisenberg's (1925) original suggestion that $x(t)$, the position of the electron in the atom, must be replaced by

$$X_q(t) = \sum_a R(n, n-a) \exp[iv(n, n-a)t]$$

The exponent ensures that the Ritz combination rule of atomic spectra can be satisfied, namely

$$v(n, n-a) + v(n-a, n-a-b) = v(n, n-a-b).$$

This result in needed when we form variables like $X_q(t)^2$ which appear in the discussion of a quantum oscillator. Heisenberg then proposed that the amplitudes combine as

$$R(n, n - b) = \sum_a R(n, n - a) R(n - a, n - b)$$

This is immediately recognised as the rule for matrix multiplication. It is when this matrix idea is extended to momentum we find the need for the Heisenberg commutation relations. Notice here we are talking about transitions between stationary states, one being characterised by quantum number n and the other characterised by $(n - a)$. Thus we are talking about transitions between one state and another, that is between structures defining what has been to what will be.

I will continue in the same theme by recalling Feynman's classic paper where he sets out his thinking that led to his 'sum over paths' approach (Feynman 1948). There he starts by dividing space-time into two regions R' and R''. R' consists of a region of space occupied by the wave function before time t', while R'' is the region occupied by the wave function after time t'', i.e $t' < t''$. Then he suggested that we should regard the wave function in region R' as contain information coming from the 'past', while the conjugate wave function in the region R'' representing information coming from the 'future'[3]. The possible present is then the intersection between the two, which is simply represented by the transition probability amplitude $\langle \psi(R'') | \psi(R') \rangle$. But what I want to discuss here is $| \psi(R') \rangle \langle \psi(R'') |$. This is where all the action is!

Before taking up this point I would like to call attention to a similar notion introduced by Stuart Kauffman (1996) in his discussion of biological evolution, again an evolution of structure. He talks about the evolution of biological structures from their present form into the 'adjacent possible'. This means that only certain forms can develop out of the past. Thus not only does the future form contain a trace of the past, but it is also constrained by what is 'immediately' possible. So any development is governed by the *tension between the persistence of the past, and an anticipation of the future.*

What I would now like to do is to build this notion into a dynamics. Somehow we have to relate the past to the future, not in a completely deterministic way, but in a way that constrains the possible future development. My basic notion is thus an extended structure in both space and time. I have elsewhere called it a 'moment' (see Hiley and Fernandes 1997). In spatial terms it is fundamentally non-local; it is also 'non-local' in *time*. I see this as an a-local concept, which has extension in time. It is a kind of 'extension' or 'duron'. We can think of this as a necessary consequence of the energy-time uncertainty

---

[3] This is essentially the same idea that led to the notion of the anti-particle 'going backward in time', but here we are not considering exotic anti-matter.

principle. For a process with a given energy cannot be described as unfolding at an instant except in some approximation.

How then are we to discuss the dynamics of process, which depends on this notion of a moment? I will start in the simplest possible way by proposing that the basic dynamical function will involve two times. Thus we will discuss the time development of two-point functions of the form $[A(t_1), B(t_2)]$ and show that we capture the usual equations of motion in the limit $t_1 \rightarrow t_2$.

Fortunately even in classical physics two-point functions abound. They are implicit in all variational principles that form the basis of modern physics. For example in his classic work on optics, Hamilton (1967) recognising the importance of Fermat's least-time principle, and suggested that both optics and classical mechanics could be united into a common formalism by introducing a two-point characteristic function, $\Omega(A, B)$. Following on from Hamilton's work Synge (1964), in his unique approach to general relativity, proposed that a two-point function, which he called the world function, lies at the heart of general relativity[4]. Can we exploit these two-point functions to develop a new way of looking at dynamics?

I want to pick up on a very small aspect of this well-known work and show how ideas already implicit in that structure are relevant to what I have in mind. As is well known use of the variational principle produces the classical Hamilton-Jacobi equation (see Goldstein 1950). This emerges by considering a variation of the initial point A of the trajectory. Standard theory shows that by varying the initial point A we can obtain the relations

$$\frac{\partial S}{\partial x_1} = p(x_1) \qquad \frac{\partial S}{\partial t_1} + H(t_1) = 0 \qquad (14)$$

where we have written $H(t_1) = H\left(x_1(t_1), \frac{\partial S}{\partial x_1}(t_1)\right)$ for convenience and we have replaced the world function Ω by the classical action function S.

What is not so well known is that if we vary the final point B, we find another pair of equations

---

[4] In modern parlance these functions are the generating functions of the symplectomorphisms in classical mechanics (see de Gosson 2001).

$$\frac{\partial S}{\partial x_2} = -p(x_2) \qquad \frac{\partial S}{\partial t_2} - H(t_2) = 0 \tag{15}$$

Here the second Hamilton-Jacobi equation formally becomes the same by writing $t_2 = -t_1$. Could this be taken to signify a wave coming from the 'future' and fit into the general scheme I am developing here?

Leaving that speculation aside, let us see how we can formally exploit these two Hamilton-Jacobi equations. Consider a pair of points with co-ordinates (x_1, t_1) and (x_2, t_2) in configuration space. The world function (generalised action) for this pair can be written as $S(x_1, x_2, t_1, t_2)$

We will find it more convenient to use 'sums' and 'differences' rather than the co-ordinates themselves. Thus we change to co-ordinates $(X, \Delta x, T, \Delta t)$ where

$$X = \frac{x_1 + x_2}{2} \qquad T = \frac{t_1 + t_2}{2} \qquad \text{and} \qquad \Delta x = x_2 - x_1 \qquad \Delta t = t_2 - t_1$$

so that the generalised action becomes

$$S(x_1, x_2, t_1, t_2) = S(X, \Delta x, T, \Delta t)$$

Then equations (14) and (15) can be replaced by

$$\frac{\partial S}{\partial X} = \Delta p \qquad \frac{\partial S}{\partial T} = \left[H(t_2) - H(t_1) \right] \tag{16}$$

$$\frac{\partial S}{\partial \Delta x} = P \qquad \frac{\partial S}{\partial \Delta t} = \tfrac{1}{2} \left[H(t_2) + H(t_1) \right] \tag{17}$$

In order to see the meaning of the two equations let us make a Legendre transformation

$$K(X, P, T, E) = P\Delta x + E\Delta t - S(X, \Delta x, T, \Delta t) \tag{18}$$

so that

$$\frac{\partial S}{\partial T} = -\frac{\partial K}{\partial T} \qquad \frac{\partial S}{\partial \Delta t} = E$$

A general background discussion to these ideas can be found in Bohm and Hiley (1981).

Then when we go to the limit as $\Delta t \to 0$, we define

$$\lim_{\Delta t \to 0} \frac{\partial S}{\partial T} = -\left[H(t_2) - H(t_1) \right] \Rightarrow \frac{\partial S}{\partial T} + \frac{\partial H}{\partial P} \Delta p + \frac{\partial H}{\partial X} \Delta x \approx 0 \qquad (19)$$

But

$$\Delta p = -\frac{\partial K}{\partial X} \qquad \Delta x = \frac{\partial K}{\partial P}$$

Then equation (19) becomes

$$\frac{\partial K}{\partial T} + \{K, H\} = 0 \qquad (20)$$

where $\{.\}$ is the Poisson bracket so that equation (20) becomes the classical equation of motion for the dynamical variable K. Indeed when this K is identified with the probability distribution this is nothing more than the Liouville equation. The second equation (16) becomes

$$\frac{\partial S}{\partial \Delta t} = \tfrac{1}{2} \left[H(t_2) + H(t_1) \right] \qquad \Rightarrow \qquad \frac{\partial K}{\partial \Delta t} = E \qquad (21)$$

which is simply the equation for the total energy of the system.

14

In order to anticipate the approach the quantum mechanics I will describe in the next section, I need to introduce the notion of a generalised Poisson bracket defined by

$$\{\ \} = \frac{\partial}{\partial X}\frac{\partial}{\partial \Delta p} - \frac{\partial}{\partial \Delta p}\frac{\partial}{\partial X} + \frac{\partial}{\partial \Delta x}\frac{\partial}{\partial P} - \frac{\partial}{\partial P}\frac{\partial}{\partial \Delta x}$$

so that we find the following relationships

$$\{X, \Delta p\} = \{\Delta x, P\} = 1$$

$$\{X, P\} = \{\Delta x, \Delta p\} = \{X, \Delta x\} = \{P, \Delta p\} = 0 \qquad (22)$$

This suggests another pair of brackets of the form

$$\{T, H(t_2) - H(t_1)\} = \{\Delta t, H(t_2) + H(t_1)\} = 1$$

If we were to introduce the quantity $L(t_1, t_2) = H(t_2) - H(t_1)$ we have the classical correspondence to the Liouville operator introduced by Prigogine (1980). We will discuss this connection further when we generalise these results to the quantum domain.

Quantum Pasts and Futures.

Now let me return to the quantum domain and consider Feynman's suggestion mentioned earlier in more detail. Introduce a world function defined by

$$\hat{\rho}(t_1, t_2) = |\psi(t_1)\rangle\langle\psi(t_2)| \qquad (24)$$

I use the symbol $\hat{\rho}(t_1, t_2)$ because I am dealing essentially with a generalised density operator. Then let us form

$$\frac{\partial}{\partial T}\left(|\psi(t_1)\rangle\langle\psi(t_2)|\right) = \left(\frac{\partial}{\partial t_1}|\psi(t_1)\rangle\right)\langle\psi(t_2)| + |\psi(t_1)\rangle\left(\frac{\partial}{\partial t_2}\langle\psi(t_2)|\right) \qquad (25)$$

Since Feynman has already derived the Schrödinger equation from these considerations we can substitute the two equations

$$i\frac{\partial}{\partial t_1}|\psi(t_1)\rangle = \hat{H}_1|\psi(t_1)\rangle \qquad \text{and} \qquad -i\frac{\partial}{\partial t_2}\langle\psi(t_2)| = \langle\psi(t_2)|\hat{H}_2$$

into equation (25) and we find

$$i\frac{\partial\hat{\rho}(t_1,t_2)}{\partial T} + \hat{\rho}(t_1,t_2)\hat{H}_2 - \hat{H}_1\hat{\rho}(t_1,t_2) = 0 \qquad (26)$$

If we now take the limit as $\Delta t \to 0$ when $T \to t$, we find

$$i\frac{\partial\hat{\rho}}{\partial t} + \left[\hat{\rho},\hat{H}\right]_- = 0 \qquad (27)$$

Here $\hat{\rho}$ has become the usual density operator for the pure state $|\psi(t)\rangle$. This equation is then recognised as the Liouville equation.

Now let us consider

$$2\frac{\partial}{\partial\Delta t}\left(|\psi(t_1)\rangle\langle\psi(t_2)|\right) = -\left(\frac{\partial}{\partial t_1}|\psi(t_1)\rangle\right)\langle\psi(t_2)| + |\psi(t_1)\rangle\left(\frac{\partial}{\partial t_2}\langle\psi(t_2)|\right)$$

So that by using the two Schrödinger equations we find

$$2i\frac{\partial}{\partial\Delta t}\hat{\rho}(t_1,t_2) + \hat{\rho}(t_1,t_2)\hat{H}_2 + \hat{H}_1\hat{\rho}(t_1,t_2) = 0 \qquad (28)$$

Here we cannot go directly to the limit because of the appearance of Δt in the denominator. There are two ways to proceed. Firstly let me use the approach that directly links with the classical Legendre transformation (18). Take the Wigner transformation defined by

$$\hat{\rho}(T,\Delta t) = \int \hat{\rho}_E(E,T)\exp[iE\Delta t]dE \qquad (29)$$

Then

$$i\frac{\partial}{\partial\Delta t}\hat{\rho}(t_1,t_2) = i\frac{\partial}{\partial\Delta t}\hat{\rho}(T,\Delta t) = -\int E\hat{\rho}_E(E,T)\exp[iE\Delta t]dE = -\overline{E}$$

where we can regard $\overline{E}$ as the mean energy over the interval Δt. Thus we can finally write equation (28) as

$$2\overline{E} = \left[\hat{\rho},\hat{H}\right]_+ \qquad (30)$$

This is an expression of the conservation of energy equation.

16

Collecting together the main results so far we find

$$i\frac{\partial\hat{\rho}}{\partial t}+\left[\hat{\rho},\hat{H}\right]_{-}=0 \qquad\Leftrightarrow\qquad \frac{\partial K}{\partial T}+\{K,H\}=0$$

and

$$2\overline{E}=\left[\hat{\rho},\hat{H}\right]_{+} \qquad\Leftrightarrow\qquad E=\frac{\partial K}{\partial\Delta t}$$

Again if K is the classical analogue of the density operator then we would have a correspondence between the classical 'Liouville' equation (20) and the quantum Liouville equation (27). In turn the quantum energy equation (30) then corresponds to the classical energy equation (21). Thus we have a clear correspondence between the classical and the quantum levels.

There is a second way to approach the limit $\Delta t \to 0$ that does not involve a Wigner transformation and perhaps produces a cleaner result. In fact this method produces exactly the same results that are derived in Brown and Hiley (2000), but from a different standpoint. The emphasis there was to do everything in the algebra itself and was probably too abstract for most physicists. This means replacing $|\psi(t_1)\rangle$ by an element of a minimal left ideal, $\hat{\Psi}_L(t_1)$, of a form similar to that of the spinor used in section 2. In the same way we can replace $\langle\psi(t_2)|$ by an element of a right ideal, $\hat{\Psi}_R(t_2)$. Then we write these algebraic elements in polar form

$$\hat{\Psi}_L(t_1)=\hat{R}(t_1)\exp[i\hat{S}(t_1)] \qquad\text{and}\qquad \hat{\Psi}_R(t_2)=\exp[-i\hat{S}(t_2)]\hat{R}(t_2)$$

Here we have put 'hats' on the $\hat{\Psi}$, $\hat{R}$ and $\hat{S}$ to emphasise that they are elements of the algebra (ie. *operators*) and *not* elements of a Hilbert space. Then

$$2\frac{\partial}{\partial\Delta t}\hat{\rho}(t_1,t_2)=\left[-\frac{\partial\hat{R}(t_1)}{\partial t_1}\hat{R}(t_2)+\hat{R}(t_1)\frac{\partial\hat{R}(t_2)}{\partial t_2}-i\hat{R}(t_1)\hat{R}(t_2)\left[\frac{\partial\hat{S}(t_1)}{\partial t_1}+\frac{\partial\hat{S}(t_2)}{\partial t_2}\right]\right] \\ \times\exp\left[-i\left(\hat{S}(t_2)-\hat{S}(t_1)\right)\right] \tag{31}$$

where we have assumed that $\hat{R}$ and $\hat{S}$ commute. Then when we go to the limit $\Delta t \to 0$ with $T \to t$ we find

$$\lim_{\Delta t\to 0}2\frac{\partial}{\partial\Delta t}\hat{\rho}(t_1,t_2)=-i\hat{R}^2\frac{\partial\hat{S}}{\partial t} \tag{32}$$

17

Thus equation (28) then becomes

$$2\hat{R}^2 \frac{\partial \hat{S}}{\partial t} + \left[\hat{\rho}, \hat{H}\right]_+ = 0 \qquad (33)$$

This equation is identical to the anti-commutator equation (11) derived in Brown and Hiley (2000). A yet different derivation of this equation will also be found in Hiley (2002b). The reason why I have re-derived this equation in different ways is because I have not seen this equation written down in this form in the literature and I wanted to make sure it was mathematically sound.

In Brown and Hiley (2000) we showed that there were two important consequences following from this equation. Firstly we showed that the Berry phase and the Aharonov-Bohm effect followed immediately from this equation in a very simple way. Secondly we used this quantum equation to see where the quantum potential introduced by Bohm emerges from what is essentially the Heisenberg picture (see also Hiley 2002a). We found that this potential only appeared as a result of *projecting* the algebraic elements onto a representation space. This led us to speculate that all the 'action' of quantum phenomena takes place in the algebra itself, in the pre-space.

It is well-known that we cannot display quantum processes in a phase space because we are using a non-commutative structure. Following on from the work of Gel'fand this means that there is no unique manifold underlying the algebra. You have to rely on shadow manifolds, which are constructed by projections. In this projection we get distortions like those found in maps produced by a Mercator's projection. Therefore it is not surprising to find it necessary to introduce forces to account for the predicted behaviour in the shadow manifold. This is exactly how the gravitation force is manifested in general relativity (For a more detailed discussion see Hiley 2002a)

Bi-Algebras and super-algebras.

In this final section I want to connect this work with the proposals made by Umezawa (1993) in his discussions of thermal quantum field theory. The aim here is to find a common formalism in which both quantum and thermal effects can be incorporated. Unlike the work presented here, Umezawa uses Hilbert space and shows that if we double the Hilbert space then the thermal state can also be represented by a single vector in this double space. For example, in more familiar notation, the thermal wave function can be written in the form

$$|\Omega(\beta)\rangle = Z^{-\frac{1}{2}} \sum \exp[-\beta E_n / 2] |\psi_n\rangle \otimes |\psi_n\rangle \qquad (34)$$

Here $\beta = \frac{1}{kT}$ and $|\psi_n\rangle$ are the energy eigenkets. Z is the partition function. The ensemble average of some quantum operator A would then be given by

$$\langle \Omega(\beta)|A|\Omega(\beta)\rangle = Tr(\rho A)$$

where ρ is the thermal density operator. The more usual form of the density operator is

$$\rho = \exp[-H\beta]$$

These results show the essential relation between the two approaches.

Those familiar with algebraic quantum field theory will recognise that this is essentially the GNS construction (Emch 1972 and Hiley 2002b). However the Umezawa approach proceeds by doubling the number field elements so that an algebraic theory would have double the algebra. This means that we would introduce a pair of annihilation and creation operators for each degree of freedom, $\{a, a^\dagger, \tilde{a}, \tilde{a}^\dagger\}$

Now let us connect this with what I am doing here. So far I have essentially been dealing with a two-time quantum theory. This has been straightforward to deal with because time is a parameter and not an operator in the quantum domain. If I were in a classical theory I would simply generalise the two-time theory by considering two points in phase space at different times co-ordinated by $\{x_1, p_1, t_1, x_2, p_2, t_2\}$. This would lead me to a structure encompassing the generalised Poisson brackets defined in equation (22).

When I move on to quantum theory I need now to consider the position and momentum as *operators* so I must base the theory on *pairs of algebraic* elements $\hat{x}_1, \hat{x}_2, \hat{p}_1,$ and $\hat{p}_2$. Again I have added the 'hat' to emphasise that these are elements in the algebra (i.e. operators). In other words we are moving on to consider doubling up the algebra so that we are essentially dealing with bi-algebraic structures.

Let us continue the idea of regions of ambiguity linked by quantum process. Now there will be regions in the algebra that correspond to the regions R' and R'' so let us proceed quite naively by forming the set of operators

$$2\hat{X} = \hat{x}_1 \otimes 1 + 1 \otimes \hat{x}_2, \qquad \hat{\eta} = \hat{x}_1 \otimes 1 - 1 \otimes \hat{x}_2, \tag{35}$$

$$2\hat{P} = \hat{p}_1 \otimes 1 + 1 \otimes \hat{p}_2, \qquad \hat{\pi} = \hat{p}_1 \otimes 1 - 1 \otimes \hat{p}_2. \tag{36}$$

Then we find that the following commutator relations hold

$$\left[\hat{X}, \hat{\pi}\right] = \left[\hat{\eta}, \hat{P}\right] = i$$

and

$$\left[\hat{X}, \hat{P}\right] = \left[\hat{\eta}, \hat{\pi}\right] = \left[\hat{X}, \hat{\eta}\right] = \left[\hat{P}, \hat{\pi}\right] = 0 \tag{37}$$

These relations are the quantum analogues of the generalised Poisson brackets defined in equation (22). These results were already reported in Bohm and Hiley (1981). What we have achieved so far is a formal correspondence between the classical and quantum structures based on the doubling of the variables. The important question is whether this structure will lead to new physics. I think it will but I will only outline two possibilities.

Both possibilities are connected with the introduction of irreversibility into quantum physics. The first suggestion we follow is that of Prigogine (1980). He suggested that we need a theory in which irreversibility plays a fundamental role directly in the dynamics itself. Then perhaps time could then be introduced, not as a parameter, but by an operator. It is the absence of such an operator that has handicapped my own attempts to find a fully algebraic description of physical processes.

In order to show how a time operator emerges from the work here, first note that we can write the quantum Liouville equation (27) in the form

$$i\frac{\partial \hat{\rho}_V}{\partial t} + \hat{L}\hat{\rho}_V = 0 \tag{38}$$

Here $\hat{\rho}_V$ is a vector equivalent of the density operator and $\hat{L} = \hat{H} \otimes 1 - 1 \otimes \hat{H}$. Thus we have simply re-expressed the Liouville equation in terms of the language of bi-algebras. The appearance of the super-operator enables us to introduced a time operator $\hat{T}$, defined through the relation

$$\left[\hat{T}, \hat{L}\right] = i \tag{39}$$

20

Note that this is the quantum version of the classical form presented by the first equation in (23).

Prigogine (1980) argues that this time operator, $\hat{T}$ represents the 'age' of the system. I don't want to discuss the reasons for this as I have already made some comments on it in Bohm and Hiley (1981) and in Hiley and Fernandes, (1997). A more general discussion of Prigogine's point of view will be found in George and Prigogine (1979), and in Prigogine (1980),

What I want to do now is to go on to the bi-algebraic generalisation of equation (30). This requires the introduction of the super-operator corresponding to the anti-commutator, which can be written in the form

$$\bar{E} = \left(\hat{H}\otimes 1 + 1 \otimes \hat{H}\right)\hat{\rho}_V = E_+\hat{\rho}_V \qquad (40)$$

Such an operator was first introduced by George et al (1978) in their general discussion of dissipative processes. They, like us, regard this as an expression of the total energy of the system. This is only other discussion I have seen in non-relativistic quantum theory where the role the anti-commutator is taken to correspond to the energy of the system. The only reason why I want to mention this equation here is that it adds further legitimacy to equation (33). However I should point out that Fairlie and Manogue (1991) have discussed an analogous equation based on the cosine Moyal bracket introduced by Baker (1958).

I now want to move on a bit further and remark that not only can we introduce an 'age' operator $\hat{T}$, but we can also introduce a 'time difference' operator $\hat{\tau}$, the duron. This satisfies the commutator relations

$$\left[\hat{T},\hat{\varepsilon}\right] = \left[\hat{\tau},\hat{E}\right] = i$$

and

$$\left[\hat{T},\hat{E}\right] = \left[\hat{\tau},\hat{\varepsilon}\right] = \left[\hat{T},\hat{\tau}\right] = \left[\hat{E},\hat{\varepsilon}\right] \qquad (41)$$

where we have written $\hat{\varepsilon}$ for $\hat{L}$ to bring out the symmetry. Hiley and Fernandes (1997) have already discussed these relationships in the context of finding operators for time. In particular they interpreted $\hat{\tau}$ as the mean time spent passing between two energy states.

Bi-algebras and the Bogoliubov transformations.

Before discussing the meaning of $\hat{\tau}$ in more detail let me return to my way of thinking about the bi-algebra. I have proposed that the evolution of a quantum process does not proceed at an instant of time at a point in space, but through the ambiguous region of phase space that I have called a 'moment'. We consider the relation between the two sides of this moment, describing one side as information coming from the past while the other side is to do with the possible developments for the future.

I have spoken at times rather dramatically about this latter feature as 'information coming from the future'. But such a way of talking is not that outrageous that it has not been suggested before. For example Cramer (1986) in his transactional interpretation of quantum mechanics uses the advanced potentials to carry information from the future. The transaction is a 'handshake' between emitter and the absorber participants of a quantum event. This notion, in turn, has a resonance with an earlier proposal of Lewis (1926) who has based his thinking on the following idea. In the rest frame of a photon time dilation suggests that there is no time lapse between emission and absorption and because of the length contraction, there is no distance between the emitter and absorber either. The light ray is a primary contact between the two ends of the process. These are both very radical ideas and unfortunately I have never known what to make of them so I tend to discuss the notion of a 'moment' hoping that Δt is small, but as these two examples show this may be a rather conservative view to adopt!

Recently was very happy to meet with Giuseppe Vitiello and to discuss some of his extremely interesting ideas on dissipative quantum systems. His ideas are, perhaps, even more conservative and therefore probably more reliable, yet they seem to fit into the overall scheme I am discussing here. His work is reported in a series of papers by Vitiello (1995), Celeghini, Rasetti and Vitiello (1992), Celeghini *et al* (1998) and Iorio and Vitiello (1995). I rely heavily on the mathematics contained in these papers.

They are interested in quantum dissipation, which they explore in terms of a pair of coupled dissipative oscillators, one emitting energy, the other absorbing energy. In terms of our two-sided evolution discussed above, we find one 'side' of the process is seen as representing the system while the other 'side' is seen as representing the environment, the latter acting as a sink for the dissipated energy.

In this model the degrees of freedom of the system are described by the set of annihilation operators $\{a_k\}$, while the environment is described by the set $\{\tilde{a}_k\}$. Thus there is a doubling of the mathematical structure. The extra field variables $\{\tilde{a}_k\}$

22

describing the 'environment' are a mirror image of the variables used to describe the system. Not only is a spatial mirror image but it is also a *'time-reversed* mirror image' as Vitiello (1996) puts it. So the 'environment sink' appears to be acting as if it were 'anticipating the future'.

Let us leave the imagery for the moment and move on to see how the ideas work out mathematically. For this we will need to introduce some more formalism. So far we have introduced elements of our bi-algebra by effectively defining two sets of co-products which we will now express formally as

$$\Delta_+ \hat{A} = \hat{A} \otimes 1 + 1 \otimes \hat{A} \qquad \text{and} \qquad \Delta_- \hat{A} = \hat{A} \otimes 1 - 1 \otimes \hat{A} \qquad (42)$$

We have then shown that when we go to the limit $\Delta t \to 0$, we produce two dynamical equations, namely,

$$i\frac{\partial \hat{\rho}_V}{\partial t} + \hat{L}\hat{\rho}_V = 0 \qquad \text{and} \qquad \underset{\Delta t \to 0}{Lim}\left(i\frac{\partial \hat{\rho}_V}{\partial \Delta t} \right) + \tfrac{1}{2}\hat{H}_+ \hat{\rho}_V = 0 \qquad (43)$$

But what do we make of the general co-products and the commutation relations listed in equations (35) – (37)? To explore these let us first make a Bargmann transformation from the Heisenberg algebra to the boson algebra of annihilation and creation operators. This will enable us to immediately relate our work to that of Vitiello (1995) and Celeghini *et al* (1998). Thus writing

$$\begin{aligned} a &= \hat{x}_1 + i\hat{p}_1 & \tilde{a} &= \hat{x}_2 + i\hat{p}_2 \\ a^\dagger &= \hat{x}_1 - i\hat{p}_1 & \tilde{a}^\dagger &= \hat{x}_2 - i\hat{p}_2 \end{aligned}$$

We can immediately make contact with equation (34) by using the well-known generator of the Bogoliubov transformation

$$G = -i\left(a^\dagger \tilde{a}^\dagger - a\tilde{a}\right) \qquad (44)$$

Then applying this to the vacuum state $|0, \hat{0}\rangle$, we find a new vacuum state $|0(\theta)\rangle$ given by

$$|0(\theta)\rangle = \exp[i\theta G]|0, 0\rangle = \sum_n c_n(\theta)|n\rangle \otimes |n\rangle. \qquad (45)$$

This means that by doubling the algebra we can immediately make contact with equation (34) provided we find the correct relationship between θ and β. Recall that in equation

23

(34) β is proportional to the inverse of the temperature. Thus we have a way of combining thermodynamics and quantum mechanics in a single mathematical structure.

But let's go deeper and develop the boson bi-algebra by defining the following co-products based on equations (35) and (36),

$$\Delta_+ a = a \otimes 1 + 1 \otimes a = a + \tilde{a} \qquad \Delta_- a = a \otimes 1 - 1 \otimes a = a - \tilde{a} \qquad (46)$$

$$\Delta_+ a^\dagger = a^\dagger \otimes 1 + 1 \otimes a^\dagger = a^\dagger + \tilde{a}^\dagger \qquad \Delta_- a^\dagger = a^\dagger \otimes 1 - 1 \otimes a^\dagger = a^\dagger - \tilde{a}^\dagger \qquad (47)$$

We see immediately that these co-products are identical to those introduced by Celeghini *et al* (1998) but we can go further and form

$$A = \frac{1}{\sqrt{2}}(a + \tilde{a}) = \sqrt{2}\left(\hat{X} + i\hat{P}\right) \qquad \text{and} \qquad A^\dagger = \frac{1}{\sqrt{2}}\left(a^\dagger + \tilde{a}^\dagger\right) = \sqrt{2}\left(\hat{X} - i\hat{P}\right) \qquad (48)$$

$$B = \frac{1}{\sqrt{2}}(a - \tilde{a}) = -\frac{1}{\sqrt{2}}\left(\hat{\eta} + i\hat{\pi}\right) \qquad \text{and} \qquad B^\dagger = \frac{1}{\sqrt{2}}\left(a^\dagger - \tilde{a}^\dagger\right) = -\frac{1}{\sqrt{2}}\left(\hat{\eta} - i\hat{\pi}\right) \qquad (49)$$

These operators lie at the heart of their approach. In our approach we see that these operators have a very simple interpretation. They are simply the annihilation and creation operators of the mean position variables and the difference variables respectively. Thus

$$\hat{X} = \frac{1}{2\sqrt{2}}\left(A + A^\dagger\right) \qquad \text{and} \qquad \hat{P} = \frac{i}{2\sqrt{2}}\left(A - A^\dagger\right)$$

$$\hat{\eta} = -\frac{1}{\sqrt{2}}\left(B + B^\dagger\right) \qquad \text{and} \qquad \hat{\pi} = \frac{i}{\sqrt{2}}\left(B - B^\dagger\right)$$

In other words the operators A and B are the algebraic way of defining the ambiguous moments of in our algebraic phase space. They are the variables that we need to describe the unfolding process that forms the basis of our paper.

Now I want to follow Celeghini *et al* (1998) further and generalise our approach by deforming the bi-algebra. We do this by defining the co-product

$$\Delta_+ a_q = a_q \otimes q + q^{-1} \otimes a_q \qquad \text{and} \qquad \Delta_+ a^\dagger_q = a^\dagger_q \otimes q + q^{-1} \otimes a^\dagger_q \qquad (50)$$

24

where we will write $q = e^{\theta}$ where θ is some parameter the physical meaning of which has yet to be determined. Then

$$A_q = \frac{\Delta a_q}{\sqrt{[2]}_q} = \frac{1}{\sqrt{[2]}_q}\left(e^{\theta}a + e^{-\theta}\tilde{a}\right) \qquad \text{and} \qquad B_q = \frac{1}{\sqrt{[2]}_q}\frac{\delta}{\delta\theta}\Delta a_q = \frac{1}{\sqrt{[2]}_q}\left(e^{\theta}a - e^{-\theta}\tilde{a}\right)$$

+h.c. (51)

The A_q and B_q are then the deformed equivalents of equations (48) and (49). Notice also that

$$\Delta_- A_{\theta} = \frac{\delta}{\delta\theta}\Delta_+ A_{\theta} \qquad \text{and} \qquad \Delta_- A = \lim_{\theta \to 0}\frac{\delta}{\delta\theta}\Delta_+ A \qquad (53)$$

so that the two sets of co-products defined in equations (46) and (47) are not independent. With these definitions it is not difficult to show that we can write

$$A(\theta) = \frac{1}{\sqrt{2}}(a(\theta) + \tilde{a}(\theta)) \qquad \text{and} \qquad B(\theta) = \frac{1}{\sqrt{2}}(a(\theta) - \tilde{a}(\theta)) \qquad (54)$$

So that

$$a(\theta) = \frac{1}{\sqrt{2}}(A(\theta) + B(\theta)) = a\cosh\theta - \tilde{a}^{\dagger}\sinh\theta \qquad (55)$$

and

$$\tilde{a}(\theta) = \frac{1}{\sqrt{2}}(A(\theta) - B(\theta)) = \tilde{a}\cosh\theta - a^{\dagger}\sinh\theta \qquad (56)$$

This is immediately recognised as nothing but the Bogoliubov transformation from the set of annihilation and creation operators $\{a, \tilde{a}\}$ to a new set $\{a(\theta), \tilde{a}(\theta)\}$. This result justifies the use of the Bogoliubov generator given in equation (44), which was used to construct the GNS ket given in equation (45).

Unfolding through inequivalent representations?

Having put the formalism in place I now want to consider how all this leads to a radically new way of looking at the way quantum processes unfold in time. My ideas go back to the early eighties when David Bohm and I were discussing how we could think about the type of process underlying quantum phenomenon. Most of this work was unpublished essentially because I did not have an adequate understanding of the mathematics needed. However Bohm (1986) did publish some of the background relevant to the ideas I am developing here. There perhaps for the first time he makes a clear statement as to what we were thinking. I quote

> All these relationships (of moments of enfoldment) have to be understood primarily as being between the implicate "counterparts" of these explicate moments. That is to say, we no longer suppose that space-time is primarily an arena and that the laws describe necessary relationships in the development of events as they succeed each other in this arena. Rather, each law is a structure that interpenetrates and pervades the totality of the implicate order.

Implicit in this was the idea that space-time itself would emerge at some higher explicit level (Hiley 1991). All of this was easily dismissed as 'somewhat vague', but we did try to make it more specific by arguing that the inequivalent representations contained within quantum field theory would play a key role. However we could not see how to make the mathematics work.

In the general context of Bohm's ideas, the vacuum state should not be regarded as absolute and self-contained. Rather each vacuum state provides the basis for what we called an explicate order so that a set of inequivalent vacuum states could be thought of as providing an array of explicate orders, all embedded in the overall implicate order in which all movement is assumed to take place. The movement between inequivalent representations, between inequivalent vacuum states, is then regarded as a movement from one explicate order to another. It was the implicate order that enabled this transformation to take place as an unfolding of moments.

Within this structure we found the explanation as to why in a single Hilbert space formalism nothing *actually* happens. The inner automorphisms of the algebra of operators are simply a re-description of the *potentialities* of the process so that every unitary transformation becomes merely a re-expression of the order. In this sense everything is *potentiality*. But what about the actual occasions? This has been the continuing difficulty of the 'measurement problem'. Where do the *actual events* arise in the quantum formalism? First we should notice that in quantum field theory the vacuum kets $|0(\theta)\rangle$ belong to inequivalent representations of the boson algebra. Our suggestion is that not only is there a movement within each inequivalent representation but there is also another movement involved and this is the movement between inequivalent representations and thus between these inequivalent vacuum states. The key question is how this movement is described mathematically.

The answer appears to lie in the relationship between the two co-products described by equation (53) as Celeghini *et al* (1998) have already pointed out. It is this feature that allows us to discuss the movement between inequivalent representations. To explain this idea let us define

$$p_\theta = -i\frac{\delta}{\delta\theta} \qquad (57)$$

We can then think of p_θ as a conjugate momentum to the internal degree of freedom θ so that this momentum can be thought of as describing the movement between inequivalent Hilbert spaces. This identification becomes even more compelling once we realise that

$$-i\frac{\delta}{\delta\theta}a(\theta) = [G, a(\theta)] \qquad \text{and} \qquad -i\frac{\delta}{\delta\theta}\tilde{a}(\theta) = [G, \tilde{a}(\theta)] \qquad (58)$$

Here G is the generator of the Bogoliubov transformation given in equation (44). Indeed if we use the generator (44) then for a fixed value of $\bar{\theta}$ we have

$$\exp[i\hat{\theta}p_\theta]a(\theta) = \exp[i\hat{\theta}G]a(\theta)\exp[-i\hat{\theta}G] = a(\theta + \bar{\theta}) \qquad (59)$$

which is equivalent to the transformation from $|0(\theta)\rangle \rightarrow |0(\theta + \bar{\theta})\rangle$. Furthermore and even more importantly from our point of view the movement is expressed in terms of an inner automorphism of the algebra[5].

Finally I want to turn my attention to the question of time. In the bi-algebra we have two time operators,

$$T = \Delta_+ t = t \otimes 1 + 1 \otimes t \qquad \text{and} \qquad \tau = \Delta_- t = t \otimes 1 - 1 \otimes t \qquad (60)$$

Since Δ_+ and Δ_- are related, T and τ are not independent. If we regard T as being represented by θ then τ will take the form $-i\frac{\delta}{\delta\theta}$. The conjugate representation would

---

[5] The inner automorphism is a way of expressing the enfolding and unfolding movement.

involve taking τ to be represented by ϕ while T will take the form $i\dfrac{\delta}{\delta\phi}$ Here I am merely exploiting the analogy between the x- and the p-representations where the operators are $\left(x,-i\dfrac{\partial}{\partial x}\right)$ and $\left(p,i\dfrac{\partial}{\partial p}\right)$ respectively.

How are we to use this structure? When T is diagonal we remain within one of the inequivalent Hilbert spaces parameterised by θ. In that Hilbert space T now behaves as a parameter, which is proportional to the t that appears in the two equations (27) and (33) and hence in the Schrödinger equation. The system remains within this Hilbert space, getting older as it were but not actualising. All that is happening is that the potentialities are changing with time. Bohm (1987) calls T the implication parameter and regards it as a measure of the age of the system.

In this proposal an actual change comes about by a transformation to a different inequivalent representation or, in other words, to a new Hilbert space. Notice that during the transformation T is no longer diagonal implying that Schrödinger time is ambiguous during the transition process. Instead τ becomes diagonal meaning that the time between states is well defined. This would then tie in with the idea of Hiley and Fernandes (1997) mentioned above, where we regarded τ as a measure of the time between states. In the present paper it is a measure of times between inequivalent vacuum states. The fact that θ and its conjugate p_θ do not commute implies that transition between inequivalent states is not sharp and requires just the kind of ambiguity we have suggest accompanies the notion of a moment.

In some ways this ambiguity is necessary because quantum theory tells us that energy and time are complementary variables. So why do we insist on the evolution of a process with a definite energy occurring at a definite instant of time? Surely to have movement we must have this ambiguity in each moment of time. We must have a moment where *what has been* is separated from *what is yet to come*. We must exploit the tension between what has gone with what is to come. In emphasising this point I am proposing that not only does quantum theory contain spatial non-locality but that it also contains a 'non-locality' in time. That is several instants of time coexist in the same moment in the manner suggested by Bohm (1986).

I have yet to connect the parameter θ with the temperature. Superficially it is tempting to regard θ as the inverse of β, i.e. θ is proportional to the temperature. However I am reluctant to make this a definitive step at this stage because I am very aware of the idea of modular flow introduced by Rovelli (1993) and Connes and Rovelli (1994) which has some direct relevance to what I am discussing here. These papers have an extensive discussion on the thermodynamic origin of time. They have probed deeper into the mathematical structure implicit in the work I am discussing and have shown how the Tomita-Takesaki theorem provides this connection between time and the thermal evolution of a quantum system. There are clearly connections between this work and the tentative proposals I have outlined in my paper. There is much more to be said but this must be left for another publication.

Acknowledgements.

I would like to thank the members of the TPRU for their invaluable help in trying to straighten out the ideas expressed in this paper. In particular I would like to thank Melvin Brown for many stimulating discussions. I should also like to thank Keith Bowden for inviting me to present this talk at the ANPA 23 meeting.

References.

G. A. Baker, (1958), *Formulation of Quantum Mechanics based on the Quasi-probability Distribution Induced on Phase Space*, Phys. Rev. **109**, 2198-206.

D. Bohm, (1965),*Space, Time and the Quantum Theory understood in Terms of Discrete structure Process*, Proc. Int. Conf. Elementary Particles, Kyoto,.

D. Bohm, (1986), *Time, The Implicate Order, And Pre-Space*, in Physics and the Ultimate Significance of Time, Ed., D. R. Griffin, 177-208, SUNY Press, Albany.

D. Bohm, (1987), *The Implicate Order and Prigogine's Notions of Irreversibility*, Fond. Phys. **17**, 667-77.

D. Bohm and B. J. Hiley, (1981), *On a Quantum Algebraic Approach to a Generalised Phase Space*, Found. Phys., **11**, 179-203.

D. Bohm and B. J. Hiley, (1993), *The Undivided Universe: an Ontological Interpretation of Quantum Theory*, Routledge, London.

N. Bohr, (1961), *Atomic Physics and Human Knowledge*, Science Editions, New York,.

O. Bratteli and D. W. Robinson, (1979), *Operator Algebras and Quantum Statistical Mechanics I,* Springer, Berlin.

M. R. Brown and B. J. Hiley, (2000), *Schrödinger Revisited: an algebraic approach*, quant-ph/0005025.

E. Celeghini, M. Rasetti and G. Vitiello, (1992), *Quantum Dissipation*, Ann. Phys., **215**, 156-170,.

E. Celeghini, S. De Martino, S. De Siena, A. Iorio, M. Rasetti, and G. Vitiello, (1998), *Thermo Field Dynamics and Quantum Algebras*, Phys. Lett. **A244**, 455-461.

A. Connes and C. Rovelli, (1994),*Von Neumann algebra automorphisms and time-thermodynamics relation in general covariant quantum theories*, Class. Quantum Grav., **11**, 2899-2917.

J. G. Cramer, (1986), *The Transactional Interpretation of Quantum Mechanics*, Rev. Mod. Phys., **58**, 647-687.

A. Eddington, (1958), *The Philosophy of Physical Science*, University of Michigan Press, Ann Arbor.

G. G. Emch, (1972), *Algebraic Methods in Statistical Mechanics and Quantum Field Theory*, Wiley-Interscience, New York.

D. B. Fairlie and C. A. Manogue, (1991), *The formulation of quantum mechanics in terms of phase space functions—the third equation*, J. Phys. A: Math. Gen. **24**, 3807-3815.

M. Fernandes, (1996), *Geometric Aspects and Foundations of Quantum Theory*, PhD thesis, London University.

R. P. Feynman, (1948), *Space-time Approach to Non-Relativistic Quantum Mechanics*, Rev. Mod. Phys. **20**, 367-387.

J. G. Fichte, *Introductions to the Wissenschaftslehr*, (1994), Translated by D. Breazeale, p. 26, Hackett Press, Indianapolis.

D. R. Finkelstein, (1997), *Quantum Relativity: a Synthesis of the Ideas of Einstein and Heisenberg*, Springer, Berlin.

C. George, F, Henin, F. Mayne, and I. Prigogine, (1978), *Hadronic Journal*, **1**, 520.

C. George and I. Prigogine, (1979), *Physica*, **A99**, 369.

H. Goldstein, (1950), *Classical Mechanics*, Addison-Wesley, Reading.

M. de Gosson, (2001), *The Principles of Newtonian and Quantum Mechanics*, Imperial College Press, London.

H. Grassmann, (1995), *A New Branch of Mathematics: the Ausdehnungslehre of 1844, and other works*, trans. by L. C. Kannenberg, Open Court, Chicago.

A. Griffor, (1999), *On the Non-commutative Combinatorial Hierarchy*, in Aspects II, Proc. ANPNA **20**, Ed K. G. Bowden, 13-22, ANPA, London.

A. Griffor, (2001), *From Strings to Clifford Algebras*, in Implications, Proc. ANPNA **22**, Ed. K. G. Bowden, 30-55, ANPA, London.

W. R. Hamilton, (1967), *Mathematical Papers*, Ed. H. Halberstam and R. E. Ingram, Cambridge Uni Press, Cambridge.

W. Heisenberg, (1925), *Quantum-theoretic Re-interpretation of Kinematic and Mechanical Relations*, Z. Phys., **33**, 879-893.

B. J. Hiley, (1991), *Vacuum or Holomovement*, in The Philosophy of Vacuum, ed., S. Saunders and H. R. Brown, pp. 217-249, Clarendon Press, Oxford.

B.J. Hiley, (1995), *The Algebra of Process*, Consciousness at the Crossroads of Cognative Science and Philosophy, Maribor, Aug. 1994, pp. 52-67.

B.J. Hiley and M. Fernandes, (1997), *Process and Time*, in Time, Temporality and Now, ed., H. Atmanspacher and E. Ruhnau, 365-383, Springer Berlin.

B. J. Hiley, (2002a), *From the Heisenberg Picture to Bohm: a New Perspective on Active Information and its relation to Shannon Information,* Quantum Theory: reconsideration of foundations *Proc. Int. Conf.* Vexjo, Sweden, June 2001. (To appear in 2002)

B. J. Hiley, (2002b), *Algebraic Quantum Mechanics, Algebraic Spinors and Hilbert Space*, (To appear in 2002).

A. Iorio and G. Vitiello, (1995), Quantum Dissipation and Quantum Groups, *Ann. Phys.* (N.Y), **241**, 496-506.

L. H. Kauffman, (1980), *Complex numbers and Algebraic Logic*, 10th Int, Symp. Multiple Valued Logic, IEEE Pub.

L. H. Kauffman, (1987), *Self-reference and Recursive Forms*, J. Social Bio. Struct. 10, 53-72.

L. H. Kauffman, (1982), *Sign and Space*, in In Religious Experience and Scientific Paradigms, Proc. of the IAWSR Conf., Inst, Adv. Stud. World Religions, Stony Brook, New York, 118-164.

S. A. Kauffman, (1996), Lecture 7, Investigations : The Nature of Autonomous Agents and the Worlds They Mutually Create.

G. N. Lewis, (1926), Light Waves and Light Corpuscles, *Nature*, **117**, 236-238.

G. N. Lewis, (1926), The Nature of Light, *Proc. Nat. Acad. Sci.*, **12**, 22-29.

A. F. Paker-Rhodes, (19810 The Theory of Indistinguishables, Reidel, Dordrecht.

A. Prigogine, (1980), *From Being to Becoming*, Freeman, San Francisco.

I. Raptis and R. R, Zapatrin, (2001), *Algebraic Description of Spacetime Foam,* Class. Quant. Grav. **18**, 4187-4212.

C. Rovelli, (1993), *Statistical Mechanics of gravity and the thermodynamical origin of time,* Class. Quantum Grav., **10**, 1549-1566.

M. Schönberg, (1958), *Quantum Mechanics and Geometry*, Ann. Acad. Brasil. Cien., **30**,1-20.

B. L. Synge, (1960), *Relativity: The General Theory*, North-Holland, Amsterdam.

H. Umezawa, (1993), *Advanced Field Theory: Micro, Macro and Thermal Physics*, AIP Press, New York.

G. Vitiello, (1995), *Dissipation and Memory Capacity in the Quantum Brain Model*, Int. J. Mod. Phys., **9B**, 973-989.

G. Vitiello, (1996), *Living Matter Physics and the Quantum Brain Model*, Phys. Essays, **9**, 548-555.

R. R. Zapatrin, (2001), *Incidence Algebras of Simplicial Complexes*, Pure Math. Appl., **11**, 105-118.

Comparing Quantum Entanglement and Topological Entanglement

Louis H. Kauffman
Department of Mathematics, Statistics
and Computer Science (m/c 249)
851 South Morgan Street
University of Illinois at Chicago
Chicago, Illinois 60607-7045
<kauffman@uic.edu>
and
Samuel J. Lomonaco Jr.
Department of Computer Science and Electrical Engineering
University of Maryland Baltimore County
1000 Hilltop Circle, Baltimore, MD 21250
<lomonaco@umbc.edu>

Abstract

This paper discusses relationships between topological entanglement and quantum entanglement. Specifically, we propose that it is more fundamental to view topological entanglements such as braids as entanglement operators and to associate to them unitary operators that are capable of creating quantum entanglement.

1 Introduction

This paper discusses relationships between topological entanglemenet and quantum entanglement. The present paper is an expanded version of [9].

Specifically, we propose that it is more fundamental to view topological entanglements such as braids as *entanglement operators* and to associate to them unitary operators that perform quantum entanglement. Then one can compare the way the unitary operator corresponding to an elementary braid has (or has not) the capacity to entangle quantum states. Along with this, one can examine the capacity of the same operator to detect linking. The detection of linking involves working with closed braids or with link diagrams. In both cases, the algorithms for computing link invariants are very interesting to examine in the light of quantum computing. These algorithms can usually be decomposed into one part that is a straight composition of unitary operators, and hence can be seen as a sequence of quantum computer instructions, and another part that can be seen either as preparation/detection, or as a quantum network with cycles in the underlying graph.

The paper is organized as follows. Section 2 discusses the basic analogy between topological entanglement and quantum entanglement. Section 3 proposes the viewpoint of braiding operators and gives a specific example of a unitary braiding operator, showing that it does entangle quantum states. Section 3 ends with a list of problems. Section 4 discusses the link invariants associated with the braiding operator R introduced in the previous section. Section 5 is a discussion of the structure of entanglement in relation to measurement. Section 6 is an introduction to the virtual braid group, an extension of the classical braid group by the symmetric group. We contend that unitary representations of the virtual braid group provide a good context and language for quantum computing. Section 7 is a discussion of ideas and concepts that have arisen in the course of this research.

Acknowledgement. Most of this effort was sponsored by the Defense Advanced Research Projects Agency (DARPA) and Air Force Research Laboratory, Air Force Materiel Command, USAF, under agreement F30602-01-2-05022. Some of this effort was also sponsored by the National Institute for Standards and Technology (NIST). The U.S. Government is authorized to reproduce and distribute reprints for Government purposes notwithstanding any copyright annotations thereon. The views and conclusions contained herein are those of the authors and should not be interpreted as necessarily representing the official policies or endorsements, either expressed or implied, of the Defense Advanced Research Projects Agency, the Air Force Research

Laboratory, or the U.S. Government. (Copyright 2002.) It gives the first author great pleasure to thank Fernando Souza for interesting conversations in the course of preparing this paper.

2   The Temptation of Tangled States

It is quite tempting to make an analogy between topological entanglement in the form of linked loops in three dimensional space and the entanglement of quantum states. A topological entanglement is a non-local structural feature of a topological system. A quantum entanglement is a non-local structural feature of a quantum system. Take the case of the Hopf link of linking number one. See Figure 1. In this Figure we show a simple link of two components and state its inequivalence to the disjoint union of two unlinked loops. The analogy that one wishes to draw is with a state of the form

$$\psi = (|01> -|10>)/\sqrt{2}$$

which is *quantum entangled*. That is, this state is not of the form $\psi_1 \otimes \psi_2 \in H \otimes H$ where H is a complex vector space of dimension two. Cutting a component of the link removes its topological entanglement. Observing the state removes its quantum entanglement in this case.

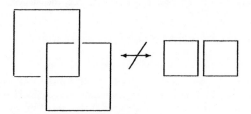

Figure 1 - The Hopf Link

An example of Aravind [1] makes the possibility of such a connection even more tantalizing. Aravind compares the Borommean Rings (See Figure 2) and the GHZ state

$$|\psi> = (|\beta_1> |\beta_2> |\beta_3> -|\alpha_1> |\alpha_2> |\alpha_3>)/\sqrt{2}.$$

3

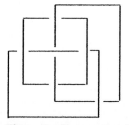

Figure 2 - Borommean Rings

The Borommean Rings are a three component link with the property that the triplet of components is indeed topologically linked, but the removal of any single component leaves a pair of unlinked rings. Thus, the Borommean Rings are of independent intellectual interest as an example of a tripartite relation that is not expressed in terms of binary relations. The GHZ state can be viewed as an entangled superposition of three particles with (say) all their spins in the $z-$ direction. If we measure one particle of the three particle quantum system, then the state becomes disentangled (That is, it becomes a tensor product). Thus the GHZ state appears to be a quantum analog to the Borommean Rings!

However, Aravind points out that this analogy is basis dependent, for if one changes basis, rewriting to

$$|\psi> = (|\beta_{1x}>/\sqrt{2})(|\beta_2>|\beta_3>-|\alpha_2>|\alpha_3>)/\sqrt{2}$$
$$+(|\alpha_{1x}>/\sqrt{2})(|\beta_2>|\beta_3>+|\alpha_2>|\alpha_3>)/\sqrt{2},$$

where $|\beta_{1x}>$ and $|\alpha_{1x}>$ denote the spin-up and spin-down states of particle 1 in the x direction, then one sees that a measurement of the spin of particle 1 in the x direction will yield an entangled state of the other two particles. Thus, in this basis, the state $|\psi>$ behaves like a triplet of loops such that each pair of loops is linked! Seeing the state as analogous to a specific link depends upon the choice of basis. From a physical standpoint, seeing the state as analogous to a link depends upon the choice of an observable.

These examples show that the analogy between topological linking and quantum entanglement is surely complex. One might expect a collection of links to exemplify the entanglement properties of a single quantum state. It is attractive to consider the question: *What patterns of linking are inherent in a given quantum state?* This is essentially a problem in linear algebra and should be investigated further. We will not pursue it in this paper.

On top of this, there is quite a bit of ingenuity required to produce links with given properties. For example, in Figure 3 we illustrate a Brunnian Link of four components. This link has the same property as the Borommean Rings but for four components rather than three. Remove any component and the link falls apart. The obvious generalization of th GHZ state with this property just involves adding one more tensor product in the two-term formula. This raises a question about the relationship of toplogical complexity and algebraic complexity of the corresponding quantum state. The other difficulties with this analogy are that topological properties of linked loops are not related to quantum mechanics in any clear way. Nevertheless, it is clear that this is an analogy worth pursuing.

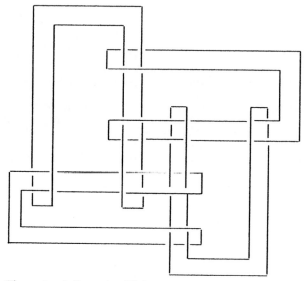

Figure 3 - A Brunnian Link

3   Entanglement Operators

Braids and the Artin braid group form a first instance in topology where
a space (or topological configuration) is also seen as an *operator* on spaces
and configurations. It is a shift that transmutes the elements of a topological
category to morphisms in an associated category. While we shall concentrate
on braids as an exemplar of this shift, it is worth noting that such a shift is
the basis of quantum topology and topological quantum field theory, where
spaces are viewed (through appropriate functors) as morphisms in a category
analogous to a category of Feynman diagrams. This pivot from spaces to
morphisms and back is the fundamental concept behind topological quantum
field theory.

Braids are patterns of entangled strings. A braid has the form of a collection of strings extending from one set of points to another, with a constant number of points in each cross section. Braids start in one row of points and end in another. As a result, one can multiply two braids to form a third braid by attaching the end points of the first braid to the initial points of the second braid. Up to topological equivalence, this multiplication gives rise to a group, the Artin Braid Group B_n on n strands.

Each braid is, in itself, a pattern of entanglement. Each braid is an operator that operates on other patterns of entanglement (braids) to produce new entanglements (braids again).

We wish to explore the analogy between topological entanglement and quantum entanglement. From the point of view of braids this means *the association of a unitary operator with a braid that respects the topological structure of the braid and allows exploration of the entanglement properties of the operator.* In other words, we propose to study the analogy between topological entanglement and quantum entanglement by looking at *unitary representations of the Artin Braid Group.* It is not the purpose of this paper to give an exhaustive account of such representations. Rather, we shall concentrate on one particularly simple representation and analyze the relationships between topological and quantum entanglement that are implicit in this representation. The main point for the exploration of the analogy is that, from the point of view of a braid group representation, each braid is seen as an operator rather than a state. See Figure 4.

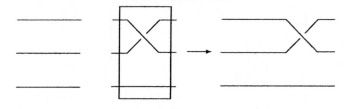

Braiding Operator

Figure 4 - A Braiding Operator

142

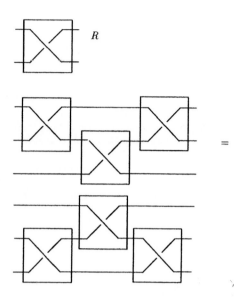

The Yang-Baxter Equation

Figure 5 - The Yang-Baxter Equation

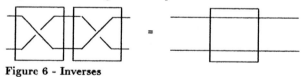

Figure 6 - Inverses

We will consider representations of the braid group constructed in the following manner. To an elementary two strand braid there is associated an operator

$$R : V \otimes V \longrightarrow V \otimes V.$$

Here V is a complex vector space, and for our purposes, V will be two dimensional so that V can hold a single qubit of information. One should

8

think of the two input and two output lines from the braid as representing this map of tensor products. Thus the left endpoints of R as shown in Figures 4, 5 and 6 represent the tensor product $V \otimes V$ that forms the domain of R and the right endpoints of the diagram for R represent $V \otimes V$ as the range of the maping. In the diagrams with three lines shown in Figure 5, we have mappings from $V \otimes V \otimes V$ to itself. The identity shown in Figure 5 is called the Yang-Baxter Equation, and it reads algebraically as follows, where I denotes the identity transformation on V.

$$(R \otimes I)(I \otimes R)(R \otimes I) = (I \otimes R)(R \otimes I)(I \otimes R).$$

This equation expresses the fundamental topological relation in the Artin Braid group, and is the main requirement for producing a representation of the braid group by this method. We also need an inverse to R and this will be associated with the reversed elementary braid on two strands as shown in Figure 6. One then defines a representation τ of the Artin Braid Group to automorphisms of $V^{\otimes n}$ by the equation

$$\tau(\sigma_k) = I \otimes \cdots \otimes I \otimes R \otimes I \cdots \otimes I,$$

where the R occupies the k and $k+1$ places in this tensor product. If R satisfies the Yang-Baxter equation and is invertible, then this formula describes a representation of the braid group. If R is unitary, then this construction provides a unitary representation of the braid group.

Here is the specific R matrix that we shall examine. The point of this case study is that R, being unitary, can be considered as a quantum gate *and* since R is the key ingredient in a unitary representation of the braid group, it can be considered as a operator that performs topological entanglement. We shall see that it can also perform quantum entanglement in its action on quantum states.

$$R = \begin{bmatrix} a & 0 & 0 & 0 \\ 0 & 0 & d & 0 \\ 0 & c & 0 & 0 \\ 0 & 0 & 0 & b \end{bmatrix}.$$

Here a, b, c, d can be any scalars on the unit circle in the complex plane. *Then R is a unitary matrix and it is a solution to the Yang-Baxter Equation.* It

144

is an interesting and illuminating exercise to verify that R is a solution to the Yang-Baxter Equation. We will omit this verification here, but urge the reader to perform it. In fact, the following more general construction gives a large class of unitary R matrices: Let $M = (M_{ij})$ denote an $n \times n$ matrix with entries in the unit circle in the complex plane. Let R be defined by the equation

$$R^{ij}_{kl} = \delta^i_l \delta^j_k M_{ij}.$$

It is easy to see that R is a unitary solution to the Yang-Baxter equation. Our explicit example is the special case of R where the matrix M is 2×2. It turns out, just as we shall show here for the special case, R detects no more than linking numbers for braids, knots and links. This is interesting, but it would be even more interesting to see other unitary R matrices that have subtler topological properties. The reader may enjoy comparing this situation with the unitary representation of the Artin Braid Group discussed in [8].

One can use that representation to calculate the Jones polynomial for three-strand braids. There is still a problem about designing a quantum computer to find the Jones polynomial, but this braid group representation does encode subtle topology. At the same time the representation in [8] cannot entangle quantum states. Thus the question of the precise relationship between topological entanglement and quantum entanglement certainly awaits the arrival of more examples of unitary representations of the braid group. We are indebted to David Meyer for asking sharp questions in this domain [14].

Now let P be the swap permutation matrix

$$P - \begin{bmatrix} 1 & 0 & 0 & 0 \\ 0 & 0 & 1 & 0 \\ 0 & 1 & 0 & 0 \\ 0 & 0 & 0 & 1 \end{bmatrix}.$$

and let $\tau = RP$ so that

10

$$\tau = \begin{bmatrix} a & 0 & 0 & 0 \\ 0 & c & 0 & 0 \\ 0 & 0 & d & 0 \\ 0 & 0 & 0 & b \end{bmatrix}.$$

Then from the point of view of quantum gates, we have the phase gate τ and the swap gate P with $\tau = RP$. From the point of view of braiding and algebra, we have that R is a solution to the braided version of the Yang-Baxter equation, τ is a solution to the algebraists version of the Yang-Baxter equation, and P is to be regarded as an algebraic permutation *or* as a representation of a virtual or flat crossing. We discuss the virtual braid group [3, 4, 5, 7] in section 5, but for here suffice it to say that it is an extension of the classical braid group by the symmetric group and so contains braiding generators and also generators of order two. Now the point is that by looking at unitary representations of the virtual braid group, we can (as with the matrices above) pick up both phase and swap gates, and hence the basic ingredients for quantum computation. This means that the virtual braid group provides a useful topological language for quantum computing. This deserves further exploration.

The matrix R can also be used to make an invariant of knots and links that is sensitive to linking numbers. We will discuss this point in section 4.

But now, consider the action of the unitary transformation R on quantum states. We have

1. $R|00> = a|00>$

2. $R|01> = c|10>$

3. $R|10> = d|01>$

4. $R|11> = b|11>$

Here is an elementary proof that the operator R can entangle quantum states. Note how this comes about through its being a composition of a phase and a swap gate. This decomposition is available in the virtual braid group.

Lemma. If R is chosen so that $ab \neq cd$, then the state $R(\psi \otimes \psi)$, with $\psi = |0> + |1>$, is entangled.

11

Proof. By definition,

$$\phi = R(\psi \otimes \psi) = R((|0> +|1>) \otimes (|0> +|1>))$$

$$= a|00> +c|10> +d|01> +b|11> .$$

If this state ϕ is unentangled, then there are constants X, Y, X', Y' such that

$$\phi = (X|0> +Y|1>) \otimes (X'|0> +Y'|1>).$$

This implies that

1. $a = XX'$

2. $c = X'Y$

3. $d = XY'$

4. $b = YY'$

It follows from these equations that $ab = cd$. Thus, when $ab \neq cd$ we can conclude that the state ϕ is entangled as a quantum state. //

Figure 7 - Braiding Operator Entangling a State

Remark. Note that if $\alpha = a|0> +b|1>$ and $\beta = c|0> +d|1>$ then $\alpha \otimes \beta = ac|00> +ad|01> +bc|10> +bd|11>$. Thus a state $\gamma = X|00> +Y|01> +Z|10> +W|11>$ is entangled if $XW \neq YZ$.

3.1   Questions

This phenomenon leads to more questions than we have answers.

1. How does one classify quantum entanglements in terms of braids (and corresponding braiding operators) that can produce them.

2. Can all quantum entangled states be lifted to braidings?

3. How do protocols for quantum computing look from this braided point of view?

4. What is the relationship between the analogy between quantum states and entangled loops when viewed through the lens of the braiding operators?

5. Does the association of unitary braiding operators shed light on quantum computing algorithms for knot invariants and statistical mechanics models? Here one can think of the computation of a knot invariant as separated into a braiding computation that is indeed a quantum computation, plus an evaluation related to the preparation and detection of a state(See [6, 8]).

6. How does one classify all unitary solutions to the Yang-Baxter equation.

4 Link Invariants from R

The unitary R matrix that we have considered in this paper gives rise to a non-trivial invariant of links. In this section we shall discuss the invariant associated with the specialization of R with $c = d$ so that

$$ R = \begin{bmatrix} a & 0 & 0 & 0 \\ 0 & 0 & c & 0 \\ 0 & c & 0 & 0 \\ 0 & 0 & 0 & b \end{bmatrix}. $$

Later we will specialize further so that $a = b$. We omit the details here, and just give the formula for this invariant in the form of a state summation. The invariant has the form

$$ Z_K = a^{-w(K)}(\sqrt{a/b})^{rot(K)} < K >, $$

where $w(K)$ is the sum of the crossing signs of the oriented link K and $rot(K)$ is the rotation number (or Whitney degree) of the planar diagram for K. See Figure 8. The bracket $< K >$ is the unnormalized state sum for the invariant. This state sum is defined through the equations shown in Figure 8.

13

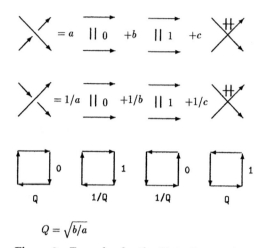

$$Q = \sqrt{b/a}$$

Figure 8 - Formulas for the State Summation

In this Figure, the first crossing is positive, the second negative. The first two diagrammatic equations correspond to terms in the matrices R and R^{-1} respectively. Note that the glyphs in these equations are labeled with 0 or 1. The first two terms correspond to the action of R on $|00 >$ and on $|11 >$ respectively. The third term refers to the fact that R acts on $|01 >$ and $|10 >$ in the same way (by multiplying by c). However, these equations are interpreted for the state summation as instructions for forming local states on the link diagram. A global state on the link diagram is a choice of replacement for each crossing in the diagram so that it is either replaced by parallel arcs (as in the first two terms of each equation) or by crossed arcs (as in the third term of each equation). The local assignments of 0 and 1 on the arcs must fit together compatibly in a global state. Thus in a global state one can think of the 0 and 1 as qubits 'circulating" around simple closed curves in the plane. Each such state of circulation is measured in terms of the qubit type and the sense of rotation. These are the evaluations of cycles indicated below the two main equations for the state sum. Each cycle is assigned either Q or $1/Q$ where $Q = \sqrt{b/a}$. The state sum is the summation

14

of evaluations of all of the possible states of qubit circulation where each state is evaluated by the product of weights a,b,c (and their inverses) coming from the expansion equations, multiplied by the porduct of the evaluations Q or $1/Q$ of the simple closed curves in the state. This completes a summary of the algorithm.

There are many ways to construe a state summation such as this. One can arrange the knot or link with respect to a given direction in the plane, and see the calculation as a vacuum-vacuum amplitude in a toy quantum field theory [6]. One can look directly at it as a generalized statistical mechanics state summation as we described it above. One can write the link as a closed braid and regard a major part of the calculation as a composition of unitary braiding operators. In this picture, a good piece of the algorithm can be construed as quantum. We believe that algorithms of this type, inherent in the study of so-called quantum link invariants, should be investigated more deeply from the point of view of quantum computing. In particular, the point of view of the algorithm as a sum over states of circulating qubits can be formalized, and will be the subject of another paper.

An example of a computation of this invariant is in order. In Figure 9 we show the admissible states for a Hopf link (a simple link of two circles) where both circles have the same rotation sense in the plane. We then see that if H denotes the Hopf link, then $< H >= a^2Q^2 + b^2Q^{-2} + 2c^2$ whence

$$Z_H = Q^{-2} < H >= a^2 + b^2Q^{-4} + 2c^2Q^{-2}.$$

From this it is easy to see that the invariant Z detects the linkedness of the Hopf link. In fact Z cannot detect linkedness of links with linking number equal to zero. For example, Z cannot detect the linkedness of the Whitehead link shown in Figure 10.

150

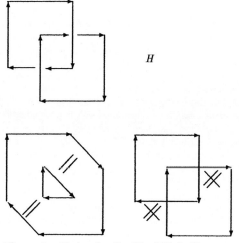

H

Figure 9 - States for the Hopf Link H

16

151

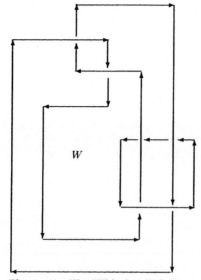

Figure 10 - The Whitehead Link

4.1 A Further Specialization of Z_K

If we let $a = b$ in the definition of Z_K, then the state summation becomes particularly simple with $Q = 1$. It is then easy to see that for a two component link Z_K is given by the formula

$$Z_K = 2(1 + (c^2/a^2)^{lk(K)})$$

where $lk(K)$ denotes the linking number of the two components of K. Thus we see that *for this specialization of the R matrix the operator R entangles quantum states exactly when it can detect linking numbers in the topological context.*

17

Here is another description of the state sum: Instead of smoothing or flattening the crossings of the diagram, label each component of the diagram with either 0 or 1. Take vertex weights of a or c (in this special case, and the corresponding matrix entries in the general case) for each local labelling of a positive crossing as shown in Figure 11. For a negative crossing the corresponding labels are $1/a$ and $1/c$ (which are the complex conjugates of a and c repsectively, when a and c are unit complex numbers). Let each state (labelling of the diagram by zeroes and ones) contribute the product of its vertex weights. Let $\Sigma(K)$ denote the sum over all the states of the products of the vertex weights. Then one can verify that $Z(K) = a^{-w(K)}\Sigma(K)$ where $w(K)$ is the sum of the crossing signs of the diagram K.

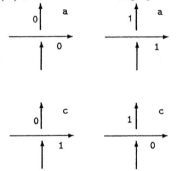

Figure 11 - Positive Crossing Weights

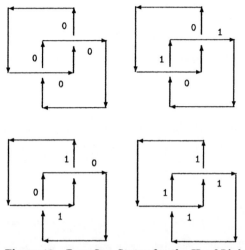

Figure 12 - Zero-One States for the Hopf Link

For example, view Figure 12. Here we show the zero-one states for the Hopf link H. The 00 and 11 states each contributes a^2, while the 01 and 10 states contribute c^2. Hence $\Sigma(H) = 2(a^2 + c^2)$ and $a^{-w(H)}\Sigma(H) = 2(1 + (c^2/a^2)^1) = 2(1 + (c^2/a^2)^{lk(H)})$, as expected.

The calculation of the invariant in this form is actually an analysis of quantum networks with cycles in the underlying graph. In this form of calculation we are concerned with those states of the network that correspond to labelings by qubits that are compatible with the entire network structure. A precise definition of this concept will be given in a sequel to this paper. Here one considers only those quantum states that are compatible with the interconnectedness of the network as a whole.

The example of the Hopf link shows how subtle properties of topological entanglement are detected through the use of the operator R in circularly interconnected quantum networks. It remains to do a deeper analysis that can really begin to disentangle the roles of quantum entanglement and circularity in such calculations.

5   A Remark about EPR

It is remarkable that the simple algebraic situation of an element in a tensor product that is not itself a a tensor product of elements of the factors corresponds to subtle nonlocality in physics. It helps to place this algebraic structure in the context of a gedanken experiment to see where the physics comes in. Consider

$$S = |0> |1> + |1> |0>.$$

In an EPR thought experiment, we think of two "parts" of this state that are separated in space. We want a notation for these parts and suggest the following:

$$L = \{|0>\}|1> + \{|1>\}|0>,$$

$$R = |0> \{|1>\} + |1> \{|0>\}.$$

In the left state L, an observer can only observe the left hand factor. In the right state R, an observer can only observe the right hand factor. These "states" L and R together comprise the EPR state S, but they are accessible individually just as are the two photons in the usual thought experiement. One can transport L and R individually and we shall write

$$S = L * R$$

to denote that they are the "parts" (but not tensor factors) of S.

The curious thing about this formalism is that it includes a little bit of macroscopic physics implicitly, and so it makes it a bit more apparent what EPR were concerned about. After all, lots of things that we can do to L or R do not affect S. For example, transporting L from one place to another, as in the original experiment where the photons separate. On the other hand, if Alice has L and Bob has R and Alice performs a local unitary transformation on "her" tensor factor, this applies to both L and R since the transformation is actually being applied to the state S. This is also a "spooky action at a distance" whose consequence does not appear until a measurement is made.

6 Virtual Braids

This section expands the remarks about how the inclusion of a swap operator in the braid group leads to a significant generalization of that structure to the virtual braid group.

The *virtual braid group* is an extension of the classical braid group by the symmetric group. If V_n denotes the n–strand virtual braid group, then V_n is generated by braid generators σ_1, ..., σ_{n-1} and virtual generators $c_1,..., c_n$ where each virtual generator c_i has the form of the braid generator σ_i with the crossing replaced by a virtual crossing. Among themselves, the braid generators satisfy the usual braiding relations. Among themselves, the virtual generators are a presentation for the symmetric group S_n. The relations that relate virtual generators and braiding geneerators are as follows:

$$\sigma_i^{\pm} c_{i+1} c_i = c_{i+1} c_i \sigma_{i+1}^{\pm},$$
$$c_i c_{i+1} \sigma_i^{\pm} = \sigma_{i+1}^{\pm} c_i c_{i+1},$$
$$c_i \sigma_{i+1}^{\pm} c_i = c_{i+1} \sigma_i^{\pm} c_{i+1}.$$

It is easy to see from this description of the virtual braid groups that all the braiding generators can be expressed in terms of the first braiding generator σ_1 (and its inverse) and the virtual generators. One can also see that Alexander's Theorem generalizes to virtuals: Every virtual knot is equivalent to a virtual braid [4]. In [7] a Markov Theorem is proven for virtual braids.

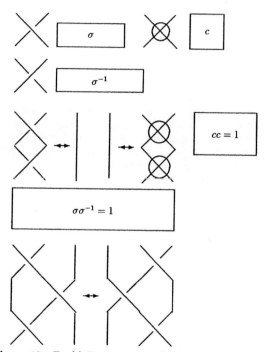

Figure 12 - Braid Generators and Virtual Braid Generators

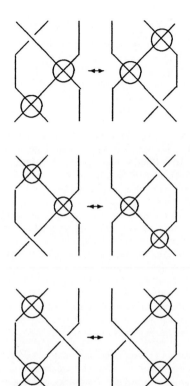

Figure 13 - Relations in the Virtual Braid Group

From the point of view of quantum computing, it is natural to add the virtual braiding operators to the Artin Braid Group. *Each virtual braiding operator can be interpreted as a swap gate.* With the virtual operators in place, we can compose them with the R matrices to obtain phase gates and other apparatus as described in Section 3. We then have the virtual braid group as a natural topologically based group structure that can be used as an underlying language for building patterns of quantum computation.

23

7   Discussion

We are now in a position to state the main problem posed by this paper. We have been exploring the analogy between topological entanglement and quantum entanglement. It has been suggested that there may be a direct connection between these two phenomena. But on closer examination, it appears that rather than a direct connection, there is a series of analogous features that are best explored by going back and forth across the boundary between topology and quantum computing. In particular, we have seen that the unitary operator R can indeed produce entangled quantum states from unentangled quantum states. The operator R is the basic ingredient for forming a representation of the Artin Braid Group. As such, it is intimately connected with topological entanglement. In fact, the operator R is also the basic ingredient in constructing the link invariant Z_K that we have studied in section 4. The construction of this link invariant is motivated by quantum statistical mechanics and its structure bears further investigation from the point of view of quantum computing. The theme that emerges is powerfully related to the circularity of the links. It is through mutual circularity that the topological linking occurs. And it is through this circularity and the measurement of circulating states of qubits that one computes the state summation model. A deep relation of quantum states and topological states will be seen through the study of the quantum states of circularly interconnected networks structurally related to three-dimensional space. These networks are both topological and quantum mechanical, and a common structure will emerge. This is the project for further papers in our series.

In the meantime, the language of the braid group and virtual braid group provides an arena for representing quantum operators that can be interpreted topologically. This framework provides a means for topology and quantum computing to converse with one another.

The papers [10, 11] and [12, 13] provide background to the considerations of the present paper. In particular, they provide a general framework for studying quantum entanglement that may be useful in investigating the role of infinitesimal braiding operators and other aspects of the representation theory of the Artin braid group.

The reader may wish to compare the points of view in this paper with

24

the paper [2]. There the author considers the possibility of anyonic computing and follows out the possible consequences in terms of representations of
the Artin Braid Group. We are in substantial agreement with his point of
view *and* we contend that braiding is fundamental to quantum computation
whether or not it is based in anyonic physics.

References

[1] P. K. Aravind, Borromean entanglement of the GHZ state. in 'Potentiality, Entanglement and Passion-at-a-Distance", ed. by R. S. Cohen et
al, pp. 53-59, Kluwer (1997).

[2] M. Freedman. A magnetic model with a possible Chern-Simons phase.
(preprint 2001), arXiv:quant-ph/0110060v1 9 Oct 2001.

[3] L. H. Kauffman, Virtual Knot Theory , European J. Comb. (1999) Vol.
20, 663-690.

[4] L. H. Kauffman, A Survey of Virtual Knot Theory in "Proceedings of
Knots in Hellas '98", World Sci. Pub. 2000 , pp. 143-202.

[5] L. H. Kauffman, Detecting Virtual Knots, *Atti. Sem. Mat. Fis. Univ.
Modena*, Supplemento al Vol. IL, 241-282 (2001).

[6] L. H. Kauffman, *Knots and Physics*, World Scientific Pub. Co.
(1991,1994, 2001).

[7] S. Kamada, Braid representation of virtual knots and welded knots, *to
appear in JKTR*.

[8] L. H. Kauffman, Quantum computing and the Jones polynomial. (to appear in the proceedings of AMS special session on quantum computing,
edited by Sam Lomonaco).

[9] L.H. Kauffman and S. J. Lomonaco, Topological entanglement and
quantum entanglement, (To appear in the Proceedings of the Dallas
Nov. 26-29, 2001, Darpa Quist Meeting on Quantum Computing.)

[10] S. J. Lomonaco Jr, A Rosetta Stone for Quantum Mechanics with an Introduction to Quantum Computation, in "Quantum Computation: A Grand Mathematical Challenge for the Twenty-First Century and the Millennium," PSAPM Vol. 58, AMS, Providence, RI (2002) (ISBN 0-8218-2084-2).

[11] S. J. Lomonaco Jr, An entangled tale of quantum entanglement in in "Quantum Computation: A Grand Mathematical Challenge for the Twenty-First Century and the Millennium," PSAPM Vol. 58, AMS, Providence, RI (2002) (ISBN 0-8218-2084-2).

[12] N. Linden and S. Popescu, On multi-particle entanglement, http://xxx.lanl.gov/abs/quant-ph/9711016.

[13] N. Linden, S. Popescu, and A. Sudbery, Non-local properties of multipaticle density matrices, http://xxx.lanl.lanl.gov/abs/quant-ph/9801076.

[14] D. Meyer, (private conversation at Darpa Quist Meeting in Dallas Texas, November 2001).

Symmetry Breaking as a Consequence of the Dirac Algebra

Peter Rowlands* and J. P. Cullerne†

*IQ Group and Science Communication Unit, Department of Physics, University of Liverpool, Oliver Lodge Laboratory, Oxford Street, Liverpool, L69 7ZE, UK. e-mail prowl@hep.ph.liv.ac.uk and prowl@csc.liv.uk

†IQ Group, Department of Computer Science, University of Liverpool, Chadwick Laboratory, Peach Street, Liverpool, L69 7ZF, UK. e-mail jpc@wincoll.ac.uk

The creation of the five Dirac gamma matrices from the eight fundamental units of space, time, mass and charge is proposed as the origin of symmetry-breaking between the strong, weak and electromagnetic interactions. The consequences are followed through with detailed analyses of the symmetries with which these interactions are associated. It is shown how the symmetry-breaking processes lead to the structures of baryons, bosons and free fermions, and to the various processes in which particle masses are generated.

THE DIRAC ALGEBRA AND ITS ORIGINS

We begin with the assumption made in many previous publications [e.g. Rowlands, 1983, 1991, 1999, 2001] that the four fundamental parameters, space, time, mass and charge, form a Klein-4 group described by the following properties:

space	real	nonconserved	countable
time	imaginary	nonconserved	noncountable
mass	real	conserved	noncountable
charge	imaginary	conserved	countable

The symmetry described by the group is taken to be both exact and exclusive as a source of information for physics. Charge is taken here as a 3-dimensional parameter incorporating the sources of strong, electromagnetic and weak interactions (s, e, w), with units described by the imaginary quaternion operators i, j, k, coupled with a real part (1) representing a unit of mass(-energy). Space and time, then, by symmetry, take on the characteristics of the vector and pseudoscalar parts of a 4-vector, with respective units $\mathbf{i}$, $\mathbf{j}$, $\mathbf{k}$ and i. However, to maintain the exactness of the symmetry, the vector units must be quaternion-like or multivariate, that is equivalent to Pauli matrices, with full products such that $\mathbf{ij} = -\mathbf{ji} = i\mathbf{k}$, and, in general terms, $\mathbf{ab} = \mathbf{a.b} + i\mathbf{a} \times \mathbf{b}$.

Another important aspect of the symmetry is that the conservation of charge must be absolute, and, therefore, extend to conservation of *type of charge*, with s, e, w not being interchangeable. This has been described previously [Rowlands, 1999, 2001] as a rotation *a*symmetry of charge, as opposed to the rotation symmetry of space, which is one manifestation of space's property of *nonconservation*. By Noether's theorem, this becomes linked to the conservation of angular momentum, and we could therefore suppose a Noether's theorem extension, in which the conservation of angular momentum becomes a manifestation of the separateness of the conservation laws of s, e, and w charges, as in the following scheme:

symmetry	conserved quantity	linked conservation
space translation	linear momentum	value of charge
time translation	energy	value of mass
space rotation	angular momentum	type of charge

Mathematically, the components of the Klein-4 group are described by a quaternion-multivariate-4-vector algebra with eight units $\mathbf{i}$, $\mathbf{j}$, $\mathbf{k}$, i, i, j, k, 1. This corresponds to a 32-part algebra isomorphic with that of the five Dirac γ matrices, which we represent as k, $i i$, $i i \mathbf{j}$, $i i \mathbf{k}$, $i j$. It is then comparatively straightforward to derive the Dirac equation, starting with the classical relativistic energy-momentum-rest mass equation:

$$E^2 - p^2 - m^2 = 0 .$$

This factorizes as:

$$(\pm kE \pm i i \, \mathbf{p} + i j \, m)\,(\pm kE \pm i i \, \mathbf{p} + i j \, m) = 0 ,$$

which is still classical. To convert it to a quantum equation, we attach the exponential term $e^{-i(Et\,-\,\mathbf{p}.\mathbf{r})}$ (which expresses the required total variation in space and time), so that

$$(\pm kE \pm i i \, \mathbf{p} + i j \, m)\,(\pm kE \pm i i \, \mathbf{p} + i j \, m) \, e^{-i(Et\,-\,\mathbf{p}.\mathbf{r})} = 0 ,$$

and replace E and $\mathbf{p}$ in the first bracket with the quantum operators, $i\partial / \partial t$ and $-i\nabla$, to give

$$\left(\pm ik\frac{\partial}{\partial t} \pm i\nabla + ijm \right)(\pm kE \pm i i \, \mathbf{p} + i j \, m) \, e^{-i(Et\,-\,\mathbf{p}.\mathbf{r})} = 0 ,$$

or,

$$\left(\pm ik\frac{\partial}{\partial t} \pm i\nabla + ijm \right) \psi = 0 .$$

The equation has four solutions representing the four possible signs of $\pm kE \pm ii$ **p**. Conventionally, these are attributed to fermion and antifermion, spin up and spin down (a multivariate **p**, of course, being equivalent to the conventional σ.**p** or σ.∇). As in conventional Dirac theory, the four solutions are conveniently represented by the four terms of a column or row vector (which we will call the quaternion state vector or QSV), but, in this case, the exponential term for a free particle (and the equivalent variable term for a bound particle) is common to all four solutions because the sign variation is incorporated into the differential operator. The QSV thus directly incorporates all the information contained in the exponential term, and it will often be convenient to describe the wavefunction by the QSV part alone.

In this formulation, both the wavefunction and the operator are nilpotent (or square roots of zero), and, even more significantly, identical; so incorporating immediate second quantization. They are written differently simply because one concerned with the conservation of mass-(energy) and charge, while the other is is expressing the *nonconservation* of space and time. Pauli exclusion is a direct consequence of a nilpotent formulation (because the product of identical nilpotents is zero), as also is universal nonlocality (as nilpotents must immediately 'know' that they are not identical to any other), although the nilpotent, as a square root of a relativistic energy expression, also automatically requires time-delayed local charge-related interaction between fermions. The fermion nilpotent can, in this sense, be regarded as a parameterization of the 'universe' – the only one allowed or necessary – and it is perfectly natural that it should be a square root of zero, generating nothing in combination with its 'dual' partner. Pauli exclusion says that there are an infinite number of such parameterizations, all correlated nonlocally. The QSV expressions in the formulation can also be used to represent creation or annihilation (with four separate operators acting simultaneously), and supersymmetry; while the 4-spinor retains its complete identity in calculations for bound states or propagators, leading to a single, rather than dual, set of equations in such cases.

For convenience, we may represent either a column or row vector as a column, without the vector brackets. So, a fermion may be represented by the row vector:

$$(kE + ii\ \mathbf{p} + ij\ m)$$
$$(kE - ii\ \mathbf{p} + ij\ m)$$
$$(-kE + ii\ \mathbf{p} + ij\ m)$$
$$(-kE - ii\ \mathbf{p} + ij\ m)$$

and an antifermion by the column vector:

$$(-kE + ii\ \mathbf{p} + ij\ m)$$
$$(-kE - ii\ \mathbf{p} + ij\ m)$$
$$(kE + ii\ \mathbf{p} + ij\ m)$$
$$(kE - ii\ \mathbf{p} + ij\ m)\ .$$

The spin 1 boson produced by their combination is then simply the scalar product:

$$(kE + ii\, \mathbf{p} + ij\, m) \quad (-kE + ii\, \mathbf{p} + ij\, m)$$
$$(kE - ii\, \mathbf{p} + ij\, m) \quad (-kE - ii\, \mathbf{p} + ij\, m)$$
$$(-kE + ii\, \mathbf{p} + ij\, m) \quad (kE + ii\, \mathbf{p} + ij\, m)$$
$$(-kE - ii\, \mathbf{p} + ij\, m) \quad (kE - ii\, \mathbf{p} + ij\, m)\,.$$

Spin 0 bosons are achieved by reversing the $\mathbf{p}$ signs in the second column, while reversing both E and $\mathbf{p}$ signs produces a bosonic-like state from two fermions with opposite spins. This can perhaps be thought of in terms of an idealized version of the unit bosonic state in a Bose-Einstein condensate, or of the Cooper pairs in a superconductor, or even of the combination of electron and magnetic flux line in the quantum Hall phenomenon. (It is notable that, in the nilpotent formulation, states such as $a_1 a_2$ and $a_1 a_2^{\dagger}$ are automatically excluded, unless $a_1 = a_2$, when the respective anticommutators become 0 and 1.)

The spin-statistics connection is easily established by connecting the ½-integral spin for the fermion with the process of square-rooting involved in the creation of its wavefunction. In numerical calculations where multivariate values of $\mathbf{p}$ or ∇ are used, then spin is automatically incorporated, but where we use ordinary vectorial versions of $\mathbf{p}$ or ∇, for example, in calculations making explicit use of polar coordinates and spherical symmetry, then we have to make specific use of additional spin terms. Following the original Dirac procedure, and writing the space derivative (or $\boldsymbol{\sigma}.\nabla$) as a function of r in polar coordinates, with an explicit use of a ½-integral spin angular momentum term ($j + $ ½), we obtain:

$$\boldsymbol{\sigma}.\nabla = \left(\frac{\partial}{\partial r} + \frac{1}{r}\right) \pm i\,\frac{j + \tfrac{1}{2}}{r}\,.$$

VACUUM

The vacuum plays a significant, even direct, role in this formulation of the Dirac algebra. We can construct a vacuum operator as a diagonal matrix, which is premultiplied by a 4-component quaternion row state vector or postmultiplied by a 4-component column quaternion state vector, representing a fermion state. In the first case, we write:

$$((kE + ii\mathbf{p} + ijm)\ (kE - ii\mathbf{p} + ijm)\ (-kE + ii\mathbf{p} + ijm)\ (-kE - ii\mathbf{p} + ijm)) \times$$

$$k\begin{pmatrix} kE + ii\mathbf{p} + ijm & 0 & 0 & 0 \\ 0 & kE - ii\mathbf{p} + ijm & 0 & 0 \\ 0 & 0 & -kE + ii\mathbf{p} + ijm & 0 \\ 0 & 0 & 0 & -kE - ii\mathbf{p} + ijm \end{pmatrix} e^{-i(Et - \mathbf{p}.\mathbf{r})}$$

$$= ((kE + ii\mathbf{p} + ijm)\ (kE - ii\mathbf{p} + ijm)\ (-kE + ii\mathbf{p} + ijm)\ (-kE - ii\mathbf{p} + ijm))\, e^{-i(Et - \mathbf{p}.\mathbf{r})}\,,$$

assuming an appropriate normalisation. Individual components of the row vector, ($\pm kE \pm ii\mathbf{p} + ijm$), which are effectively the four separate creation operators required to specify the whole system, can be considered as being postmultiplied by k ($\pm kE \pm ii\mathbf{p} + ijm$) to return to their original state, after normalisation. Clearly, this can be continued indefinitely, with the fermion acting continually on the vacuum to reproduce itself:

$$(\pm kE \pm ii\mathbf{p} + ijm) \, k \, (\pm kE \pm ii\mathbf{p} + ijm) \, k \, (\pm kE \pm ii\mathbf{p} + ijm) \, k \, (\pm kE \pm ii\mathbf{p} + ijm) \ldots$$

However, k ($\pm kE \pm ii\mathbf{p} + ijm$) k is the same as the antistate to ($\pm kE \pm ii\mathbf{p} + ijm$), or ($\mp kE \pm ii\mathbf{p} + ijm$), making this equivalent to

$$(\pm kE \pm ii\mathbf{p} + ijm) \, (\mp kE \pm ii\mathbf{p} + ijm) \, (\pm kE \pm ii\mathbf{p} + ijm) \, (\mp kE \pm ii\mathbf{p} + ijm) \ldots$$

Another way to look at this is to say that the fermion sees in the vacuum its 'image' or virtual antistate, producing a kind of virtual bosonic combination, and leading to an infinite alternating series of virtual fermions and bosons.

Each real fermion state creates a virtual mirror antifermion image of itself in the vacuum, while each real antifermion state creates a virtual mirror fermion image of itself. The combined real and virtual particle creates a virtual boson state. Real fermions and real antifermions are real mirror images of each other. Vacuum fermions and vacuum antifermions have a similar relationship, although both states, in this case, are virtual. The mirror image states of all possible fermion states constitute the zero point energy of the vacuum. Each possible state provides a virtual vacuum energy of $\hbar\omega / 2$, like the ground state of a harmonic oscillator (which, of course, it is). To create a real fermion state, we excite a virtual vacuum state of $-\hbar\omega / 2$ up to the level $\hbar\omega / 2$, using a total energy quantum of $\hbar\omega$. Counting real and virtual particles, we have the same number of fermions and antifermions in the universe, but, in a universe with a non-symmetric ground state, fermions will be predominantly real and antifermions predominantly virtual; and, counting real and virtual particles, and assigning $+E$ to fermions and $-E$ to fermions, we obtain a total energy of zero.

Real	Fermion	Antifermion
Vacuum	Antifermion	Fermion

The existence of mirror image vacuum states for all fermionic particles accounts for the structure of the Dirac quaternion state vector. We incorporate both real and virtual components (interpreting the *zitterbewegung* as a switching between them). The four creation operators create both the real particle and its dual vacuum images. All fermion wavefunctions are, in this sense, single-valued, producing an effective combination analagous to a simultaneous consideration of the two sides of Newton's third law of motion or a virial doubling of the kinetic energy in a potential energy term. Fermion and antifermion QSVs thus have identical components; only the *order* privileges either $+E$ or $-E$ states as the 'real' ones. (A similar principle applies to the spin states.)

The vacuum is really an expression of the continuous or noncountable nature of mass-energy ('mass', as the source of gravity). Continuity automatically makes mass-energy unidimensional and unipolar. Since it is also real, it is therefore restricted to a single mathematical sign, which is usually taken as positive. We can interpret this as implying a non-symmetric ground state or a filled vacuum. The filled vacuum for the ground state is that of negative energy or antifermions. In physical terms, it manifests itself in the Higgs field, which breaks charge conjugation symmetry for the weak interaction, and gives rest masses to the fermions and weak gauge bosons. (The reaction half of the system in this case, in this sense, is equivalent to what Newton called the 'impressed force' or the inertia.) It is also responsible for quantum mechanical nonlocality and the instantaneous transmission of the gravitational force. Significantly, gravitational potential energy is often represented as negative.

SYMMETRY BREAKING AND THE DIRAC ALGEBRA

One of the significant aspects of the nilpotent formulation of the Dirac equation is that charge is explicitly involved, and that symmetry-breaking between the three charges is an immediate consequence of the formulation of the Dirac state. This is because, to reduce the eight 'primitive' units of time, space, mass and charge, to the five composite units of the Dirac algebra, requires an algebraic symmetry-breaking for one of the two three-dimensional parameters, as follows:

Time	Space	Mass	Charge
i	**i j k**	1	*i j k*
Removing charge			
k	*i*	*j*	
produces			
ik	*ii ij ik*	*j*	
E	**p**	*m*	
Dirac Energy	*Dirac Momentum*	*Dirac Rest Mass*	

We will show later how this symmetry-breaking between the three charges can be interpreted in terms of the conservation of angular momentum.

$SU(3)$ AND THE STRONG INTERACTION

A product of an even number of fermionic QSVs is bosonic, and a product of an odd number is fermionic, as in conventional theory, and is similarly described by the use of Slater determinants. However, in the case of identical QSVs (that is, ones which are part of the same physical system), such a product is impossible, even for two states, unless either the signs of E or $\mathbf{p}$ or both are different in the two states. In the first case, we have a spin 1 boson, in the second case a Bose-Einstein condensate, and in the third case a spin 0 boson. There is, however, one further degree of freedom, and this involves the rotational properties of $\mathbf{p}$. Here, we have three degrees of freedom, representing the three dimensions of $\mathbf{p}$, and it is possible to construct a three-part fermionic single-system object from three fermionic QSVs (equivalent to the coloured quarks of conventional theory), if each QSV encompasses a different spatial dimension. Then an expression of the form

$$(kE \pm ii\, p_1 + ij\, m)\, (kE \pm ii\, p_2 + ij\, m)\, (kE \pm ii\, p_3 + ij\, m) \,,$$

by successively taking $\mathbf{p}$ through each of the phases representing the three dimensional components of momentum, p_1, p_2, p_3, will produce three non-zero terms equivalent to $-p^2(kE + ii\, \mathbf{p} + ij\, m)$ and three equivalent $-p^2(kE - ii\, \mathbf{p} + ij\, m)$, which we can take as equivalent to three cyclic and three anticyclic combinations. In principle, we generate all six terms in the antisymmetric baryonic colour singlet of $SU(3)$:

$$\psi \sim (BGR - BRG + GRB - GBR + RBG - RGB)\,.$$

with a mapping of the form:

BGR	$(kE + ij\, m)\, (kE + ij\, m)\, (kE + ii\, \mathbf{p} + ij\, m)$
$- BRG$	$(kE + ij\, m)\, (kE - ii\, \mathbf{p} + ij\, m)\, (kE + ij\, m)$
GRB	$(kE + ij\, m)\, (kE + ii\, \mathbf{p} + ij\, m)\, (kE + ij\, m)$
$- GBR$	$(kE + ij\, m)\, (kE + ij\, m)\, (kE - ii\, \mathbf{p} + ij\, m)$
RBG	$(kE + ii\, \mathbf{p} + ij\, m)\, (kE + ij\, m)\, (kE + ij\, m)$
$- RGB$	$(kE - ii\, \mathbf{p} + ij\, m)\, (kE + ij\, m)\, (kE + ij\, m)\,.$

With only one spin term in each combination, this representation predicts that the spin is a property of the *baryon* wavefunction as a whole, not of component quark wavefunctions. Looked at in this way, the $SU(3)$ nature of the strong interaction – the one linked with $\mathbf{p}$ in the Dirac formalism – becomes explicit. The 'interaction' is essentially a statement of the co-existence or gauge invariance of all states which would be identical under an $SU(3)$ transformation. As with other such symmetries, we can describe this gauge invariance using the idea of the 'transfer' of a gauge boson, or, in this case, of a 'transfer' of momentum or angular momentum, although in reality all possible states co-exist on an equal basis. Because the gauge invariance is exact, being exactly equivalent to that of the three dimensions of space, the gauge boson will be necessarily massless. We can also use the already existing formalism for $SU(3)$ interactions to link the angular momentum 'transfer' to that of the strong charge. The conventional expression for this symmetry requires a covariant derivative of the form:

$$\partial_\mu \to \partial_\mu + ig_s \frac{\lambda^\alpha}{2} A^{\alpha\mu}(x) ,$$

which, in component form, becomes:

$$ip_1 = \partial_1 \to \partial_1 + ig_s \frac{\lambda^\alpha}{2} A^{\alpha 1}(x)$$

$$ip_2 = \partial_2 \to \partial_2 + ig_s \frac{\lambda^\alpha}{2} A^{\alpha 2}(x)$$

$$ip_3 = \partial_3 \to \partial_3 + ig_s \frac{\lambda^\alpha}{2} A^{\alpha 3}(x)$$

$$E = i\partial_0 \to i\partial_0 - g_s \frac{\lambda^\alpha}{2} A^{\alpha 0}(x) .$$

Inserting these expressions into the differential form of the baryon state vector, we obtain:

$$\left(k \left(E - g_s \frac{\lambda^\alpha}{2} A^{\alpha 0} \right) \pm i \left(\partial_1 + ig_s \frac{\lambda^\alpha}{2} A^{\alpha 1} \right) + ij\, m \right)$$

$$\left(k \left(E - g_s \frac{\lambda^\alpha}{2} A^{\alpha 0} \right) \pm i \left(\partial_2 + ig_s \frac{\lambda^\alpha}{2} A^{\alpha 2} \right) + ij\, m \right)$$

$$\left(k \left(E - g_s \frac{\lambda^\alpha}{2} A^{\alpha 0} \right) \pm i \left(\partial_3 + ig_s \frac{\lambda^\alpha}{2} A^{\alpha 3} \right) + ij\, m \right) .$$

To preserve the nonzero fermionic nilpotent structure, we write this expression in one of the forms:

$$\left(k \left(E - g_s \frac{\lambda^\alpha}{2} A^{\alpha 0} \right) \pm i \left(\partial_1 + ig_s \frac{\lambda^\alpha}{2} \mathbf{A}^\alpha \right) + ij\, m \right)\left(k \left(E - g_s \frac{\lambda^\alpha}{2} A^{\alpha 0} \right) + ij\, m \right)\left(k \left(E - g_s \frac{\lambda^\alpha}{2} A^{\alpha 0} \right) + ij\, m \right)$$

$$\left(k \left(E - g_s \frac{\lambda^\alpha}{2} A^{\alpha 0} \right) + ij\, m \right)\left(k \left(E - g_s \frac{\lambda^\alpha}{2} A^{\alpha 0} \right) \pm i \left(\partial_1 + ig_s \frac{\lambda^\alpha}{2} \mathbf{A}^\alpha \right) + ij\, m \right)\left(k \left(E - g_s \frac{\lambda^\alpha}{2} A^{\alpha 0} \right) + ij\, m \right)$$

$$\left(k \left(E - g_s \frac{\lambda^\alpha}{2} A^{\alpha 0} \right) + ij\, m \right)\left(k \left(E - g_s \frac{\lambda^\alpha}{2} A^{\alpha 0} \right) + ij\, m \right)\left(k \left(E - g_s \frac{\lambda^\alpha}{2} A^{\alpha 0} \right) \pm i \left(\partial_1 + ig_s \frac{\lambda^\alpha}{2} \mathbf{A}^\alpha \right) + ij\, m \right)$$

Here the vector **A** term has the same function as a unit of strong charge or baryon number, and we can regard the strong interaction as equivalent to the 'transfer' of a unit of strong charge, which occurs with the 'transfer' of the active component of angular momentum. The exact gauge invariance and the equivalence of all possible states is a property of the wavefunction alone, and necessarily nonlocal. This means that the rate of 'transfer' of momentum or the strength of the interaction is necessarily independent of the spatial coordinates associated with any of the component parts of the wavefunction. The same would apply to any bosonic state (or meson) with explicit 'colour' or variation of angular momentum orientation. With the further necessity of spherical symmetry for a system in which no particular direction may be privileged, it is evident that the strong force involved in both the 3-quark or baryon system, and the quark-antiquark or meson system, is independent of the spatial separation of the system's components, or can be described by a potential which increases linearly with distance. This allows an explicit calculation of the strong force in either of these systems, which explains its observed physical properties. The calculation is completely analytic.

AN ANALYTIC SOLUTION FOR THE STRONG INTERACTION

Experimental studies of charmonium states, in addition to lattice gauge calculations from QCD [Takahashi et al., 2001], already suggest that the quark-antiquark potential in the bound meson state at the quenched (long-distance) level is, at least approximately, of the form:

$$V = -\frac{A}{r} + \sigma r + C \ .$$

In this expression, $-A / r$ is the Coulomb term, which we will show is necessary to maintain spherical symmetry; σr is the linear potential, demanded by a constant rate of 'transfer'; while C is a constant, which has no effect on the form of the results obtained, merely shifting the total energy value from E to $E - qC$, where q ($= \sqrt{\alpha_s}$) is the strong or colour charge for the quark. We thus have a potential energy

$$W = q\frac{A}{r} - q\sigma r - qC$$

for the interactions of quark and antiquark (qA being worked out theoretically at $4\alpha_s / 3$). Assuming spherical symmetry, we incorporate the potential in the E term to create the covariant time derivative, and use

$$\sigma.\nabla = \left(\frac{\partial}{\partial r} + \frac{1}{r}\right) \pm i \frac{j + \frac{1}{2}}{r}$$

for the space derivative as a function of r in polar coordinates, with the explicit ½-integral spin angular momentum term. We can now construct the nilpotent operator, as follows:

$$\pm k\left(E + q\frac{A}{r} - q\sigma r - qC\right) \pm i\left(\frac{\partial}{\partial r} + \frac{1}{r} \pm i \frac{j + \frac{1}{2}}{r}\right) + ijm \ .$$

where the complete operator is a column vector incorporating all four terms. Two of the four Dirac solutions require positive values of i $(j + \frac{1}{2})$ and two negative. Initially, we suppose that the nonquaternionic part of the wavefunction has the form

$$\psi = \exp(-ar - br^2)\, r^{\gamma} \sum_{v=0} a_v r^v ,$$

and consider the ground state (with $v = 0$) over the four Dirac solutions. The squared four-part nilpotent wavefunction defines the condition:

$$4\left(E + q\frac{A}{r} - q\sigma r - qC\right)^2 = -2\left(\frac{\partial}{\partial r} + \frac{1}{r} + i\frac{j+\frac{1}{2}}{r}\right)^2 - 2\left(\frac{\partial}{\partial r} + \frac{1}{r} - i\frac{j+\frac{1}{2}}{r}\right)^2 + 4m^2$$

for all solutions. Applying ψ and expanding, we obtain:

$$(E - qC)^2 - 2q^2 A\sigma + \frac{q^2 A^2}{r^2} + q^2\sigma^2 r^2 + \frac{2qA}{r}(E - qC) - 2q\sigma(E - qC)r$$

$$= -\left(a^2 + \frac{(\gamma + v + 1)^2}{r^2} - \frac{(j+\frac{1}{2})^2}{r^2} + 4b^2 r^2 + 4abr - 4b(\gamma + v + 1) - \frac{2a}{r}(\gamma + v + 1)\right) + m^2 .$$

The positive and negative $i(j + \frac{1}{2})$ terms cancel out over the four solutions as they do in the case of the hydrogen atom. We now equate:

(1) coefficients of r^2:

$$q^2\sigma^2 = -4b^2$$

(2) coefficients of r:

$$-2q\sigma(E - qC) = -4ab$$

(3) coefficients of $1/r$:

$$-2qA(E - qC) = 2a(\gamma + v + 1)$$

(4) coefficients of $1/r^2$:

$$q^2 A^2 = -(\gamma + v + 1)^2 + (j + \frac{1}{2})^2$$

(5) constant terms:

$$(E - qC)^2 - 2q^2 A\sigma = -a^2 + 4b(\gamma + v + 1) + m^2$$

From the first three equations, we immediately obtain:

$$b = \pm\frac{iq\sigma}{2}$$

$$a = \mp i(E - qC)$$

$$\gamma + v + 1 = \mp iqA .$$

The case where $v = 0$, then leads to

$$(j + \tfrac{1}{2})^2 = 0$$

$$m^2 = 0 \,.$$

This suggests a wavefunction with variable component

$$\psi = \exp\left(\mp i(E - qC)r \pm iq\sigma r^2/2\right) r^{\pm iqA - 1}$$

for the ground state, with $v = 0$. If we can assign physical meaning to the case where $v \neq 0$, and the power series in ψ terminates in $v = n'$, we will conclude that

$$q\sigma = -i\frac{m^2}{2n'}$$

and

$$qA = -i\frac{(j + \tfrac{1}{2})^2 - n'^2}{2n'} \,,$$

requiring the power series to be composed of negative imaginary integers.

The imaginary exponential terms in ψ can be interpreted as representing asymptotic freedom, the $\exp(\mp i(E - qC)r$ being typical for a free fermion. The complex $\exp(\pm iq\sigma r^2/2)$ term is similar to the real one used for a harmonic oscillator. The r^{-1} term is also complex, and can be written as a phase, $\phi(r) = \exp(\pm iqA \ln(r))$, which varies less rapidly with r than the rest of ψ. We can therefore write ψ in the form

$$\psi = \frac{\exp(kr + \phi(r))}{r} \,,$$

where

$$k = (\mp i(E - qC) \pm iq\sigma r/2) \,.$$

When r is small (at high energies), the first term dominates, approximating to a free fermion solution (which can be interpreted as asymptotic freedom). When r is large (at low energies) the second term dominates, bringing in the confining potential (σ) (which can be interpreted as producing infrared slavery).

Significantly, no spherically symmetric solution can be reached, under any conditions, with a potential $\propto r$, without the additional Coulomb term, because the spherical symmetry introduces terms in $1/r$ and $1/r^2$ as coefficients of i^2 which must be negated by similar terms acting as coefficients of k^2. The algebraic structure of the nilpotent representation also rules out a confining potential proportional to $\ln r$. A confining potential proportional to r implies a constant force, and, as the form of the solution remains unchanged by the presence of a constant term in the potential, the requirements for asymptotic freedom and infrared slavery are met simply by assuming that the quark confining force must be constant in magnitude and equal in all directions.

In line with theoretical expectations, we can show that, if the quark-quark potential is reduced to the Coulomb term, as might be imagined to happen effectively at short distances, we obtain a hydrogen-like spectral series. Here, we have

$$4\left(E + q\frac{A}{r} - qC\right)^2 = -2\left(\frac{\partial}{\partial r} + \frac{1}{r} + i\frac{j + \frac{1}{2}}{r}\right)^2 - 2\left(\frac{\partial}{\partial r} + \frac{1}{r} - i\frac{j + \frac{1}{2}}{r}\right)^2 + 4m^2 \quad ,$$

where the nonquaternionic part of the wavefunction must have the form

$$\psi = \exp\left(-ar\right) r^{\gamma} \sum_{\nu = 0} a_{\nu} r^{\nu},$$

with the exp $(-br^2)$ no longer required. On application of this function over the four Dirac solutions, and expansion (for the ground state), we obtain:

$$(E - qC)^2 + \frac{q^2 A^2}{r^2} + \frac{2qA}{r}(E - qC)$$

$$= -\left(a^2 + \frac{(\gamma + \nu + 1)^2}{r^2} - \frac{(j + \frac{1}{2})^2}{r^2} - \frac{2a}{r}(\gamma + \nu + 1)\right) + m^2 \quad .$$

This time, there are only three equations – for coefficients of $1 / r$, coefficients of $1 / r^2$, and constant terms:

$$2qA(E - qC) = 2a(\gamma + \nu + 1)$$

$$q^2 A^2 = -(\gamma + \nu + 1)^2 + (j + \frac{1}{2})^2$$

$$(E - qC)^2 = -a^2 + m^2 \quad ,$$

leading to:

$$a = \frac{qA(E - qC)}{(\gamma + \nu + 1)}$$

$$(\gamma + \nu + 1) = \pm\sqrt{(j + \frac{1}{2})^2 - q^2 A^2}$$

$$m^2 = (E - qC)^2 \left(1 + \frac{q^2 A^2}{(\gamma + \nu + 1)^2}\right) \quad .$$

Significantly, below a certain value of $(E - qC)$, a is real, suggesting a confined solution. Also, the status of γ is determined by the values of ν and j; while m here is nonzero. The equations are identical in form to those for the hydrogen atom with qA replacing Ze^2, and $E - qC$ replacing E. We assume a wavefunction, with nonquaternionic component:

$$\psi = \exp\left(-\sqrt{m^2 - (E - qC)^2}\right) r^{\gamma} \sum_{\nu = 0} a_{\nu} r^{\nu},$$

and, allowing the power series to terminate at $v = n'$, we obtain the characteristic hydrogen-like solution:

$$\frac{E - qC}{m} = \left(1 + \frac{q^2 A^2}{(\gamma + 1 + n')^2}\right)^{-1/2},$$

or

$$\frac{E - qC}{m} = \left(1 + \frac{q^2 A^2}{(\sqrt{(j + \frac{1}{2})^2 - q^2 A^2} + n')^2}\right)^{-1/2}.$$

For a real system, such as charmonium, involving additional electrostatic terms, we can modify the Coulomb term by adding the appropriate electrostatic term (say $4e^2 / 9r$ or $e^2 / 9r$) to qA / r.

Rather than signifying escape, as with the electron in the hydrogen atom, the condition resulting from $(E - qC)^2 > m^2$ is that of *asymptotic* freedom, because of the continued presence (but reduced effect) of the confining linear potential. We can use the full and Coulomb-like solutions to make an approximate numerical calculation of the distance at which infrared slavery becomes effective. From the full solution, let

$$k = (\mp i(E - qC) \pm iq\sigma r/2) = \frac{2\pi(r)}{\lambda},$$

and take $\lambda = \infty$ at zero energy (or infrared slavery). Then

$$q\sigma r = 2(E - qC)$$

and

$$r = \frac{2(E - qC)}{q\sigma}.$$

From the Coulomb-like solution, we take $(E - qC)$ as the mass or reduced mass of the c quark (≈ 1.5 GeV). Taking $\sigma \approx 1$ GeV fm^{-1} and $q \approx 0.4$, we find r ≈ 4 fm. The solution is thus completely analytic and yields meaningful numerical values.

Virtually identical arguments apply to the three-quark or baryon system, although the geometry of the separation is now different. The phase term in the full solution is interestingly proportional to α_s^2, and is the only place where A appears in the expression. Thus the Coulomb part of the potential – which is the component we believe to be significant in grand unification – results in a phase term (as does the $U(1)$ term for the electromagnetic interaction). It may be that we can regard this phase term as the one representing the gauge invariant 'transfer' of strong charge, or angular momentum, or vector part of the $SU(3)$ covariant derivative, between the 'coloured' components of baryons and mesons.

PHASE DIAGRAMS FOR CHARGE CONSERVATION

According to our extended Noether's theorem, the conservation properties of the weak and electromagnetic charges will be determined by those of the angular momentum operator, like those of the strong charge. Comparison with the strong charge calculation, gives us an idea of how this may be accomplished. Only one component of angular momentum is well-defined at any moment, and the strong charge appears to act in such a way that the well-defined direction manifests itself by 'privileging' one out of three independent phases making up the complete phase cycle. In a truly gauge invariant system, this can only be accomplished in relative terms. If the weak and electric charges are also related to angular momentum, then the same must apply to them, and the relative 'privileging' of phase can only be defined between the different interactions. The weak and electric charges, of course, are not directly attached to the $\mathbf{p}$ operator, like the strong charge, and are governed by entirely different symmetries. The creation of the Dirac algebra relates w to the pseudoscalar iE and e to the real scalar m, but these quantities *combine* to affect $\mathbf{p}$, and this is why we think of the electric and weak forces as being in some way combined.

We have, here, two options. If the 'privileged' or 'active' phases of E and m (or w and e) coincide with each other, then this also determines the 'privileged' phase of $\mathbf{p}$; the result is no 'privileged' relative phase. Since the strong charge is defined only through the directional variation of $\mathbf{p}$, via a 'privileged' relative phase, a system in which the phases coincide cannot be strongly bound. If, however, they are different, then this information can only be carried through $\mathbf{p}$ (or s), and the strong interaction must be present.

We can imagine the arrangements diagrammatically using a rotating vector to represent the 'privileged' direction states for the charges. Each charge has only one 'active' phase out of three at any one time to fix the angular momentum direction; the symbols e, s, and w, here refer to these states, not the actual charges. The vectors may be thought of as rotating over a complete spherical surface. In the case of the quark-based states – baryons and mesons – the total information about the angular momentum state is split between three axes, whereas the lepton states carry all the information on a single axis.

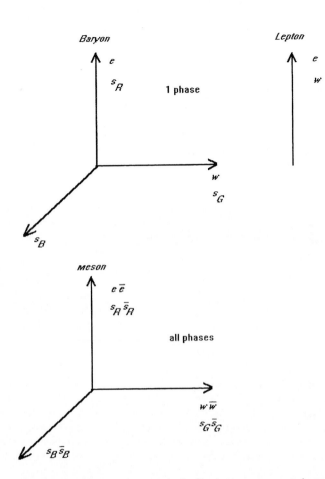

Though the axes in these diagrams, in the first instance, represent charge states, we will subsequently show that they also represent angular momentum states. In principle, each type of charge carries a different aspect of angular momentum (or helicity) conservation; s carries the directional information (linked to $\mathbf{p}$); w carries the sign information (+ or − helicity) (linked to iE); e carries information about magnitude (linked to m). Another way of looking at this is to associate these properties, respectively, with the symmetries of rotation, inversion, and translation.

HELICITY AND THE WEAK INTERACTION

Just as the character of the strong force and its relationship with the conservation of angular momentum is determined by its association with a vector operator, so we can expect that the pseudoscalar nature of iE and the scalar nature of m will determine the respective character and angular momentum relation of the weak and electric forces. In the case of the weak force, we have two sign options for iE, because we are using complex algebra, and there are necessarily two mathematical solutions. The sign option, in effect, determines the helicity state, and it is this aspect of angular momentum conservation which is linked to the weak interaction.

One of the special properties of the weak interaction is its confinement to one helicity state for fermions and the opposite state for antifermions. This is entirely a result of requiring mass-energy to be a continuum, and the consequent generation of a filled vacuum state. Essentially, there is no *physical* state corresponding to E, although the use of a complex operator requires that $-iE$ has the same *mathematical* status as iE. Charge conjugation, however, or reversal of the signs of quaternion labels, *is* permitted physically. So $-ikE$ states are interpreted as antifermion or charge-conjugated states; and the mass-energy continuum becomes a filled vacuum for the ground state of the universe, in which such states would not exist.

A filled vacuum of this type was invoked by Dirac in the process of deriving the antiparticle concept, but the filled vacuum is now specifically a k or *weak* vacuum. It requires a violation of charge conjugation symmetry for the interaction associated with the k operator alone, and a consequent violation of either time reversal symmetry or parity to maintain the invariance of CPT. A weak interaction can distinguish between particle and antiparticle, but not between + and − signs of weak charge, and making the transition in the sign of the k operator (equivalent to T), because it is now interpreted as a charge conjugation (C), comes at the price of switching the sign of the i operator (P) as well.

Where s charges are present, the effective sign of w is determined by that of s, reducing the degrees of freedom in the charge structures from the eight of $\pm w \pm s \pm e$ to the four of $\pm (w + s) \pm e$, because of the linking of the signs of two of the quaternion operators. There is no overall loss, however, because a degree of freedom is simultaneously *gained* by $E \pm \mathbf{p}$, which increases from the physical two to the mathematical four of $\pm E \pm \mathbf{p}$. Mathematically, also, with the effective transfer of this degree of freedom from w or k to E, the Dirac state ($\pm ikE \pm i\mathbf{p} + jm$) is provided with the four solutions which result from its quaternionic structure and its 4-D space-time. In principle, the unique $2^{D/2} \times 2^{D/2}$ matrix representation of the Clifford algebra, where $D = 4$, permits an exact quaternionic structure only because it is situated within a universe which has a filled k vacuum, and a single sign for the term jm in either fermion or antifermion states; and, ultimately, this is possible only because of the 4-dimensionality of the space-time signature which we have applied to the equation.

Physically, the loss of a degree of freedom for w means that both quarks and free fermions become mixed states, containing both $+w$, and suppressed $-w$, states, and involving respective violations of parity and time reversal symmetry for the latter. A violations of parity or time reversal symmetry, consequent upon the violation of charge conjugation, as we have said, also means that only one state of helicity or $\sigma.\mathbf{p}$ exists for the pure weak interaction for fermions, with the opposite helicity applying to antifermions. According to the Dirac equation, σ for fermions is -1, which implies a state of negative helicity or left-handedness. If we wish to create alternative states of positive helicity or right-handedness, as the existence of $\pm\mathbf{p}$ in the formalism would seem to require, then the only remaining mechanism is through the introduction of mass in the term jm. The j quaternion label, here, defines what we call the electric charge. The presence of m thus simultaneously mixes E and $\mathbf{p}$ terms, right-handed and left-handed components, and the effects of e and w charges.

THE ELECTROWEAK $SU(2)_L \times U(1)$

It is axiomatic in the theory described here that w, s, and e charges must be separately conserved, and therefore the interactions for which they are the sources must completely independent of each other. However, it is particularly essential to the *characterization* of the weak interaction to express its independence of the electric charge. If the mixing of E and $\mathbf{p}$ terms, or right-handed and left-handed components, is also equivalent to the mixing of e and w charges, then it is important to establish that this mixing *does not affect the weak interaction* as such. Otherwise, the whole idea of defining the weak interaction through charge-conjugation violation would be compromised. In fact, the characteristic $SU(2)_L$ 'isospin' pattern associated with the weak interaction is a direct expression of its independence from the presence or absence of the electric charge. (The $U(1)$ symmetry for the electric interaction would then produce the required phase.) There are two possible $SU(2)_L$ states, with electric charge or without electric charge, which we call the two states of weak isospin, and the weak interaction must behave in such a way that they are indistinguishable. Mathematically, $SU(2)$ these states are described by a quantum number, t_3 (the third component of weak isospin), whose value is such that $(t_3)^2 = (\frac{1}{2})^2$ in half the total number of possible states, that is, in the left-handed ones.

If we take free fermions, the quantum number for the electric force is determined by the presence or absence of the electric charge (in the same way as it is also the presence or absence of mass). That is, we take 0 and -1 as the quantum numbers (Q) (equivalent to the charges 0 and $-e$) for the absence and presence of electric charge (and mass). The $-$ sign here is purely historical in origin, with the $+$ sign being reserved for antistates. So $Q^2 = 1$ in half the total number of possible states; and there are the same number of nonzero values of Q^2 as there are of $(t_3)^2$, though they are different ones, for the states in which Q^2

= 1 include right-handed ones. There is a standard argument, reproduced in many textbooks on particle physics [e.g. Aitchison and Hey, 1989], that, if the weak and electric interactions are described by some grand unifying gauge group, irrespective of its particular structure, then, to satisfy orthogonality and normalisation conditions, the parameter which describes the mixing ratio, $\sin^2\theta_W$, is precisely determined by $\Sigma\ (t_3)^2$ / $\Sigma\ Q^2$, which in this case must be 0.25.

However, the ratio cannot apply only to free fermions. The weak interaction must also be indifferent to the presence or absence of the strong charge, that is, to the directional state of the angular momentum operator, and so the same mixing proportion must exist also for quark states, and separately for each 'colour', so that none is preferred. At the same time, however, only one directional state may be 'privileged' or 'active' for each charge, and, if we apply the lepton-like weak isospin states to this 'colour' (that is −1 and 0, or −e and 0), we also find that the only corresponding isospin states for the other colours that retain both the accepted value of $\sin^2\theta_W$ and the variation of only one 'privileged' quark phase 'instantaneously' in three are 1 and 0 (or e and 0). This is equivalent to taking the variation 0 0 −e against either an empty background or 'vacuum' (0 0 0) or a full background (e e e), so that the two states of weak isospin in the three colours become:

$$
\begin{array}{ccc}
e & e & 0 \\
0 & 0 & -e\ .
\end{array}
$$

Experimentally, we find that this is the case for all weak interactions. In the case of leptons, the pattern is

$$e + \nu \rightarrow e + \nu\,,$$

while, for quarks, it is

$$u + d \rightarrow u + d\,,$$

with d taking the place of e, and u that of ν. For weak interactions involving both leptons and quarks (for example, β decay), the pattern is once again the same:

$$d + \nu \rightarrow e + u\,.$$

In the lepton case, there are four possible vertices (assuming left-handed components only).

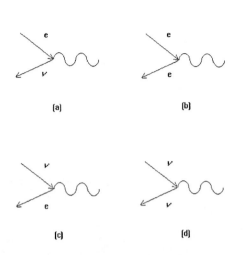

All the vertices must be true at once, and the interaction can be described as a mixing or superposition of the four possibilities. However, the second vertex (b), and this one alone, also represents a possible electromagnetic interaction, giving us a 1 to 4 ratio for the occurrence of the electromagnetic to weak interaction at the energy which the vertices characteristically represent (that of the W / Z bosons), exactly as we have predicted from the electroweak mixing ratio.

Taking the case where the spins of the interacting fermions are assumed parallel (with a total = 0 for a fermion-antifermion combination), we obtain the following quaternion state vectors for the fermionic components of the four vertices

(a) $\qquad (kE - ii\mathbf{p} + ijm) \dots (-kE + ii\mathbf{p}) \dots = 4m^2$;

(b) $\qquad (kE - ii\mathbf{p} + ijm) \dots (-kE + ii\mathbf{p} + ijm) \dots = 4m^2$;

(c) $\qquad (kE - ii\mathbf{p}) \dots (-kE + ii\mathbf{p} + ijm) \dots = 4m^2$;

(d) $\qquad (kE - ii\mathbf{p}) \dots (-kE + ii\mathbf{p}) \dots = 4m^2$.

where $(kE - ii\mathbf{p} + ijm) \dots$ represents a column or row vector with the terms:

$$(kE - ii\mathbf{p} + ijm); (kE + ii\mathbf{p} + ijm); (-kE + ii\mathbf{p} + ijm); (-kE - ii\mathbf{p} + ijm) ,$$

and so on. We may now identify with the four vertices (d), (a), (b), and (c) with the respective B^0, W^+, W^0, and W^- bosons of conventional electroweak theory. Applying a standard normalisation, these sums become m^2 / E^2, implying that, without an m term, all four vertices would become 0. The m term thus arises from the fact that $\mathbf{p}$ is not purely composed of left-handed helicity states (with – **p** right-handed), but incorporates a right-handed component, which itself cannot contribute to the weak interaction because of charge-conjugation violation and the presence of a weak filled vacuum. The right-handed component *can only arise from the presence of the electromagnetic interaction*. The weak interaction cannot exist as a pure left-handed interaction, without a mixing with the electromagnetic interaction to produce the necessary non-zero mass through the introduction of right-handed states.

Suppose we now replace the E and **p** terms of the state vectors with the covariant derivatives for the electroweak interaction, in the same way as we did previously for the strong interaction. The scalar part goes with E and the vector part with **p**. Mass is produced by the mixing of E with **p** via the relativistic connection between these terms. It is also produced by the mixing of B^0 with W^+, W^0, and W^-, which have already identified with the four vertices (d), (a), (b), and (c). By choosing the single, well-defined direction of spin or angular momentum (**p**) to be, in principle, the one where the total value for the interacting fermion-antifermion combination is 0, we can ensure that the mixing is specifically between the neutral components, B^0 and W^0, and create one massless *combination* to represent the carrier of the pure electromagnetic interaction (γ), with the other being the massive neutral weak carrier Z^0. The mixing must be such as to define the ratio of the two interactions, $\sin^2\theta_W$, at 0.25. (The other two vertices, W^+ and W^-, then fulfil the requirements for the existence of states corresponding to total spin values of +1 and –1.)

Because m is determined from the combination of E and **p**, we can, by appropriate choice of the value of m, make these compatible if we additionally define a combination of the coupling constants related to the $SU(2)_L$ and $U(1)$ symmetries, g' and g, which removes B^3 from E and W^0 from **p**. Because the combinations of g' and g, now represent the pure electromagnetic and weak coupling constants, e and w ($= g$), we must necessarily obtain the ratio $e^2 / w^2 = 0.25$, and both quarks and leptons must be structured to observe this.

The $SU(2)_L$ structure means that, for left-handed leptons, we have the covariant derivatives:

$$\partial_\mu \rightarrow \partial_\mu + ig\,\frac{\tau.W^\mu}{2} - ig'\,\frac{B^\mu}{2} \ ,$$

and, for right-handed:

$$\partial_\mu \rightarrow \partial_\mu - ig'\,\frac{B^\mu}{2} \ .$$

Taking the energy operator and the single well-defined component of spin angular momentum, we have:

$$E = i\partial_0 \rightarrow i\partial_0 + g'\,\frac{B^0}{2} + ig'\,\frac{B^3}{2}$$

and

$$ip_3 = \partial_3 \rightarrow \partial_3 + ig\,\frac{\tau.W^3}{2} + ig\,\frac{\tau.W^0}{2} \ .$$

So, we can write the state vector for the (d) vertex in the form:

$$(kE - ii\mathbf{p}) \ldots (-kE + ii\mathbf{p}) \ldots = \left(k\left(\partial_0 + g'\frac{B^0}{2} + g'\frac{B^3}{2}\right) - i\left(\partial_3 + ig\frac{\tau.W^3}{2} + ig\frac{\tau.W^0}{2}\right)\right) \times$$

$$\left(-k\left(\partial_0 + g'\frac{B^0}{2} + g'\frac{B^3}{2}\right) + i\left(\partial_3 + ig\frac{\tau.W^3}{2} + ig\frac{\tau.W^0}{2}\right)\right)$$

and the state vector for the (b) vertex in the form:

$$(kE - ii\mathbf{p} + ijm) \ldots (-kE + ii\mathbf{p} + ijm) \ldots =$$

$$\left(k\left(\partial_0 + g'\frac{B^0}{2} + g'\frac{B^3}{2}\right) - i\left(\partial_3 + ig\frac{\tau.W^3}{2} + ig\frac{\tau.W^0}{2}\right) + ijm\right) \times$$

$$\left(-k\left(\partial_0 + g'\frac{B^0}{2} + g'\frac{B^3}{2}\right) + i\left(\partial_3 + ig\frac{\tau.W^3}{2} + ig\frac{\tau.W^0}{2}\right) + ijm\right).$$

Because m is determined from the combination of E and p, we can, by appropriate choice of the value of m, make these compatible if we additionally define a combination of g' and g which removes B^3 from E and W^0 from $\mathbf{p}$. It is, of course, significant here that it is B^μ which is characteristic of right-handed lepton states, and therefore associated with the production of mass. Writing these combinations as γ^0 and Z^3, and those of g' and g, as e and w ($= g$), we obtain:

$$(kE - ii\mathbf{p} + ijm) \ldots (-kE + ii\mathbf{p} + ijm) \ldots =$$

$$\left(k\left(\partial_0 + e\frac{\gamma^0}{2}\right) - i\left(\partial_3 + iw\frac{\tau.Z^3}{2}\right) + ijm\right)\left(-k\left(\partial_0 + e\frac{\gamma^0}{2}\right) + i\left(\partial_3 + iw\frac{\tau.Z^3}{2}\right) + ijm\right).$$

Here, $\gamma^0 / 2$ becomes the same as the electrostatic potential ϕ. So, we can write this in the form:

$$(kE - ii\mathbf{p} + ijm) \ldots (-kE + ii\mathbf{p} + ijm) \ldots =$$

$$\left(k(\partial_0 + e\phi) - i\left(\partial_3 + iw\frac{\tau.Z^3}{2}\right) + ijm\right)\left(-k(\partial_0 + e\phi) + i\left(\partial_3 + iw\frac{\tau.Z^3}{2}\right) + ijm\right).$$

Because e and w now represent the pure electromagnetic and weak coupling constants, we must necessarily obtain the ratio $e^2 / w^2 = 0.25$, and both quarks and leptons must be structured to observe this.

It is significant in this analysis that *exchange* of electromagnetic charge, through, say, W^+ or W^-, is not a result of the electromagnetic interaction, which carries only phase information, but is rather an indication that the weak interaction is unable to detect the presence of the electromagnetic charge, that is, that a 'weak interaction' is a statement that all states of a particle with the same weak charge are equally probable, given the appropriate energy conditions, and that gauge invariance is maintained with respect to them. Weak bosons become massive because they act as carriers of the electromagnetic charge, whereas electromagnetic bosons (or photons) are massless because they do not – the quantitative value of the mass must be determined from the coupling of the weak charge to the asymmetric vacuum state which produces the violation of charge conjugation in the weak interaction. The weak interaction must also be indifferent to the presence of the strong charge, and so cannot distinguish between quarks and leptons – hence, the intrinsic identity of purely lepton weak interactions with quark-lepton or quark-quark ones – and, in the case of quarks, it cannot tell the difference between a filled 'electromagnetic vacuum' (up quark) and an empty one (down quark). The weak interaction, in addition, is also indifferent to the sign of the weak charge, and responds (via the vacuum) only to the status of fermion or antifermion – hence, the well-known Cabibbo-Kobayashi-Maskawa mixing between the three quark and lepton generations.

ANGULAR MOMENTUM AND CHARGE CONSERVATION

A single angular momentum ($\hat{\mathbf{p}}$) or helicity term term ($\sigma.\hat{\mathbf{p}}$) – normalised here to a unit value – carries all the information concerning the conservation of the three charge terms; the e, s, and w charges become separately conserved because they represent three different aspects of this angular momentum conservation process. We can relate this to the phase diagrams we have previously drawn for charge conservation in the different particle types. Arbitrary directions may be represented by random unit vector components $\hat{\mathbf{p}}_1$, $\hat{\mathbf{p}}_2$, $\hat{\mathbf{p}}_3$. For weak and electric charges, these randon components are associated respectively with the sign, and the magnitude of the angular momentum state, through the connections of $\mathbf{p}$ with E and $\mathbf{p}$ with m; and we can create a generalised procedure for producing possible fermion states by applying $\sigma.\hat{\mathbf{p}}_1$, $\sigma.\hat{\mathbf{p}}_2$, $\sigma.\hat{\mathbf{p}}_3$ to the quaternion operators (k and j) specifying w and e, but with the sequence of unit vectors determined separately in each case. The various alignments between the sequences of unit vectors or *phases* applied to s, w and e then determine the nature of the fermion state produced.

As we have seen previously in the diagrammatic representation, aligning the unit vectors applied to w and e also are effectively aligns the E and m phases with each other, and so necessarily with the $\mathbf{p}$ phase, meaning that the system has a single phase and so cannot be baryonic. The $\mathbf{p}$ phase is defined with E and m, and there is no strong charge. This defines a free fermion or lepton. In a baryon system, with strong charges present, the vectors assigned to the weak and electric charges, and hence to E and m, will not be aligned, and, consequently, the $\mathbf{p}$ phase is not fixed with respect to them.

To complete the representation of all possible fermions, we incorporate the effect of weak isospin and also the parity- and time-reversal-violations of the second and third generations. To reverse isospin, we replace a term such as $-j\hat{\mathbf{p}}_1$ with $-j(\hat{\mathbf{p}}_1 - 1)$, the $j1$

representing the filled 'electric vacuum' state. Charge conjugation violation may be represented by the non-algebraic symbols z_P and z_T, depending on whether it is accompanied by P or T violation. These symbols merely imply that the $-w$ of the second and third generator is treated as though it were positive in the same way as the w of the first generation. We can now express quark structures in the following form:

down	$-\boldsymbol{\sigma}.\,(-j\hat{\mathbf{p}}_a + i\hat{\mathbf{p}}_b + k\hat{\mathbf{p}}_c)$
up	$-\boldsymbol{\sigma}.\,(-j(\hat{\mathbf{p}}_a - 1) + i\hat{\mathbf{p}}_b + k\hat{\mathbf{p}}_c)$
strange	$-\boldsymbol{\sigma}.\,(-j\hat{\mathbf{p}}_a + i\hat{\mathbf{p}}_b - z_P k\hat{\mathbf{p}}_c)$
charmed	$-\boldsymbol{\sigma}.\,(-j(\hat{\mathbf{p}}_a - 1) + i\hat{\mathbf{p}}_b - z_P k\hat{\mathbf{p}}_c)$
bottom	$-\boldsymbol{\sigma}.\,(-j\hat{\mathbf{p}}_a + i\hat{\mathbf{p}}_b - z_T k\hat{\mathbf{p}}_c)$
top	$-\boldsymbol{\sigma}.\,(-j(\hat{\mathbf{p}}_a - 1) + i\hat{\mathbf{p}}_b - z_T k\hat{\mathbf{p}}_c)$

Here, $-j$ represents electric charge (which is conventionally negative), i is strong charge, k is weak charge. a, b, c are *each* randomly 1, 2, 3, except that $b \neq c$. Both $-z_P k$ and $-z_T k$ become equivalent to k, for the purposes of the weak interaction. For the corresponding leptons, the components are all in phase ($\hat{\mathbf{p}}_a$), and there is no directional component:

electron	$-\boldsymbol{\sigma}.\,(-j\hat{\mathbf{p}}_a + k\hat{\mathbf{p}}_a)$
e neutrino	$-\boldsymbol{\sigma}.\,(-j(\hat{\mathbf{p}}_a - 1) + k\hat{\mathbf{p}}_a)$
muon	$-\boldsymbol{\sigma}.\,(-j\hat{\mathbf{p}}_a - z_P k\hat{\mathbf{p}}_a)$
μ neutrino	$-\boldsymbol{\sigma}.\,(-j(\hat{\mathbf{p}}_a - 1) - z_P k\hat{\mathbf{p}}_a)$
tau	$-\boldsymbol{\sigma}.\,(-j\hat{\mathbf{p}}_a - z_T k\hat{\mathbf{p}}_a)$
τ neutrino	$-\boldsymbol{\sigma}.\,(-j(\hat{\mathbf{p}}_a - 1) - z_T k\hat{\mathbf{p}}_a)$

Both antiquarks and antileptons simply replace $-\boldsymbol{\sigma}$ with $\boldsymbol{\sigma}$. As before, the information in these representations ('charge accommodation') may be displayed in tabular form. Since $\boldsymbol{\sigma}$ and the $\hat{\mathbf{p}}$ terms all have unit values, the result is a series of 0 and 1 options for each of the charge states. Applying these to the known fermions, A-C would appear to represent the coloured quark system, with s pictured as being 'exchanged' between the three states. L includes all the left-handed leptonic states, and is equivalent to D / E in earlier representations [Rowlands and Cullerne, 1999, 2000a], with the s value zeroed.

A

		B	G	R
u	$+e$	$1j$	$1j$	$0i$
	$+s$	$1i$	$0k$	$0j$
	$+w$	$1k$	$0i$	$0k$
d	$-e$	$0j$	$0k$	$1j$
	$+s$	$1i$	$0i$	$0k$
	$+w$	$1k$	$0j$	$0i$
c	$+e$	$1j$	$1j$	$0i$
	$+s$	$1i$	$0k$	$0j$
	$-w$	$z_P k$	$0i$	$0k$
s	$-e$	$0j$	$0k$	$1j$
	$+s$	$1i$	$0i$	$0k$
	$-w$	$z_P k$	$0j$	$0i$
t	$+e$	$1j$	$1j$	$0i$
	$+s$	$1i$	$0k$	$0j$
	$-w$	$Z_T k$	$0i$	$0k$
b	$-e$	$0j$	$0k$	$1j$
	$+s$	$1i$	$0i$	$0k$
	$-w$	$Z_T k$	$0j$	$0i$

B

		B	G	R
u	$+e$	$1j$	$1j$	$0k$
	$+s$	$0i$	$0k$	$1i$
	$+w$	$1k$	$0i$	$0j$
d	$-e$	$0i$	$0k$	$1j$
	$+s$	$0j$	$0i$	$1i$
	$+w$	$1k$	$0j$	$0k$
c	$+e$	$1j$	$1j$	$0k$
	$+s$	$0i$	$0k$	$1i$
	$-w$	$z_P k$	$0i$	$0j$
s	$-e$	$0i$	$0k$	$1j$
	$+s$	$0j$	$0i$	$1i$
	$-w$	$z_P k$	$0j$	$0k$
t	$+e$	$1j$	$1j$	$0k$
	$+s$	$0i$	$0k$	$1i$
	$-w$	$Z_T k$	$0i$	$0j$
b	$-e$	$0i$	$0k$	$1j$
	$+s$	$0j$	$0i$	$1i$
	$-w$	$Z_T k$	$0j$	$0k$

C

		B	G	R
u	+e	1j	1j	0k
	+s	0i	1i	0j
	+w	1k	0k	0i
d	-e	0j	0k	1j
	+s	0i	1i	0k
	+w	1k	0j	0i
c	+e	1j	1j	0k
	+s	0i	1i	0j
	-w	z_Pk	0k	0i
s	-e	0j	0k	1j
	+s	0i	1i	0k
	-w	z_Pk	0j	0i
t	+e	1j	1j	0k
	+s	0i	1i	0j
	-w	Z_Tk	0k	0i
b	-e	0j	0k	1j
	+s	0i	1i	0k
	-w	Z_Tk	0j	0i

L

		$\bar{e}$	$\bar{e}$	v_e
	+e	1j	1j	0j
	+s	0k	0i	0i
	+w	0i	0k	1k
				e
	-e	0i	0k	1j
	+s	0j	0i	0i
	+w	0k	0j	1k
		$\bar{\mu}$	$\bar{\mu}$	v_μ
	+e	1j	1j	0j
	+s	0k	0i	0i
	-w	0i	0k	z_Pk
				μ
	-e	0i	0k	1j
	+s	0j	0i	0i
	-w	0k	0j	z_Pk
		$\bar{\tau}$	$\bar{\tau}$	v_τ
	+e	1j	1j	0j
	+s	0k	0i	0i
	-w	0i	0k	Z_Tk
				τ
	-e	0i	0k	1j
	+s	0j	0i	0i
	-w	0k	0j	Z_Tk

The tables, as we have shown in earlier publications [Rowlands, 1994, Rowlands and Cullerne, 1999, 2000a], lead to meaningful charge structures for all known composite particles, and explain many significant aspects of particle physics. The quark structures derived here are lepton-like, with integral electric charges, as in the original model of Han and Nambu [1965]. Such charge structures, however, will not be directly observed, because of the perfect gauge invariance of the strong interaction. Observed charges, as measured in QED experiments, will necessarily be fractional, as in the parallel condensed matter case of the fractional quantum Hall effect. Only experiments directly dependent on the group structure for grand unification will be able to distinguish this model from one based on 'true' fractional charges in terms of predictable results [Rowlands and Cullerne, 1999, 2000a].

In addition to establishing the separate conservation laws for the three types of charge, we can take the angular momentum operator in the nilpotent wavefunction as effectively defining the classical / quantum transition. A classical system becomes a quantum system when the direct connection between charge and angular momentum is established, so that quantizing charge becomes the same as quantizing angular momentum. Real physical processes, of course, involve discrete energy transfer between discrete charged or massive particles, and, in quantum mechanical terms, this involves the collapse of the wavefunction. The collapse may be considered as an application of the type of change which breaks the direct connection between the two fundamental conservation laws. Breaking this connection leads to decoherence through the vector addition of the noncoherent individual **p** components, and, therefore, to energy transfer, because of the overall change in **p**. Decoherence is a natural result of physical interactions between fermions, and is measured in terms of the increase in entropy or number of noncoherent states. Making a classical measurement means the application of interacting fields of sufficient size to make the whole system decohere and reduce any quantum mechanical variation in spatial coordinates during a given time interval to the level of the uncertainty principle.

MASS

The charge structures for fermions and antifermions may also be conveniently derived from a single expression:

$$\sigma_z . (i\,\hat{\mathbf{p}}_a\,(\delta_{bc} - 1) + j\,(\hat{\mathbf{p}}_b - \mathbf{1}\delta_{0m}) + k\,\hat{\mathbf{p}}_c\,(-1)^{\delta}\mathbf{1}g\ g)$$

Here, σ_z is the spin pseudovector component defined in the z direction, with $\sigma_z = -1$ defining left-handed states, and $\sigma_z = 1$ defining right-handed. With a filled weak vacuum, left-handed states become predominantly fermionic, while right-handed states become antifermionic 'holes' in the vacuum. The units of quantized angular momentum, $\hat{\mathbf{p}}_a, \hat{\mathbf{p}}_b, \hat{\mathbf{p}}_c$ are selected *randomly* and *independently* from the three orthogonal components $\hat{\mathbf{p}}_x, \hat{\mathbf{p}}_y, \hat{\mathbf{p}}_z$. As before, the quaternion operators i, j, k, stand for the respective s, e, w charges, e being conventionally negative. The other operators each create one of the fundamental divisions in fermionic structure – fermion / antifermion (σ_z); quark / lepton ($\delta_{bc} - 1$); weak up isospin / weak down isospin ($- \mathbf{1}\delta_{0m}$); and the three generations ($(-1)^{\delta}\mathbf{1}g\ g$). These are identified, respectively, by the weak, strong, electromagnetic and gravitational interactions. $b = c$ produces leptons; $b \neq c$ produces quarks. Taking into account all three directions at once, when $b \neq c$, we define baryons composed of three quarks (and mesons composed of quark and antiquark), in which each of a, b, c cycle through the directions x, y, z.

The single expression for fermions and antifermions gives us an immediate opportunity for seeing how mass can be generated by the Higgs mechanism, involved a filled weak vacuum. Mass, according to the Higgs mechanism, is generated when an element of partial right-handedness is introduced into an intrinsically left-handed system. So, in principle, anything which alters the signs of the terms in the expression ($i\,\hat{\mathbf{p}}_a\,(\delta_{bc} - 1) + j$ $(\hat{\mathbf{p}}_b - \mathbf{1}\delta_{0m}) + k\,\hat{\mathbf{p}}_c\,(-1)^{\delta}\mathbf{1}g\ g$), or reduces any of the terms to zero, is a mass generator, because it is equivalent to introducing the opposite sign of σ_z or a partially right-handed state. There are three main sources in the equation for producing mass. These can be described as weak isospin, quark confinement, and weak charge conjugation violation.

The two states of weak isospin produced by the term $(\hat{\mathbf{p}}_b - \mathbf{1}\delta_{0m})$ are effectively equivalent to taking an undisturbed system in the form $j\sigma_z.\hat{\mathbf{p}}_b$ and of taking the same system with the added 'right-handed' term $-j\sigma_z.\mathbf{1}$. In the pure lepton states, when $b = c \neq$ z, and hence the weak component, $k\sigma_z.\hat{\mathbf{p}}_c = 0$, the equation generates residual right-handed electron / muon / tau states, specified by $-j$, with the equivalent left-handed antistates specified by j. The right-handed terms may be considered as the intrinsically right-handed or non-weak-interacting parts of the fermions, generated by the presence of nonzero rest mass. (The mixing illustrates the fact that the electromagnetic interaction cannot identify the presence or absence of a weakly interacting component.) The quarks follow the same procedure as leptons in generating the two states of weak isospin, but there are no separate representations of 'right-handed' quarks, as two out of any three quarks in any baryon system will always require $c \neq$ z and $k\sigma_z.\hat{\mathbf{p}}_c = 0$.

Mass is again generated by quark confinement, because each baryonic system requires quarks in which one or more of $i\sigma_z.\hat{\mathbf{p}}_a$, $j\sigma_z.\hat{\mathbf{p}}_b$, or $k\sigma_z.\hat{\mathbf{p}}_c$ is zero. This mechanism is more likely to be relevant to composite states, such as mesons and baryons, than to 'pure' ones, such as quarks and leptons. In these cases, the mass equivalent for a zero charge would appear to be that of a fundamental unit m_f, from which we derive the electron mass as $m_e = \alpha m_f$. Such a mechanism has already been applied to derive the mass values associated with the baryons and mesons derived from quarks [Rowlands and Cullerne, 1999]. The use of a fundamental mass unit for zero charges irrespective of origin appears to derive from the fact that these 'missing' charges are a result of a perfectly random rotation of the momentum states $\hat{\mathbf{p}}_a$, $\hat{\mathbf{p}}_b$, or $\hat{\mathbf{p}}_c$, in exactly the same manner as applies in the strong interaction to produce its linear potential; $\hat{\mathbf{p}}_a$ is, of course, actually an expression of this interaction, but $\hat{\mathbf{p}}_b$ and $\hat{\mathbf{p}}_c$ follow the identical pattern of variation.

The third mechanism for mass generation arises from the fact that the sign of the intrinsically complex k term is not specified with those of the i and j terms. Physically, however, a filled weak vacuum requires that the weak interaction recognizes only one sign for the k term when the sign of σ_z is specified. Hence, negative values of $k\sigma_z.\hat{\mathbf{p}}_c$ must act, in terms of the weak interaction, as though they were positive. Reversal of a sign is equivalent to introducing opposite handedness or mass. So, the two intrinsic signs of the $k\sigma_z.\hat{\mathbf{p}}_c$ term become the source of a mass splitting between a first generation, involving no sign reversal, and a second generation in which the reversal is accomplished by charge conjugation violation. However, since charge conjugation violation may be accomplished in two different ways – either by violating parity or time reversal symmetry – there are actually two further mass generations instead of one. In addition, because the weak interaction cannot distinguish between them, the three generations represented by the quarks d, s and b, are mixed, like the left-handed and right-handed states of e, μ and τ, in some proportion related to the quark masses.

Since all of these mechanisms relate to the idea of a filled vacuum, and, since we believe that the zero point energy of the vacuum is another expression of the same principle, it is worth considering whether the two processes can be related. It is relatively straightforward, in fact, to see how rest mass could arise out of the zero point energy of the vacuum. It is well-known that the spectral density of the zero point field is given by:

$$\frac{dU}{d\omega} = \frac{\omega^2}{\pi^2 c^3} \frac{\hbar\omega}{2} = \frac{\hbar\omega^3}{2\pi^2 c^3} \ ,$$

where U is the energy density, since $\omega^2 / \pi^2 c^3$ is the number of modes per unit volume, and $(\hbar\omega / 2$ is the energy per unit mode. Suppose that we now introduce a cut-off value for ω, say ω_m. Then the energy density integrates to

$$U = \int\limits_{\omega_m}^{0} \frac{\hbar\omega^3}{2\pi^2 c^3} = \frac{\hbar\omega_m^4}{8\pi^2 c^3} \ .$$

To relate this to a mass-energy density, we need only assume that we can relate the space 'occupied' by a particle (at least in approximate terms) to the reciprocal of its mass-energy mc^2. Suppose, for example, we assume that the particle is 'confined' within a sphere of Compton radius $\hbar / mc$. Then

$$U = \frac{\hbar\omega_m^4}{8\pi^2 c^3} = \frac{3m^4 c^5}{4\pi(\hbar^3)}$$

and

$$m = \left(\frac{1}{6\pi}\right)^{1/4} \frac{\hbar\omega_m}{c^2} = 0.48 \ \frac{\hbar\omega_m}{c^2} \approx \left(\frac{1}{2}\right) \frac{\hbar\omega_m}{c^2} \ ,$$

which is effectively the zero point energy at ω_m. This mechanism based on the zero point field may be related to that of the Higgs mechanism, in which the Higgs field, treated as a plasma, acts as a high-pass filter, with the low frequencies transmitted away, and producing no stable bound states. The high-pass filter mechanism of the field allows particles to acquire mass determined by the cut-off frequency. The Higgs boson provides the minimum frequency for the plasma to have a collective mode. In principle, then, the Higgs mechanism requires a cut off in the zero point energy, and a cut off frequency is sufficient to generate mass of the right order.

SOME PREDICTIONS

Theories are often judged on their predictions, and some of ours have already proved to be true, while others are yet to be tested. The predictions we have made include the violation of CP symmetry in *all* states incorporating 0 or $\pm$ 2*w* weak charge as alternatives. This was, of course, first observed in mixed states of K^0 and $\overline{K}^0$ in 1964, but recent observations have shown that it also occurs in K^0 and $\overline{K}^0$ as separate states. In our theory, this must also be extended to K^+ and K^- ($u\bar{s}$ and $s\bar{u}$), and also to $u\bar{s}$ and $c\bar{u}$ states. In addition, it also occurs with the b quark generation, as has also been recently observed, and will, according to our understanding, occur with all bosonic mixtures of u, d with d, s or b, t. We think, also, that it will occur in the weak decays of other bosonic or quasi-bosonic structures which have $\pm 2w$ weak charge states acting as $0w$. All bosonic-type states made of two fermions are of this type, and we could consider Bose-Einstein condensates, Cooper pairs, and perhaps states involving the Berry phase or the quantum Hall effect, as possible candidates, although it is, of course, difficult to imagine immediately a simple way in which a *weak* decay of such a state could be identified and observed .

While the masses of the composite particles made up of quarks seem to be obtainable by a relatively logical construction, the masses of the leptons have so far resisted easy explanation. This may be because we should really think of them as mixed states, paralleling those for the quarks in the Cabibbo-Kobayashi-Maskawa (CKM) matrix. This would be the logical consequence of seeing this mixing as generated by the electroweak, rather than the strong, interaction, and it could even be responsible for reported neutrino oscillations. It is possible that the muon $g - 2$ anomaly recently claimed may be a result of 'down' weak isospin lepton mixing; if so, then even higher anomalies could be predicted. The mixing requires a higher than observed mass for the mixed state and a value of $g - 2$ which is higher than the predicted one. It may be that the CKM mixing, which is fixed (apparently arbitrarily) for quarks in the 'down' phase (d, s, b), may really occur in this manner, and that a similar mixing between the equivalent leptons might preserve the complete left-right asymmetry of neutrinos in the Standard Model [Rowlands and Cullerne, 2001b].

We have suggested a mass of 182 GeV for the Higgs boson on symmetry grounds, assuming the fundamental significance of four quark / lepton tables with all charges zeroed [Rowlands and Cullerne, 1999]. The present paper confirms the significance of the four tables, but, without a more detailed analysis, this value can still only be considered a guess rather than a firm prediction, though it would provide a neat solution for the mass problem. However, the reduction of alpha to 1/118 at 14 TeV (rather than 1/125, as in minimal $SU(5)$) is precise and numerical, and will be tested with the next generation of colliders [Rowlands and Cullerne, 2000b, 2001a]. A successful negative prediction we have always made (since at least as early as 1981-82) has been the nondecay of the proton [Rowlands, 1983], while another successful prediction has been an acceleration in the cosmological redshift with deceleration parameter –1 [Rowlands, 1994]. A *conceptual* prediction that conservation of type of charge would be linked to conservation of angular momentum is part of the driving force behind the theoretical work presented here.

190

REFERENCES

Aitchison, I. J. R. and Hey, A. J. G. [1989], *Gauge Theories in Particle Physics*, second edition (Adam Hilger).

Han, M. Y. and Nambu, Y. [1965], 'Three-Triplet Model with Double SU(3) Symmetry', *Phys. Rev*, **139 B**, 1006-10.

Rowlands, P. [1983], 'The fundamental parameters of physics', *Speculat. Sci. Tech.*, 6, 69-80.

Rowlands, P. [1991], *The Fundamental Parameters of Physics: An Approach towards a Unified Theory* (PD Publications, Liverpool).

Rowlands, P. [1994], *A Revolution Too Far: The Establishment of General Relativity* (PD Publications, Liverpool).

Rowlands, P. [1999], 'Physics; let's get down to basics', in K. Bowden (ed.), *Aspects II, 1999* (*Proceedings of XX ANPA Conference*, Cambridge, September 1998), 123-134.

Rowlands, P. [2001], A foundational approach to physics, arXiv:physics/0106054.

Rowlands, P. and Cullerne, J. P. [1999], 'A derivation of particle structures and the Dirac equation from fundamental symmetries', in K. Bowden (ed.), *Aspects II* (*Proceedings of XX ANPA Conference*, Cambridge, September 1998), 155-191.

Rowlands, P. and Cullerne, J. P. [2000a], 'The Dirac algebra and charge accommodation', in K. Bowden (ed.), *Participations* (*Proceedings of XXI ANPA Conference*, Cambridge, September 1999), 89-111.

Rowlands, P. and Cullerne, J. P. [2000b], '*SU*(5) and grand unification, in K. Bowden (ed.), *Participations* (*Proceedings of XXI ANPA Conference*, Cambridge, September 1999), 124-146.

Rowlands, P. and Cullerne, J. P. [2001a], 'The connection between the Han-Nambu quark theory, the Dirac equation and fundamental symmetries' *Nuclear Physics* **A 684**, 713-5.

Rowlands, P. and Cullerne, J. P. [2001a], 'The Dirac algebra and grand unification', arXiv:quant-ph/0106111.

Takahashi, T. T., Matsufuru, H., Nemoto, Y., and Sugunama, H. [2001], *Phys. Rev. Lett.*, **86**, 18.

A Comparison between two versions of the Dirac Algebra

Peter Rowlands[1], J. P. Cullerne[2], and Brian D. Koberlein[3]

[1] IQ Group and Science Communication Unit, Department of Physics, University of Liverpool, Oliver Lodge Laboratory, Oxford Street, Liverpool, L69 7ZE, UK. e-mail prowl@hep.ph.liv.ac.uk and prowl@csc.liv.uk

[2] IQ Group, Department of Computer Science, University of Liverpool, Chadwick Laboratory, Peach Street, Liverpool, L69 7ZF, UK. e-mail jpc@wincoll.ac.uk

[3] Department of Physics, SUNY Geneseo State College, 1 College Circle, Geneseo, NY 14454, USA. e-mail kober@geneseo.edu

Some discussion has arisen from presentations at previous ANPA meetings concerning the relations between different versions of the Dirac algebra, and specifically between the respective versions presented by Basil Hiley (BJH) and ourselves (RC). Essentially, the differences have arisen because of a difference in aims. BJH aims at deriving the algebra from fundamental logical principles; he also wishes to show the equivalence of two different representations, the conventional and the Bohmian. The RC version is aimed at elucidating the structures of fundamental particles. The situation parallels, and is related to, the differences between Lagrangian and Hamiltonian dynamics. However, it is possible to convert mathematically between the two systems, and so it should be possible, in principle, to derive a version of the Dirac algebra from fundamental logical principles, which can then be converted for use in deriving particle structures. The process is significant not only in relating two algebraic formalisms which are concerned with the same physical reality but which were designed for different immediate purposes, but also in highlighting some profound dualities at the heart of fundamental physics. In this short note, we will first discuss the conceptual issues, and then proceed to a mathematical analysis.

BJH's plan is to use an algebra of process to generate Clifford algebras. He uses mathematical expressions for the strength of process, directed process, the order of succession, and the order of existence. He produces symplectic spinors and othogonal Clifford algebras. The methodology requires the definition of an instant in time, and this leads to a doubling of the Clifford algebras with two expressions for the wavefunction. A left ideal represents ideas coming from the past while a right ideal represents information coming from the future. Together, the left and right spinors produce *zitterbewegung*. BJH uses Heisenberg symplectic spinors for his left and right ideals, and introduces a Dirac idempotent via the Heisenberg algebra.

In a physical system, however, energy is unique as well as time, and the RC formulation uses a fixed or unique element of energy, rather than a fixed moment in time. The RC formulation is thus not about time directly. This comes from the fact that, in the fundamental parameter group, energy is conserved while time is not. Reversing their roles will produce a reversed algebra. Another fundamental difference is that energy really is unique. It only has one sign; mass is real and positive, and we have CPT rather than MCPT symmetry. Time, on the other hand, while physically unique, has two signs. The RC process thus fixes primarily on conservation, rather than nonconservation. It says that mass-energy is a conserved quantity, and that it can, therefore, be described uniquely in mathematical terms. Thus, in principle, it ought to be possible to fix a unique-energy wavefunction as a single object, rather than as the two separate objects required by fixing a moment in time. So, in RC, ikE and $-ikE$ are contained in a single wavefunction.

In principle, if you choose unique energy rather than unique time, it becomes a *single* representation because energy has only one real physical solution, but unique time requires a *double* representation because time has a built-in $\pm i$ because of its complex nature. So BJH doubles the algebra, as he requires, while RC double the physical representation. The particular value of RC with relation to particle structures arises *because* it uses a single mathematical representation with everything compactified within it. The RC nilpotent is self-dual, which means that it is already second quantized, and immediately creates boson states from fermions and vice versa. The nilpotent as a square root of zero produces both solutions at the same time. In more general terms, it uses the method of getting discreteness from continuity which occurs in all aspects of physics. The change from 2π rotation to 4π rotation for fermion states occurs, in both BJH and RC, by doubling the algebra. This is explicit in BJH, but compactified in the nilpotent formulation, where we can *privilege* positive mass-energy. The RC algebra is thus already a double algebra. This is why we can have a nilpotent wavefunction.

The nilpotent wavefunction in RC is *not* the same as the nilpotent operator used in the BJH system, and it is a quantum field operator rather than a conventional wavefunction. The RC nilpotent uses a 4-spinor not a 2-spinor, and all the terms in the free-particle state have the same exponential. Many representations of the Dirac wavefunction use two 2-spinors, which are split in conventional calculations, but this one doesn't, and we don't need to regard the spinor as a bispinor at all. When we write down propagators we have only one summation, whereas conventional Dirac algebra uses two summations, one for each spin state. When we create the energy states for the hydrogen atom, we use only one series of simultaneous equations, derived from coefficients of r^2, r^1, r^0, r^{-1}, r^{-2}, etc., not two, as in the conventional method. The strong interaction solution shows how we can extend this to a problem where the solution isn't well worked out.

This seems to be comparable with using Hamiltonian rather than Lagrangian dynamics – one equation is needed rather than two. This is because we can group $\pm E$ as well as $\pm \mathbf{p}$. It doesn't make any sense in RC to group just one of them. E, $\mathbf{p}$ together is effectively the same as including space and time together as the Hamiltonian method does, not as separate variations as the Lagrangian method does. Doubling the algebra is the same as the general symmetry-doubling, as in the discrete-continuous symmetry. The doubling occurs because we are making something discrete (space, charge, the Dirac state) from something continuous (time, the vacuum). It is also an expression of the duality of conserved / nonconserved properties; we are creating a conserved quantity against a 'background' of nonconservation (space, time).

Doubling is thus present in both formulations; it is the *method* of doubling that distinguishes them. Fixing space-time is a Heisenberg option and is used by BJH, leading to two expressions; fixing E, $\mathbf{p}$, is a Schrödinger option, which is used by RC, but RC also *combine* them in a single expression. BJH has a duality between space and momentum; but RC have a duality between the combined space-time and the combined energy-momentum. This is precisely because the spinor is not split into two, so the E and $\mathbf{p}$ and the + and – values of each are all on the same footing, producing 4 equal states. Conventional Dirac splits either the space ($\mathbf{p}$) and the time (E) into two (with different exponentials); the RC nilpotent incorporates all 4 by using the same exponential. You can always make all four have the same exponential by using a nilpotent because you can then transfer the sign variation onto the differential operator, and therefore also onto the E, $\mathbf{p}$ part of the wavefunction. So there is no split between space and time, and the nilpotent becomes dual.

BJH's duality is that of $\mathbf{x}$ and $\mathbf{p}$, with each expression incorporating half of the total duality available at any time. The duality comes in separate expressions because he has idempotents and left and right ideals (corresponding to $\mathbf{x}$ and $\mathbf{p}$). He chooses $\mathbf{x}$ for Bohm and $\mathbf{p}$ for conventional quantum mechanics, and shows the duality between these, as is his primary aim. But the RC nilpotent collapses this to one because left and right ideals become identical, and the duality is incorporated directly, leading to a quantum field representation, and automatic second quantization, which is more directly relevant to describing particle states.

To obtain such second quantization requires the combination of the Heisenberg and Schrödinger approaches. Heisenberg, the basis for BJH, puts the $\mathbf{p}$ operator on space and the E operator on time, which achieves first quantization; second quantization requires their combination. The RC nilpotent, which is founded on Schrödinger, combines the Heisenberg-like vector term (*k*E + *ii***p** + *ij*m) with the Schrödinger-like exponential. (Because of the variability of time, it is probably easier to incorporate Heisenberg using the Schrödinger approach, as in RC, than it would be to incorporate Schrödinger using the Heisenberg approach.) BJH uses the symplectic group for his Heisenberg-related spinors, and 2-equation duality. It may be that the metaplectic group, as the double cover of the symplectic group, will lead to the integrated duality of the RC nilpotent.

In more mathematical terms, BJH derives the quantum equation from an algebraic version of the Heisenburg formalism, that is

$$[H,e] = Ee ,$$

where H is the Hamiltonian, E is the energy operator, and e is a left / right dual operator. He then defines this formally, in terms of two vector states A and B, such that

$$[H,e] = He - eH = (HA)B - A(BH) = i\frac{\partial A}{\partial t}B + iA\frac{\partial B}{\partial t} .$$

This can then be separated into the two conjugate Schrödinger equations,

$$i\frac{\partial A}{\partial t} = HA$$
$$-i\frac{\partial B}{\partial t} = BH ,$$

in which A and B are operators in the algebra (not the usual states). They are related to the usual states by saying that $A^* = B$, forming the position / momentum duals. However, if that is the case, then AB is time independent (and their total energy is zero). This would then give

$$[H,e] = He - eH = 0 .$$

We could, in fact, propose a different form of this algebraic equation, by defining $e = AB$. The equation for quantum mechanics then becomes

$$He = Ee ,$$

where E is the net energy and H is a one-directional operator:

$$He = H(AB) = (HA)B + A(HB) = (HA)B - A(BH) = [H,e] .$$

Thus, it is equivalent to the BJH form. If one then imposes the condition that this state is the product of the position and momentum values of the same state, then $E = 0$ and $He = 0$. Thus, they form a nilpotent identity. Here both H and e are 'operators', even though H is the Hamiltonian operator, and e is the 'state' operator. Thus the operator and state are on the same footing. One could then take this further by transforming the operators to be equivalent. This would then give the general equation

$$H'H' = EH'$$

or, for the dual case,

$$H'H' = 0 \ .$$

If we normalize things so that $E = 1$, then the state operator is either nilpotent (and it is then a pure dual state), or it is eigenpotent (and it is a product state). (The idempotent is the product state of the nilpotent, but it can also be turned around; it seems to be linked to the boson / fermion duality, and supersymmetry operators, in that one can be seen as the product of the other.) The RC algebra thus becomes equivalent to the two separate algebras of BJH combined. Of course, separate algebras are BJH's requirement for showing equivalence between Bohmian and conventional quantum mechanics, but a combined algebra is more appropriate to the RC requirement for a self-dual quantum-field equivalent. BJH is thus useful for providing a 'visualization' of the dual state, while RC is more useful for more complex systems. For a single object, the two are the same.

It is interesting that this combination can be obtained by *incorporating* Bohmian quantum mechanics into the conventional version, and that this becomes equivalent to incorporating the vacuum state with the fermion, or the fermion with the vacuum state, or even to incorporating Heisenberg (fermion) within Schrödinger (vacuum). This leads us into consideration of that whole class of dualities which make physics workable, and which are characterized by the appearance of alternative representations related by the numerical factor 2.

Charge accommodation and the combinatorial hierarchy

Peter Rowlands* and J. P. Cullerne†

*IQ Group and Science Communication Unit, Department of Physics, University of Liverpool, Oliver Lodge Laboratory, Oxford Street, Liverpool, L69 7ZE, UK. e-mail prowl@hep.ph.liv.ac.uk and prowl@csc.liv.uk

†IQ Group, Department of Computer Science, University of Liverpool, Chadwick Laboratory, Peach Street, Liverpool, L69 7ZF, UK. e-mail jpc@wincoll.ac.uk

This is a contribution to the work begun by Ted Bastin and Clive Kilmister (BK), as represented in the last two ANPA meetings, in investigating the relationship between the charge accommodation algebra (CA) for explaining the symmetries of the standard model and the combinatorial hierarchy (CH), which has been developed to explain the emergence of physical properties. It should be regarded as a preliminary note, intended to lead to a fuller investigation.

BK see our work as a bridge between CH and physics. The key link seems to be in the use of quaternion representations, and existence/non-existence conditions, represented by 1 and 0. The CH describes events in terms of a statistical flux of elementary particles. There is a constant flux of new elements, which can either be created or removed. It aims to set up a framework, which has some degree of independence with respect to the changes, and uses the process of 'discrimination' to decide what is new. The CH envisages a continual flux of discriminations in which something remains stable with respect to the flux. It uses labelled entities that are labelled to be checked against what is different, and if different, to create a new entity called the 'discriminant', using a construction due to Conway. This involves a discriminantly closed subset (dcs), the smallest of which has 3 members, any two entities and their subset. Another feature called 'aspect' suggests that the discrimination of A against B is not necessarily the same as that of B against A.

Aspect modifies Conway's original rule, so that 6 elements are now required instead of 3, at the first level. With the 2 signals y and z, this produces 8 elements, which is the same as in the quaternion group. A duality between the two 3-element equivalence classes allows one to express their relation in the form a, $-a$, b, $-b$, c, $-c$, with the + / – expressed in the group multiplication sense.

As BK emphasize, the combinatorial scheme that we have developed to explain quark 'colour' structure uses a 3×3 array with quark colours plotted against the 'charges' or source strengths (e, s, w) for the the electromagnetic, strong and weak interactions, and with unit values defined as 1 or 0, according to the presence or absence of these quantities. The mechanism used for generating the 1 and 0 values is a combination of the rotation symmetry of the quaternion operators i, j, k, which apply to the charge units in our system, and the rotation *a*symmetry which applies to the charges themselves due to fundamental conservation laws. This is what we call 'charge accommodation' (CA). One additional mathematical representation we devised for this was to apply arbitrary unit vectors $\mathbf{i}, \mathbf{j}, \mathbf{k}$ to each quaternion operator to express the rotation symmetry, and then to take the scalar product of the whole system with the combined unit vector quantity $\mathbf{1}$, so generating the 1 and 0 values by a mathematical process. Originally, this approach was taken from the purely mathematical combination of vectors and quaternions that we used in the Dirac equation. More recently, it has come to seem that it has a real physical basis in the relationship between charge units and and units of quantized angular momentum, and that this has its origin in the creation of the quantized Dirac state.

This is significant because it relates the three-dimensionalities of charge and space in a fundamental way, the spatial component coming from the angular momentum direction. Within both the Dirac algebra and CA, there is a kind of combination or 3 × 3 'nesting' of three-dimensional elements. BK believe this can be related to Aspect, and, through its relationship to the Standard Model of conventional particle physics theory, connect the CH and Aspect to results accessible by experiment. The key requirement is to link the 1 and 0 of CH with the 1 and 0 of CA, either directly or indirectly, since both represent existence conditions, and are related to 'creation' and 'annihilation' in a background flux. From our point of view, this is related to our need to define the meaning of the existence / nonexistence concepts in a more rigorously mathematical way and to obtain the 1 and 0 values by a more axiomatically-defined process.

Our work is rapidly developing, and we have now arrived at a more fundamental approach, which has created a mathematically deductive basis for some of the ideas that were expressed previously in a more intuitive manner. The charge accommodation algebra is now linked to a mathematical connection between the conservation laws, conservation of type of charge and conservation of angular momentum. This actually creates the states of 1 and 0 in a more fundamental way. There are possibly further areas where connections between the CH and CA formalisms might be made. One is the use of C_2 symmetries. We see fundamental physics as developing out of a D_2 group, which incorporates 3 interrelated C_2 symmetries, but which can be extended in various ways to a whole series of higher group symmetries by a process of duality [Rowlands, Cullerne and Koberlein, 2001]. Duality is fundamental to our system. In principle, we want physics to show us how to create something from nothing, or 1 from 0 (as BK wish to do in CH), but it is our belief that this can only be done by creating that something as part of a dual pair. To any 'probe' we put forward, nature will always provide a symmetric 'response' (effectively based on C_2). This is why we have to create −1 at the same time as 1. As soon as we do this, we are effectively also creating the whole concept of number ordering and repetitive ordering processes.

Indeed, our concept of nonconservation is a process of repetitive ordering of space or time elements. What we mean by nonconservation is the way in which space and time elements are devoid of identity, have translational symmetry, and are associated with conservation laws (Noether's theorem). We see this as the direct opposite of conservation. In fact, we go as far as to say that symmetries and conservation laws may be predicted using this powerful duality concept. Our connection between the conservation of type of charge and conservation of angular momentum is an example of this predicting tool.

Our fundamental grouping has three major categories, which were based originally on induction from empirical evidence, but which we have always believed had a more fundamental origin in ideas such as the universal necessity of duality. These are the divisions between the discrete and the continuous, the real and the imaginary, and the conserved and the nonconserved. Essentially, we believe that the creation of 1 from 0 produces the first division, and that the automatic creation of the dual $(-1 \, / \, 1)$ effectively leads to the second, while the third is another way of expressing the origin of number ordering as a repetitive process. The fact that the three are interrelated also has connections with the interrelatedness of the C_2 groupings in the basic D_2 group.

A significant product of both the C_2 sub-groupings and the main D_2 group is the idea that the whole system of parameterizing the 'universe' or 'reality' comes in a package which is made up of a combination of the eight units (quaternion and mirror-symmetric multivariate 4-vector) which make up the elements of the D_2 group: space, time, mass and charge. This package is a nilpotent, or square root of zero, which establishes a unique relation between the units, applicable only to a single object. That is, the combined units ik, ii, ij, ik, j are related by a unique set of conserved quantities, E, $\mathbf{p}$ and m, whose combined value normalizes to unity. It disallows or 'discriminates' against any object that is not new (Pauli exclusion), and, though measured in a discrete way, incorporates its own continuous background which allows a continual flux of creation and annihilation of such objects to occur. Its status as a square root of zero allows us to generate 'something for nothing' by simultaneously creating the dual vacuum antistate as part of its own composition. As a nilpotent, derived ultimately from the concept of applying integer measurement to space, it may well also be relevant in the context of topos theory, another subject of special interest to ANPA members.

REFERENCES

Rowlands, P., Cullerne, J. P. and Koberlein, B. D. [2001], The group structure bases of a foundational approach to physics, arXiv:quant-ph/0110092.

THE HOLOGRAPHIC PRINCIPLE IN BIOLOGICAL DEVELOPMENT AND QUANTUM PHYSICS

STEPHEN WOOD

3c Dawlish Road, Leyton, London E10 6QB

stephenwood60@hotmail.com

22/02/02

INTRODUCTION

I would like to introduce the themes of this paper in the form of a dialogue:

Q: How should we build complex forms, such as living things?

A: Organise them as a hierarchy of stable subassemblies, or homologous organs.

Q: Surely the genes are all you need to explain living organisation?

A: But the same organ can be the result of different genes! When we look at the genes as more than simply stretches of nucleic acid, but see them switching each other on and off, then a hierarchical organisation emerges spontaneously.

Q: Anyway, hadn't Darwin explained homology?

A: No, his explanation fails, and the pre-Darwinian understanding of homology is much closer to the hierarchical approach.

Q: Isn't there a quantitative approach that explains form?

A: No, form is a qualitative distinction between an inside and an outside. Living things are autonomous forms, themselves maintaining this boundary.

Q: Is such a boundary a purely material skin?

A: A boundary can be seen as the interface between the parts inside and the rest of the universe outside, through which information flows.

Q: Can't an organism be described in isolation?

A: But then it would be a stone! An organism is a process of interaction with its environment, a process of creating and discovering.

Q: Creating and discovering? Is that a linguistic process?

A: Yes, a living thing is a focus of a linguistic process, where meanings are recognised and transformed.

Q: Eventually we will be able to reduce form to physics and chemistry, won't we?

A: Could you reduce the meaning of these words to the chemistry of the ink? The same form may be realised in many different physicochemical configurations. The Cartesian method just won't work.

Q: Do you mean to say that genetic and morphological descriptions of living things are radically different?

A: Yes, they are complementary yet incompatible. Continuity of morphological information is a kind of memory without mechanical storage. Without this holistic memory, the mechanically stored genetic information would deteriorate over time.

Q: I know that many quantitative models of morphogenesis have been proposed. So how can you say that form is a qualitative?

A: Morphogenetic models exhibit bifurcation points, where the system shifts suddenly from one form to a quite different form.

Q: I feel uncomfortable with this idea of sudden jumps.

A: You feel happy about the sudden jumps in quantum physics, don't you?

Q: But how do you decide between all the different interpretations?

A: Things become a lot clearer once you understand that the most important thing is the form of the quantum system, not the energy.

Q: Isn't that a very organic way of putting things?

A: Yes, the ageing of a living system is much closer to the development of a quantum process than to anything Newton described.

Q: But how deep could the comparison be?

A: Well, certain forms of the equations for both look very similar, the same equations that describe a hologram. You can talk about a quantum process as a hierarchy of surfaces through which information flows.

Q: 'Surfaces through which information flows'—that's how you described living things and their organs, isn't it?

A: Yes, that's right! And these surfaces turn out to be holographic.

Q: Oh so that's where the holographic principle in your title comes from?

A: Yes, the holographic principle may hold the key to bringing quantum physics together with relativity. Looks like it might bring in life and non-linear systems too!

1. MORPHOLOGICAL STABILITY

The parable of the two watchmakers is first presented by Simon (1962: 470), and has been variously adapted by Koestler (1967: 45-47) and Allen and Starr (1982: 49-51). In Simon's account, the two watchmakers are named Hora and Tempus, whereas Koestler renames them Bios and Mekhos, and Allen and Starr provide a factual exemplar of the fictional Hora. Both Hora and Tempus make watches that consist of 1000 parts. However, Hora manufactures his watches in subassemblies of 10 parts each, whereas Tempus puts his watches together part by part. The workshop is a busy place, often disturbed by the telephone ringing. Hora and Tempus must leave their work to answer the telephone, in case it is a new customer on the line. Who gets his work done more quickly? Hora's subassemblies are stable in themselves. They do not fall apart when their maker leaves them to answer the phone. But for Tempus only the completed watch is stable. A disruption at any stage except the last means he will have to start from scratch again. Hora's strategy is the better one for dealing with disturbances from the environment, since his use of stable subassemblies minimises the effect of those disturbances. Watches built by Hora as a hierarchy of subassemblies will come to predominate in the market at the expense of the watches of Tempus.

Living things are not simply aggregates of parts, nor are they indecomposable wholes. They are loosely coupled, or near decomposable (see Simon, 1962, 1973; Koestler, 1967: 64-65; Allen and Starr, 1982: 70-74). Living things consist of sub-wholes, parts in relation within the whole. A kidney is defined in terms of its function within the body, but may also be transplanted from one body to another. Its function within the body is an aspect of its *partness*, the fact that it can be transplanted an aspect of its *wholeness*. Koestler (1967: 48) describes such semi-autonomous sub-wholes as *holons* (from Greek: *holos*, meaning whole, and *-on* as in electron, proton). 'The evolutionary stability of sub-assemblies—organelles, organs, organ-systems—is reflected by their remarkable degree of *autonomy* or self-government. Each of them—a piece of tissue or a whole heart—is capable of functioning *in vitro* as a quasi-independent whole, even though isolated from the organism or transplanted into another organism. Each is a *sub-whole* which, towards its subordinated parts, behaves

2

as a self-contained whole, and towards its superior controls as a dependent part.'
Koestler (1974: 62).

'Among possible complex forms, hierarchies are the ones that have time to evolve'
(Simon, 1962: 473). Simon's conclusion from the watchmaker parable has been
tested recently in evolutionary computing. The final solution of a problem specified
for a population of genetic algorithms emerges from a synthesis of several partial
solutions, known as building blocks. Wagner (1995) draws the following lesson for
the evolution of living things: '... a system consisting of building blocks has a much
better chance to be improved by mutation and natural selection than an unstructured
system ... Hence the building block hypothesis can explain why it makes sense to
organize a complex organism into individualized characters called homologues.'
Living things consist of a wide variety of standard parts (Raff, 1996: 330), building
blocks (Wagner, 1995) or modules (Wagner and Altenberg, 1996). 'The most
fundamental principle of evolutionary strategy, related to the watchmakers' parable, is
the *standardisation* of subassemblies ... Animals and plants are made out of
homologous organelles like the mitochondria, homologous organs like the gills and
lungs, homologous limbs such as arms and wings. They are the stable holons in the
evolutionary flux' (Koestler, 1967: 135, 139).

Riedl introduces a concept of morphological stability, or fixation, to account for the
fact of homology: 'Actually, every homologue is characterised by the fact that it
shows adaptive freedom in only a few directions, but fixation in many others. If this
were different, if every character were free to change in every direction, the living
world would appear as a random chaotic mixture of patterns, as chaos, and the single
relationship left among representatives would not relate to common ancestry but only
to common functions, such as analogous limbs, horns, wings, jaws, and so forth'
(Riedl, 1977: 354; cf. Alberch, 1982: 315-316). Parts of organisms possess a stability,
which permits us to recognise relationships between them that are not the result of
shared function.

3

2. METABOLIC STABILITY

'A living thing is a complex net of interactions between thousands or millions of chemical species' (Kauffman, 1969: 437; 1970: 18). How is it possible for an organism to arrive at a stable metabolism among these chemical species? The answer lies in how the organism is able to construct a number of specialised compartments as it develops, the different cell types. It then has at its disposal a range of environments in which specialised metabolic reactions can take place. The problem of metabolic stability is a problem of cellular differentiation.

Kauffman (1969, 1970) describes cellular differentiation in terms of the Jacob-Monod theory of gene expression. Genes are modelled as binary switches, turning each other on or off. Each gene executes a certain Boolean operation on its own state, on or off, and the states of the genes connected to it in order to generate the state at the next point in time. Connections among genes are randomly assigned. Kauffman discovers how, with these model genomic networks, the behaviour of the system is related to its connectedness. With one connection the behaviour is frozen, the activities of the genetic elements are not coordinated. When the number of connections is large, chaos reigns and the array does not reach a stable pattern of activity. However, when the number of connections is poised at two, complex behaviour emerges. Here the system of elements divides into a number of functionally isolated subsystems, loosely coupled to each other, each of which settles down into a regular pattern of gene activity. Metabolic stability emerges out of randomness. Kauffman is able to introduce perturbations to test this stability, either by changing the state of a particular gene, or by altering its Boolean function. Genes will generally return to the same state cycle, or shift to a limited number of other cycles (Kauffman, 1969: 463; 1970: 34). The emergent subsystems are therefore 'poised', that is, they are to transform into a very limited number of other subsystems (Kauffman, 1992). This is the very nature of differentiation. Remarkably, the number of subsystems for a particular number of genes is of the same order of magnitude as the number of cell types found in organisms possessing that number of genes. Kauffman concludes that the genomes of organisms may indeed be constructed more or less randomly, and rely on the order that spontaneously emerges from such randomness for their coordination.

4

Kauffman (1983: 218) explains how a compartmented organisation of the genome is advantageous in evolution: 'Selective evolution [evolution by natural selection] requires the capacity to accumulate partial successes sequentially. Were the genome organized such that a small change in connections could alter coordinated dynamical patterns of gene activities throughout the network preservation of past favourable combinations of activities would be difficult. Accumulation of partial successes requires either genuinely isolated subsystems, hard to maintain in a scrambling genome, or functionally isolated subsystems which are otherwise loosely coupled, as arise inevitably in these model genomes. Selective modification of the combinations of gene activities in one functionally isolated subsystem would not alter the dynamics of the remaining system, hence allowing piecewise evolution of favourable new cell types.' Kauffman's findings harmonise very well with Simon's proposal that hierarchically organised, near-decomposable systems are the most likely to evolve. As Wagner (1995) perceives, each subsystem is a partial success, or building block, to which new improvements can be added. Kauffman's model of cellular differentiation is discussed in the chapter on modularity in Raff (1996: chapter 10). Cell types are described as modular units of gene expression (Raff, 1996: 328).

3. THE HIERARCHY OF TYPES

'What can be more curious than that the hand of man, formed for grasping, that of a mole for digging, the leg of the horse, the paddle of the porpoise, and the wing of the bat, should be all constructed on the same pattern, and should include the same bones, in the same relative positions' (Darwin, 1859 [1968: 415]). The forelimbs of the different mammals are homologous and overall, the mammals, indeed all vertebrates, show the same plan of organisation, or unity of type.

The bones in the forelimbs of mammals maintain the same relative positions: 'An organ is sooner altered, atrophied, or annihilated than transposed' (Geoffroy Saint-Hilaire, 1818: xxx; translated in Appel, 1987: 99). The criterion for their homology is the principle of connections. Geoffroy Saint-Hilaire discovered this principle through his attempt to establish the homology of the opercular bones, the bones that cover the gill opening in fishes. By considering only their connections, he reached the conclusion that the opercular bones are located in the middle ear of mammals, as the malleus, incus and stapes (Geoffroy Saint-Hilaire, 1818: 37). Similarly, by considering its connections to bones of the ankle, the horse's hoof is the enlarged nail of the third toe (Goodwin, 1994: 131).

The explanation of homology that Darwin proposes is that the two structures trace back to a structure in the common ancestor (see also, Ghiselin, 1976): 'If we suppose that the ancient progenitor, the archetype of all mammals, had its limbs constructed on the existing general pattern, for whatever purpose they served, we can at once perceive the plain signification of the homologous construction of the limbs throughout the whole class' (Darwin, 1859 [1968: 416]). Darwin's explanation assumes that bodily organs are replicated and handed on entire from generation to generation. But we know that this is not the case: 'Only replicators like genes pass on their own structure to their descendants directly. Morphological structures are not replicators ... The notion of continuity of descent is not problematic for genes but is less clear for organs' (Wagner, 1989b: 55, 56).

There are two possible ways of revising the Darwinian explanation of homology:

1. The homology of structures in different animals is due to the same genes handed down from the common ancestor.
2. Homologous structures form from the same cells in development.

However, counterexamples can be given to both explanations:

1. 'In the fruit fly *Drosophila* there is a particular gene which governs the formation of the eyes and there is an allelomorph (a mutant alternative) of this gene which in the homozygous state produces an eyeless condition. Now [T. H.] Morgan showed that, if a pure homozygous eyeless stock is inbred, the other genes in the gene complex, by reassortment, may come to be recombined in such a way that they will deputise for the missing normal eye-forming allelomorph, and lo and behold flies appear in the "eyeless" stock with the eyes as good as ever! These eyes must surely be regarded as homologous with the eyes of normal flies, yet their production is not controlled by the same genes' (Hardy, 1965: 212). This is the phenomenon of genetic piracy (Roth, 1988).

6

and integrative tendencies is inherent in the concept of hierarchic order; and a universal characteristic of life. The self-assertive tendencies are the dynamic expression of holon wholeness, the integrative tendencies of its partness' (Koestler, 1967: 343).

The distinctiveness of an element, the fact that we can recognise its identity across numerous organisms, derives from its wholeness, the tendency of a holon to assert itself. If an element cannot be recognised individually, this lack of distinctiveness emphasises the partness of the holon, its tendency to integrate itself among other elements as part of a larger whole, such as a series. We may understand serial homology in this light: 'The phenomenon of serial resemblance is in fact an expression of the capacity of repeated parts to vary similarly and simultaneously. In proportion as in their variations such parts retain this capacity the relationship is preserved, and in proportion as it is lost, and the parts begin to vary independently, exhibiting differentiation, the relationship is set aside' (Bateson, 1894: 569). When elements of a series vary similarly and simultaneously they cannot be recognised as distinct. They remain parts integrated into the larger whole, the series. When elements differentiate, they become individually recognisable and thus assert themselves as wholes distinct in themselves. The first element in the vertebral series asserted itself, weakening its integration into the rest of the series, and became individualised as the axis in tetrapods. Whether an element appears as a part or a whole depends on the broader context.

All teleost fishes have a recognisable palatine bone, in the context of the palatopterygoquadrate arch, but vary in the extent to which parts of the palatine are developed. Hence, we can describe a number of states of the palatine bone, recording differences in the shape and orientation of the boss and prong, for example. States within a character represent divergent differentiations of parts within the context of whole. A character representing the presence or absence of the palatine describes the expression or suppression of the self-assertive tendency of the holon, the acquisition or loss of its individuality. For example, the prootic and epiotic of reptiles lost their separate individualities and fused to form the mammalian petrosal, which then in its turn has followed its own path of differentiation.

A good example of where members of a series have individualised is the thorax of insects (Wagner, 1986: 151; 1989a: 1162; 1989b: 63). The thorax most probably arose as a differentiation of segments 7, 8 and 9 in the annelid-like ancestors of insects. However, the thorax as an entity in itself is not homologous to the corresponding segments in centipedes, which have remained closer to the annelid form. 'The thorax is the unit differentiated from the rest of the body in terms of appendages and internal anatomy, a condition not found in centipedes' (Wagner, 1986: 151; 1989a: 1162; 1989b: 63). There is no direct homologue with the thorax in the segments of the centipedes—we cannot establish a one-to-one mapping. The thorax represents a new condition of form, a new autonomous whole, which serves to "individuate" the taxon Insecta (in the sense of von Baer, 1828; see Rieppel, 1994: 90).

Nelson (1989) suggests that instead of taxa being seen as groups of units, such as species or organisms, they should be seen as relationships. A taxon is a relationship inherited by organisms, and a homology, then, is a relationship inherited by parts of organisms. 'Conceived as relationships, taxa and homologies do not literally descend from one another. Taxa come into being with organisms that literally descend' (Nelson, 1989: 281). A taxon is not a group of organisms tracing back to an ancestral organism, but a type, a relationship inherited by organisms. Homology is not the tracing back of structures to an ancestral structure, but a relationship inherited by parts of organisms. Taxa are relationships and have homologies for their parts (Nelson, 1989: 279). Nelson's view is much closer to the spirit of Geoffroy Saint-Hilaire. Homology is not the conservation of material structures among descendant lineages, but rather the conservation of positional relationships within the developmental process: '... systematics and comparative anatomy ... are possible only to the extent that ontogeny is orderly ... the concept of evolution is an extrapolation, or interpretation, of the orderliness of ontogeny.' (Nelson, 1978: 336).

The four laws of von Baer affirm the orderliness of the developmental process (von Baer, 1828: 224; modified from the translation in Gould, 1977: 56):

1. The general features of a broad animal type appear earlier in the embryo than the special features.

2. Less general characters are developed from the most general, and so forth, until finally the most specialized appear.

3. Each embryo of a given species, instead of passing through the stages of other animals, departs more and more from them.

4. Fundamentally therefore, the embryo of a higher animal is never like the adult of a lower animal, but only like its embryo.

A human embryo has a tail and clefts in its pharynx early in its life. These homologues humans share with all animals of the chordate type, including lancelets, sea squirts, and all vertebrates. It is only within the first year that the human infant walks upright, demonstrating the homology of the human type. More general characters, which specify more inclusive types, appear earlier in development than the more special characters, which specify less inclusive types.

The human embryo shows itself to be of the metazoan type when it develops more than one cell layer. Its left-right symmetry displays the bilateralian type, not the radiate type, where animals such as jellyfish have a rotational symmetry. The embryo then develops a polarity such that the anus is the first to form, not the mouth, therefore adopting the deuterostomian type, rather the prostomian, where the mouth develops first. The human body plan becomes specified in more and more detail as the embryo develops. The embryo displays in turn the homologies of each type in the hierarchy of types that it has inherited. The order of classification is the order of development.

4. BOUNDARIES AND INDICATIONS

It is a simple business to talk of tables and chairs. We attach our language to them as labels. We count them and attach numbers to them. Tables and chairs are separate from one another and external to one another. They are solid bodies. Our calculus of number and language of nouns suit solid bodies. Yet, consider living beings. Is a strawberry plant separate and external to other bodies? You may have planted a single individual, but the strawberry has sent out a long stolon, which has taken root and given rise to a series of new plants. We are able to distinguish different plants; together they remain one whole. We have distinction before we have number (see Bortoft, 1996). It is among solids that 'our action finds its fulcrum and our industry its tools' (Bergson, 1911: ix). Our preference for a quantitative logic of solids is understandable then, but it is not nature's logic and life confounds it. Far from being illogical, life teaches a deeper, qualitative logic.

Within Bohm's metaphysics of process, characteristic forms in nature arise through the coincidence of vast processes, which extend over the whole universe. Each centre or focus of process maintains itself within its environment through self-regulation: 'Because the basic order of process is eternal change of everything, we can no longer appeal to the mechanical notion that certain basic objects, entities, etc., 'simply exist' with constant and invariable properties. Rather, the survival of any particular thing, however 'basic' it may be thought to be, demands a complex process of regulation, which provides for the stability of this thing, in the face of the eternal change in all that serves to constitute what it is' (Bohm, 1969: 42, 52).

A living thing is a distinction between inside and outside, autonomously defining its boundaries and maintaining them through a process of self-regulation. Not only is there distinction, but also indication, that one of the two distinguished states is primary, namely the inside, not the outside, the living system as opposed to its environment (Varela, 1979: 84). In his *Laws of Form*, Spencer-Brown elegantly captures an essential fact of life: '... a universe comes into being when a space is severed or taken apart. The skin of a living organism cuts off an outside from an inside. So does the circumference of a circle in a plane' (Spencer-Brown, 1969: v). In his book, he describes the calculus of indications, the qualitative logic of life.

Despite their autonomy, living things do not exist in isolation. They interact with surrounding physical systems and with fellow members of the ecological community or social group: 'No man is an island—he is a holon. A Janus-faced entity who, looking inward, see himself as a self-contained unique whole, looking outward as a dependent part' (Koestler, 1967: 56). Janus is Koestler's emblem of hierarchy, named after the Roman god of two faces, the guardian of doorways and, with the month of January, the passage of the years.

Living things exist far from thermodynamic equilibrium, and must maintain themselves through constant interaction and exchange with the environment. Homeostasis, the maintenance of stable conditions necessary for life, may be the most obvious in the higher vertebrates, the birds and mammals, but is required by all living things. Living things, then, are constantly interacting with their environment. They adapt their internal environment to suit themselves, regulating temperature, salinity and pH.

Animals are active; they are able to make choices about where they live and actively shape their external environment, whether physical or social (Bateson, 1988: 193). '[An animal] does not merely adapt to the environment, but constantly adapts the environment to itself—it eats and drinks its environment, fights and mates with it, burrows and builds in it; it does not merely respond to the environment, but asks questions by exploring it' (Koestler, 1967: 153). Indeed, all living things have the characteristic of irritability or sensitivity. They are able to choose or discriminate between aspects of the environment that are pleasant and beneficial, and those that are harmful. How a living thing influences its external environment has consequences for itself and its descendants. A plant dropping its leaves will change the pH of the soil for itself and other plants including any offspring that disperse nearby; a beaver building a dam changes the environment of the flooded valley (Bateson, 1988: 195). Living things choose which questions to put to their environment and are able to respond to their discoveries. 'Life is matter which chooses' (Margulis and Sagan, 1995).

Living things are not solid bodies, because they are never complete. They never achieve a definite state, but rather exhibit certain tendencies. Every tendency has its antagonist. The two thwart each other's aims, never allowing the other to reach completion: 'In particular, it may be said of individuality; that, while the tendency to individuate is everywhere present in the organized world, it is everywhere opposed by the tendency towards reproduction. For the individuality to be perfect, it would be necessary that no detached part of the organism could live separately. But then reproduction would be impossible. For what is reproduction, but the building up of a new organism with a detached fragment of the old? Individuality therefore harbours its enemy at home. Its very need of perpetuating itself in time condemns it never to be complete in space' (Bergson, 1911: 13-14).

A living body defines its own boundary, marking an inside in contrast to an outside. Each organ of a living body maintains its identity in contrast to fellow organs and within the context of the system of which it is a part. There are many insides and outsides within each living body, which exist relative to one another: 'At a given level in the hierarchy, a particular system can be seen as an outside to systems below it, and as an inside to systems above it; thus, the status (i.e. the mark of distinction) of a given system changes as one passes through its level in either the upward or the downward direction' (Varela, 1979: 86).

Without the conflict of opposing tendencies, each organ of the body would solidify. Each must have its own vital tendency, its power of self-assertion, to contend with the integrative power of the whole organism: 'The organized elements composing the individual have themselves a certain individuality, and each will claim its vital principle if the individual pretends to have its own. But, on the other hand, the individual itself is not sufficiently independent, not sufficiently cut off from other things, for us to allow it a "vital principle" of its own' (Bergson, 1911: 45).

Marking a holon specifies a particular frame reference. If the boundary marked coincides with the boundary that the holon, as an autonomous unit, defines and maintains, then the observer makes a discovery about the holon, rather than merely conceiving it: 'If the scientist does, in fact, define an object holon which can be associated with a phenomenon, then in finding and observing within the inertial frame of a holon, he has achieved, for that portion of the study, a main scientific objective; in the context of his procedures he views the world in terms that are compatible with those of the holon he investigates. Subsequent observation of the holon concurs with his predictions' (Allen and Starr, 1982: 242). Systematists identify the palatine bone as a boundary that is maintained in fishes of the teleost type. The systematists' mark corresponds to a boundary that the holon itself maintains. The name palatine is an *indication* of the organic holon. The palatine boundary maintains itself in the context

13

of the palatopterygoquadrate arch and itself defines the context within which the boss
and prong boundaries define themselves.

5. THE FLOW OF INFORMATION

Koestler (1967) describes two hierarchies in living things, motor and sensory[1]. In the
motor hierarchy, information in the form of a goal cascades down from the inside to
the outside, triggering each holon into action as a whole. At each level of the
hierarchy, the goal is spelled out in greater detail, and the action becomes increasingly
particularised. To make a catch, we need only look at the ball, and not worry about
the coordination of muscular contractions with each shift in the ball's position.

In the sensory hierarchy, information in the form a stimulus cascades down from
outside, holons passing the stimulus up to higher levels of the hierarchy. Holons scan
for relevant information, taking what is relevant and passing on a digested,
generalised version to the next level. One does not remember all the frequencies and
harmonics in the shout 'Catch!' but only the imperative to throw out one's hands.

Bohm distinguishes the horizontal aspect of a hierarchy—the normal functioning of
the holons—from the vertical aspect—the flow of information, which serves to
regulate the internal functioning of the holons. He takes the example of a government
department: 'There is an upward movement in which the higher level officials are
informed about what is 'essential', 'relevant', 'significant' ... Then there is a
downward movement in which the higher level officials inform those lower in the
hierarchy how they are to order their actions in the light of the general aims of the
government, and in the light of information of all sorts coming from other
departments and levels' (Bohm, 1969: 52-53).

Holons at different levels in the hierarchy pass information to one another in the form
of signals: 'A signal is a string of energy or matter in transit between communicating
entities ... At departure, the signal represents a freezing of the infinitely rich dynamics
of the transmitting holon as expressed by the medium of energy or matter of which the

---

[1] Compare the flow of information through the hierarchies of Manthey (1998). Information trickles
down in the form of goals and bubbles up in the form of sensations.

signal stream is made. Although meanings can change, a single meaning has no dynamics of its own, in contrast to, say, a process or a system. In capturing the dynamics of the holon, the structure of the signal is a sign of the state of the holon; and signs have no rate or dynamics' (Allen and Starr, 1982: 17-18). We have a contrast between the internal functioning of each holon, based on rate-dependent dynamics, and the rules governing the flow of information between holons, based on rate-independent constraints (Pattee, 1978). The horizontal hierarchy, describing the functioning of each holon, is based in time, whereas the vertical hierarchy of information flow is timeless (Bohm, 1969: 53-54). 'Constraints always carry information which has meaning for the entities involved in natural processes. This information is not dynamically involved in the processes occurring in time and cannot be directly altered by them, but has instead a timeless quality. Furthermore, it is not altered by the rate at which some entity interprets it' (Salthe, 1985: 71).

Holons constrain or filter information that passes through them. Higher holons provide the environment and context for all lower holons with which they communicate, because the lower holons only receive information filtered by the higher level. The information emerging from a higher holon is an integration of information from its parts. 'In summary, entities (holons) in a hierarchy may be viewed as the interface between the parts and the rest of the universe. On its journey to the outside, signal from the parts is integrated through the whole... as are signals reaching the parts from the rest of the universe' (Allen and Starr, 1982: 15). Holons are surfaces through which information enters and departs.

6. CREATION AND DISCOVERY

'No man is an island—he is a holon. A Janus-faced entity who, looking inward, see himself as a self-contained unique whole, looking outward as a dependent part' (Koestler, 1967: 56). To talk of the part looking out and the whole looking in is to describe the sensations of partness and wholeness. These sensations involve the discovery of self and other: 'On the one hand an organism tends to go out of itself, to open itself to other forms around, and on the other hand it tends to organise itself, to centre on itself' (Griffiths, 1989). Going out of oneself, opening oneself to others, may lead to disintegration, that is, integration with one's environment. Going into oneself, entering reflection and meditation, restores balance and inner coordination. Spencer-Brown (1969) is talking about the activity of distinction. When we make a mark, we cross from inside to outside and describe the part looking in and the whole looking out. Distinction is the creative act, which brings an autonomous whole—a universe—into being.

Self-assertion and integration appear differently in motor and sensory aspects. Manifesting its self-assertive tendency in the motor aspect, the holon looks out as an autonomous individual. In the sensory aspect, the holon looks in on itself, gathering itself, collecting itself. Manifesting its integrative tendency in the motor aspect, the holon looks in on itself, the parts integrating themselves by coordinating their actions. In the sensory aspect, the holon looks out and opens itself to that beyond itself, losing itself in its environment.

	Motor	Sensory
Self-assertive	looking out – whole	looking in – whole
Integrative	looking in – part	looking out – part [2]

Varela (1979: 206) describes two complementarities, which match those in the previous table, namely autonomy/control and closure/interaction. Our characterisation of the system, as autonomous or controlled, depends on the tendency we highlight, self-assertive or integrative respectively. Emphasising the self-assertive

---

[2] We can construct a similar diagram if we follow Varela's (1979: 98-99) account of the general system theory of Goguen (1971). An outward functor regards a component at a lower level as a whole system at the next: 'Generally speaking, *a holon on the |n| level of the hierarchy is represented on the |n +1| level as a unit and triggered off as a unit*' (Koestler, 1967: 72). An inward functor computes the behaviour of the whole system, viewing the result as a single object at the lower level. Each pair of outward and inward functor is adjoint. The inward functor is the overlap or intersection between objects, the categorical limit. The limit has a dual, the colimit, which is the integration of systems.

	Motor	Sensory
Self-assertive	looking out – whole	looking in – whole
	outward functor	inward functor
Integrative	looking in – part	looking out – part
	inward functor (limit)	outward functor (colimit)

Here the complementarity of whole/part or self-assertion/integration is equivalent to the adjointness of an outward functor and an inward functor. Motor and sensory aspects are expressed in the duality of limit and colimit.

tendency, we focus on the autonomy of the living system. Emphasising the integrative tendency, we focus on the controls and constraints imposed on the system from outside. How we represent the system, as closed or interacting, depends on whether we consider the motor or the sensory aspects. Regarding the motor activity of an organism, we represent it as a closed system, maintaining a stable behaviour and identity by coordinating its parts. Regarding the sensations of the organism, we represent it in interaction, compensating for perturbations in its environment as a dissipative, thermodynamically open system.

The terms of Peirce and Uexküll may help us to understand the four aspects. Salthe (1993: 14-15) summarises Peirce as follows. Firstness is independent being. Secondness is being relative to, reacting with another being. Thirdness is mediation, whereby a first and a second are brought into relation. Uexküll (see Salthe, 1993: 176) contrasts a being's inner life, its Innenwelt, with the outer world, or Umwelt, that two beings come to share through their interaction. Looking in, a holon has a private inner life, an Innenwelt. The holon looking out as a self-asserting, active whole is a first. The holon looking out as an integrating, sensing part is a second. The thirdness is the immediate environment of the holons and their system of interactions. Holons encounter one another within their environment as active first and sensing second. Through this meeting of firstness and secondness, the holons' environment becomes a world, an Umwelt or thirdness.

'To share in the interpretation of a world and the response to it is to communicate' (McCabe, 1987: 119). A hierarchy is a system of communication, whether we are talking of a social group, or of parts organised within a body (Allen and Starr, 1982: 37). 'All life at any level is a matter of communication. Every organism is an organism by virtue of its power of communication.' (McCabe, 1987: 118). Firstness is creation, whereas secondness is discovery. Thirdness exists in the tension between the two. Living things 'realise' meanings in their world, in the sense of 'to discover' and 'to make real' (McCabe, 1987: 120). Living things find meanings to be 'real' (discovery) and at the same time make them 'real' (creation).

Living things organise their environment by relevance to their activities and needs. The fruits of an organism's exploration turn the environment into a world. A living thing's body and senses organise its world; they make the world meaningful to it. For example, fishes live in worlds very different our own, because of their different sensory powers. Sharks respond to electricity. Electric receptors allow them to detect the currents generated by the muscles of struggling prey. Elephant snout fishes are able to create an electric field around themselves. Nearby non-conducting objects will distort the field, and the fish can sense this. Elephant snout fishes live in murky African rivers and use their electric sense to electrolocate, in the same way that bats and dolphins use high frequency sounds to echolocate.

7. FEATURES, SIMILARITIES AND HOMOLOGIES

Living things are processes of creation and discovery. Their interactions form a language that can be understood through Peirce's triad of first, second and third. The classification of living things is also a linguistic process, and Peirce's triad emerges here too.

The first stage of classification involves the collection of representative specimens of the species to be studied. In the second stage, characters are conceptualised and the character states for particular species recorded. The third stage is the generation of a classification as the most economical summary of the data and the discovery of the defining characters of taxa.

Each stage of classification involves a different kind of pattern, to be understood in the terminology of Peirce. A pattern of firstness consists of the observed features of all morphological variants of a given species, which are at this stage not yet conceptualised. A pattern of secondness is a pattern of similarity shared by a number of species. A pattern of thirdness describes the pattern of homologies inherited by organisms. Sharing is meaning in the second context, and congruence, the nested hierarchical relationship between patterns of secondness, is meaning in the third context.

Features are firsts; they exist in one species considered alone. Similarities are seconds; they relate one species to another. Homologies are thirds; they show that two species are more closely related to one another than they are to a third. The third species reveals the thirdness of the sister species; it provides the context within which the other two find their relationship.

Character concepts begin life in the first stage as features identified in single species. The second stage of character conceptualisation is the clash between firsts. Character concepts are tested against specimens of different species, and if found not to be applicable are modified or abandoned. The third stage is the clash between seconds. Similarities that are not congruent with the most economical pattern are meaningless. They are homoplasies not homologies, confusing rather than revealing thirdness in the study group. As Peirce pointed out, the three stages exist together. The choice of study species and the conceptualisation of relevant characters are made with a background of existing classifications. Classification is a process of cyclic illumination (Hennig, 1966; Kluge, 1991).

Peirce's triad of first, second and third relates to referent, sign and system of interpretance. Species patterns of features are referents. Patterns of similarity between species are signs of affinity. The types, the patterns of homology, form the system of interpretance, the context that reveals the significance of patterns of similarity: 'More or less similarity is evidence for or against homology, not of more or less homology' (Nelson, 1989: 282). Homology is not the kind or degree of similarity. Meaning in one context cannot be reduced in that way to meaning in another. At each stage meanings are transformed through the context of comparison and analysis

8. ORDER ABOVE HETEROGENEITY

Physicists and chemists are used to dealing with homogeneous matter, with molecules, atoms, and particles that, if they are of the same kind, are indistinguishable from one another. The most surprising confirmation of the homogeneity of matter is spectroscopy. The elemental composition of distant stars can be compared with that of the Sun and the Earth. Each element has its own distinct pattern of spectral lines, which is replicated throughout the universe of stars.

The Cartesian method proceeds by reducing the complexity of large phenomena to the simplicity of the small. If phenomena are indeed homogeneous in the small, then this method works admirably and has had great success in physics and chemistry. Living things are also chemically homogeneous, in that the variety of participating atoms is small. Four elements, C, O, H, N, make up 99% of living tissue. The same genetic code applies to all living things, specifying the same twenty or so aminoacids. Does the unity of biochemistry assure us of the success of the Cartesian method in biology?

Our everyday experience of living things, especially one another, is that we are not at all uniform, but diverse and individual, with our own inclinations, habits and personalities. Physiological and biochemical studies of the human animal confirm this. 'Human stomachs vary greatly in size and shape... It is evident that some stomachs hold six or eight times as much as others. It is no wonder from this standpoint that our eating 'habits' are not all alike... The position of the stomach in the body is also widely variable... With the tip of the breastbone (sternum) used as a point of reference, the bottom of the stomach may be anywhere from about 1 to about 9 inches below this position. It is not abnormal to have the bottom of the stomach within an inch or two of the level of the base of the sternum, because about 25 per cent of people have their stomachs in this position; neither is it abnormal to have it about 7 inches lower, because more than 10 per cent have their stomachs in this position' (Williams, 1956; quoted by Elsasser, 1998: 62). Are there any reductionists who would claim that the stomach is not homologous in humans, because its size and its absolute position in the body vary widely? Individual chemical components of bone, that solid and functionally important material, may differ between human samples by not just a few per cent, but ten times! Earlier we saw how two structures are homologous, even if they emerge through different pathways of development, or under the control of different genes. In his *Reflections on a Theory of Organisms*, Elsasser puts it thus: 'Under these circumstances there can be regularity in the large where there is heterogeneity in the small: "order above heterogeneity"' (Elsasser, 1998: 4).

Tennant (1986) provides an interesting discussion of how it might be possible to define a morphological homology such as the gastrula. Is it possible to reduce the homology to a precise definition in physical and chemical terms? We might start by defining the gastrula as certain types of cells in particular topological configurations. A gastrula is thus a hollow ball of cells, where the outer layer of cells is ciliated and the inner layer is unciliated and free to divide. However, in a purely reductionist exercise each cell would have to be described in terms of particular configurations of nuclear, cytoplasmic and membranous components. Each of these components could be reduced to configurations of different sorts of molecules, and so on *ad infinitum*. We might take a different approach and describe the gastrula of each species in terms of its characteristic cell types, and the characteristic rate at which these differentiate. But even with this approach, the term would become complicated and unwieldy. Moreover, the term would lose what Tennant calls its 'open-textured meaning'. Experts teach the student to recognise a gastrula by showing him an example, probably together with a simple diagram. After some exposure, the student grasps the concept intuitively. Equipped with this knowledge, he is able to apply it even to a previously undescribed species. Any description of the gastrula purely in physical and chemical terms would have to be altered with the discovery of each new example. The term itself, nevertheless, would survive this extension unchanged. The beauty of morphological terms lies in their openness, and the problem with attempts to reduce them is that this openness is lost. Morphological homologies, such as the gastrula, describe certain orders in the large, which admit heterogeneity in the small. Tennant believes that ultimately the meaning of morphological homologies will be reduced to atoms and molecules, despite these difficulties. This belief is nothing more than an act of faith. The Cartesian method fails in the face of order above heterogeneity. There is no way, in this case, to reduce complexity to simplicity. No wonder that homology has never yielded to the Darwinian explanation.

9. GENETIC AND MORPHOLOGICAL APPROACHES

In the morphological approach to systematics, we study the outward form of organisms to generate classifications. We can also study sequences of nucleotide bases of DNA or RNA, with the aim of tracing the pathways of genetic transmission. This is the genetic approach to systematics. There is an intuitive element in

21

establishing characters, but this can be eliminated using suitable automations. Nucleotide sequences may be aligned by eye, gaps being inserted by inspection to produce the closest visual match between the sequences. Bishop and Thompson (1986) automate the alignment of pairs of sequences under a model of evolution that incorporates sequence substitution, deletion and insertion events. Their achievement shows that genetic data are fundamentally different from morphological data. Patterson (1988) discusses the attempts made by Jardine and Jardine (1967) to develop a mathematical means of comparing morphologies. He notes significantly that the authors quickly saw the computer program they wrote to be 'only an aid' (Jardine, 1970: 332). Patterson links the failure of their attempt to the fact that morphology exists in three dimensions, rather than one. We may link it to the fact that, unlike DNA sequences, morphologies are hierarchically organised. There are emergent properties, homologies, which are irreducible to any quantitative model of physics and chemistry.

The genetic approach deals with linear DNA sequences, which are aligned according to a dynamical model of the causal process of evolution, a process assumed to take place independently of the observer. The context of morphology, with its inherent hierarchical organisation, dictates that character concepts are the result of the interpretations made by a community of observers. The morphological approach derives its data through a process of interpretation, similar to that involved in any linguistic communication.

The structure of the DNA can be understood in terms of physical *laws*, whereas its function can only be comprehended in terms of *rules* of interpretation specific to living organisms (Pattee, 1978: 195-196). The coding relationship between DNA triplet and aminoacid is not reducible to physical laws, but rather to be understood as a property of the whole organism. The two approaches to systematics we have discussed are readily understood in these terms. The genetic approach assumes a process of evolution that, at least for the purpose of the analysis, lawfully governs all sequence alignments over the whole study group. The aim of the approach is to improve the fit between the model and the data. The aim of the morphological approach is to discover rules for the interpretation of biological structure. Thus, the underlying aims of the two approaches can be seen to have the character of law or rule respectively. The genetic approach generates its data using a dynamical, necessarily rate-dependent model of evolution. The morphological approach derives its data through a process of interpretation and the results of the interpretation are independent of the rate at which the interpretation is carried out. The genetic approach is dynamic, the morphological approach linguistic. The two are complementary, yet incompatible in the sense of Pattee (1978).

The aim of the morphological approach is to discover the hierarchy of types, the aim of the genetic approach to discovery the family tree of life. The hierarchy summarises putative homologies, in such a way that the greatest number agree (are congruent). This is a purely logical, linguistic criterion, as to the most efficient summary of symbols. The family tree expresses the most likely pathways of genetic transmission, based on a dynamic model of genetic change. The two approaches are complementary in the sense of Rieppel (1988: 159): 'Classification emphasises discontinuity and the subordinated hierarchy of types and subtypes ... By its logical construction, the hierarchy of types is static, i.e. ahistorical ... By its abstraction from specific form and function, the hierarchy of types is acausal: it abstracts from the causes (structural and functional) of similarity versus dissimilarity and change, but remains restricted to the representation of formal, i.e. topological relations of similarity.'

10. TWO PARALLEL STREAMS OF INFORMATION

Elsasser (1998) takes order above heterogeneity as the foundation of a theory of organisms. It is the first of four principles, which he puts forth. They, and their corollaries, are listed below:

1. The principle of ordered heterogeneity
'Take a cell of 1 micron^3; if an atom occupies somewhat less than 1 angström^3, there will be over 10^{12} atoms in such a cell. Some fraction of these will be carbon atoms; given the capability of carbon atoms to from complex, three-dimensional structures, a tremendous number of such structures becomes possible ... *the number of theoretically possible structures is vastly in excess of the number of living cells that*

could possibly exist in a universe of the space-time extension determined by astronomers' (Elsasser, 1998: 30).

1a. The postulate of finiteness

'If a heterogeneous object is sufficiently complex it may and often does occur that the investigator runs out of samples of a class of objects (cells, organisms) before he has been able to determine the structure of the objects with sufficient precision. ... *'The laws of physics do not preclude unbounded repetition of an experiment, the regularities of biology (morphology) do'* (Elsasser, 1998: 41).

2. The principle of creative selection

'Our chief statement is then that a cell of certain (morphological) characteristics can exist in many more different molecular patterns then there are actual cells in the world. Hence *a choice is made in nature* among the immense number of possible patterns ... *the availability of such a choice is the basic and irreplaceable criterion of holistic or nonmechanistic biology* ... those aspects of morphology that cannot be "reduced" to mechanistic causality appear here as direct expression of a scientifically justifiable form of creativity' (Elsasser, 1998: 5).

3. The principle of holistic memory

'that the content of that which is created results from a selection, among the immense number of patterns available, of a pattern that resembles some earlier pattern of the same organism or of preceding (parental) organisms. *The main point of the third principle is that no mechanism for the transmission of information over time is specified. We therefore postulate here the transmission of information over a time-interval without an intervening device, such as computer engineers call a "storage" mechanism'* (Elsasser, 1998: 5).

3a. Homogeneous and heterogeneous replication

'If we now assume that there is a process of information transfer without intermediate storage, *we claim in effect that organisms make use of two separate and quite different processes for information transfer over time'* (Elsasser, 1998: 7). 'The molecular process underlying genetics will from now on be designated as *homogeneous replication*, where by the term "homogeneous" we mean that in order to duplicate molecular copying in the laboratory in macroscopic terms one must have a homogeneous assembly of identical DNA molecules. The process just considered, of information transfer without intervening storage will from now on be designated as *heterogeneous reproduction*' (Elsasser, 1998: 43).

4. The principle of operative symbolism (releasers)

'We now interpret the discrete, genetic message as a *symbol* of the complete reproductive process. *Here a symbol is defined as an incomplete message* [or releaser], *from which the organism can reconstruct a structure by the process of heterogeneous reproduction such that the final structure is similar to an ancestral structure.* ... For instance, if the gene induces the appearance of an enzyme, then the enzyme is an operative component, indispensable for the reconstruction of the future message, "necessary but not sufficient" in the mathematician's language' (Elsasser, 1998: 45).

The autonomy of living things is a creative act, which is irreducible to underlying physics and chemistry. There is a creative selection among the immense number of possible physical configurations, so that the form established is similar to previous forms. Living things possess a memory of their type, which shapes their development. This holistic memory is not stored in the genes, but is transmitted through an alternative process of reproduction. As Wagner (1989b) said, homologues do not literally descend, yet, in some way, they are continuous from generation to generation. Van Valen (1982) proposes that homology is correspondence caused by continuity of information, but information that is not genetic but morphological. There are two kinds of information stability in living things. Genes are an information store, physically embodied in DNA molecules, and homogeneously replicated from generation to generation. Homologies are stable information memories, transferred without mechanical storage by heterogeneous reproduction. They are mnemes of Semon (1921). Genes do not bear sole responsibility for the development of living things. They are releasers of patterns of memory, Post-It notes in the realm of life. Tuning to a particular radio frequency releases a particular

25

pattern of sounds to be reproduced in the radio receiver. Tuning to a particular gene frequency releases a particular morphological pattern in the population.

After discussing discussed the problems with the Darwinian explanation of homology, Hardy (1965) considers his own mnemonic theory. In addition to the genetic stream, there is a psychic stream, which is a species' experience of habit, form and development. 'There would be two parallel streams of information—the DNA code supplying the varying physical form of the organic stream to be acted on by selection—and the psychic stream of shared experience—the subconscious species "blueprint"—which together with the environment, would select those members in the population better able to carry on the race ... Such an internal conserving selective element might explain the secret of homology in face of an ever changing gene complex' (Hardy, 1965: 258, 259). Homologies are conserved morphological information, responsible for maintaining the peculiarities of individuals over their own lifetimes, the stability of species over millions of years, and the permanence of higher types, such as the mammals and the vertebrates (Elsasser, 1998: 110).

Genetic replication is simply a form of chemical copying. 'The conditions for heterogeneous reproduction are quite different. The process makes sense only if there is an immense reservoir of potential variants which differ from each other in structural or dynamical details but such that certain sets of them have a similarity in the large. This similarity in the large ... is taken in such a scheme as the very foundation of a holistic view of organisms' (Elsasser, 1998: 73). Homology is this similarity in the large, and is therefore foundation of holism in biology. Genetic replication, given that it is homogeneous, is prone to errors according to Shannon's Law: 'The latter expresses a phenomenon purely of statistics that holds in any system which obeys mechanical laws ... provided there are many equal components (atoms or molecules) present' (Elsasser, 1998: 44). Holistic memory, on the other hand, is not made up of separate parts to which the law could apply, so does not deteriorate over time. The permanence of type is an empirical fact demonstrated by the fossil record: 'species live in the average for several million years from their first appearance to their extinction. During this long time the characteristics of the species change very little, mostly in barely perceptible ways' (Elsasser, 1998: 44). Elsasser (1998: 118) therefore declares that 'holistic memory is a primary phenomenon of nature whose existence is postulated but cannot be deduced from any "laws".' It is similar to the invariance of the speed of light in special relativity. No wonder that the permanence of type has never succumbed to Darwinian explanation.

11. HIERARCHIES OF CONSTRAINT

In order to take into account how the genes are mapped onto the phenotype, population genetics has to invoke a number of postulates, for example, pleiotropy, penetrance and covariance (see Wagner, 1989, and Wagner et al., 1994, summarised in Wagner and Altenberg, 1996). Alberch (1991) regards these as ad hoc: 'This phenomenological treatment ... prevents the possibility of studying the role of development in evolution' (Alberch, 1991: 5). Alberch rejects a simple genotype-phenotype map, in which genes control developmental parameters, which in turn control morphology. Rather genes, through protein synthesis, lead to changes in cell properties and tissue geometry, which, through inductive relationships, lead to new patterns of gene expression. 'The implications of this cyclical/feedback scheme drastically alter our perception of how complex morphologies evolve. Development cannot be reduced to a problem of gene expression, since gene expression itself is under epigenetic control' (Alberch, 1991: 6). Alberch proposes that there exist certain developmental constraints, which are not determined by the genes, but rather by the non-linear character of the developmental system as a whole (see also Arnold et al., 1989).

Turning to an earlier treatment, Alberch (1982) describes the idea of developmental constraints with the aid of a thought experiment. He considers, for sake of example, that the whole diversity of a phenotype can be expressed in terms of two variables, x and y. (Alberch, 1991, considers a more realistic experiment, where there are m parameters that describe the spatial and temporal interactions that occur during development). The distribution of forms found in nature is not continuous. Instead, phenotypes cluster and certain regions of the xy space remain empty. Now let us take a population of one of the natural forms and breed the population for a large number of generations. The effect of natural selection is eliminated as far as possible, by enforcing random mating and minimising competition. The overall genetic variability of the population can also be increased using mutagens. Score all the new phenotypes in terms of x and y, including teratologies. We will get the same phenotype clusters as before, plus new ones, which will be naturally lethal or non-functional phenotypes. 'However, there will still be states that are prohibited by developmental constraints' (Alberch, 1982: 318). The basic effect of developmental constraints on the apportionment of morphological variation is that 'a continuous distribution of genotypes can result in a discontinuous distribution of phenotypes' (Alberch, 1982: 319). Homology of structures thus emerges from the discontinuous apportionment of genotypic variation.

The theoretical framework that Alberch (1982) provides for understanding developmental constraints is that of non-linear systems: 'Developmental systems are complex non-linear dynamical systems. It is an intrinsic property of such systems that they will fall into a discrete number of stable states, i.e. we should find a discrete and bounded distribution of phenotypes. Furthermore, non-linear dynamical systems will exhibit preferred transitions of form' (Alberch, 1982: 327-328). The analysis of development as a dynamical system, in terms of some model of pattern generation, enables possible stable states of morphology to be identified and the preferred transformations between those states. Stable states of the morphogenetic system, like those of the genome, are poised. The morphogenetic process is conceived as a set of simple, locally acting assembly rules (Alberch, 1982: 321). Genetic or environmental change perturbs the values of the parameters of the developmental system, but as long as the values stay within certain limits, the morphology remains unchanged. The morphology is said to be self-regulating or canalised (Waddington, 1957). However, if a particular parameter reaches a threshold value then a sudden shift to a different stable state occurs. This effect is known in the language of non-linear systems theory as 'bifurcation'. The parameter space for a particular dynamical system is said to have 'bifurcation boundaries' at which the global behaviour of the system, such as the resulting morphology, shifts from one stable state to another. Oster and Alberch (1982) describe 'how the bifurcations in the developmental program acts as a filter, giving order to the random mutations in the genome, so as to present natural selection with a small subset of the possible phenotypes' (figure 11, legend). Thus developmental bifurcations 'filter random mutations, giving them a non-random character' (p. 454).

Signals pass out from the genome and modify the environment to produce the phenotype. This is what we call development. Development is an interaction between the genetic signals and the environment. The dividing line between the phenotype and the environment is not precise: the phenotype 'is a bit of the environment locally modified by the genetic information' (Cairns-Smith, 1982: 80). It is possible to imagine that the phenotype, the manifestation of the effects of the genetic signals, extends into the environment beyond the bounds of the body housing the corresponding genes. This is the 'extended phenotype' (Dawkins, 1982).

'Hierarchies can be profitably viewed as systems of constraint' (Allen and Starr, 1982: 11). We can envisage the phenotype itself as a set of holons, which differ in the extent to which they filter genetic signals as they pass out into the environment. Genetic signals that pass through few phenotypic holons will be expressed relatively unfiltered. On the other hand, genetic signals that pass through many levels of the hierarchy will be significantly filtered. Continuous genetic differences between organisms in a population may be expressed as continuous phenotypic differences, if the corresponding genetic signals are relatively unfiltered, or as discontinuities, if the genetic signals are significantly filtered. The accumulation of genetic changes will cause gradual modifications of the phenotype in the first case, but sudden shifts between stable states in the second. In this way, phenotypic holons can be said to constrain the dynamics of genetic change. These constraints are properties of the developmental system: they are *developmental constraints*. Genetic signal is filtered in such a way that across individuals, and indeed across species, qualitatively different morphologies are produced.

Homologies are developmental constraints conserved among organisms. Homologies are the rules operating at the phenotypic level that constrain the dynamics of the genetic level (cf. Allen and Starr, 1982: 42). Through descent with modification, organisms accumulate inherited constraints on their genetic dynamics, or as Riedl (1977) would put it, on their adaptive freedom: 'Structures from two individuals or

29

from the same individual are homologous if they share a set of developmental constraints, caused by locally acting self-regulatory mechanisms of organ differentiation. These structures are thus developmentally individualised parts of the phenotype' (Wagner, 1989b: 62). The taxon or type is the totality of constraints inherited by the organism, characterising 'a set of species sharing a common pattern of constraints and adaptive opportunities ... the key event in the origin of a taxon is a change in the pattern of constraints' (Wagner, 1986: 154-155). The thorax individuates the insect type, yet it cannot be a structure, since there is no continuity of morphological structures from one generation to the next. The thorax is relationship of developmental constraint inherited by insects, which individuates them as such. Through descent with modification, organisms accumulate inherited developmental constraints, and thus become increasingly individualised.

I have described above a 'feedback regulatory cycle' operating between genotype and phenotype, similar to that envisaged by Riedl (1977). In order to explain the stability of homologues over evolutionary time, Riedl saw the necessity of 'feedback loops of cause and effect both from the genome to the phenome and in the *reverse* direction' (Riedl, 1977: 364). The dynamics of gene frequencies may be the cause of phenotypic change, but the effects are constrained by the phenotype itself. Thus information flows both ways: from genotype to phenotype in the causal relationship enshrined in the 'central dogma' of molecular biology, and from phenotype to genotype as constraints enshrined in the systems approach (Riedl, 1977; Wagner, 1986).

12. QUANTUM FORMS

In Bohr's principle of complementarity, we must renounce full knowledge of systems that undergo discontinuous changes. We know a quantum system as either a particle or a wave, but cannot combine the two descriptions in a picture of what the system is between measurements. To extrapolate behaviour between measurements would assume that they change continuously, an assumption broken by the quantum of action. The agencies of measurement and the measured system form an indivisible and unanalysable whole. It is inherently ambiguous to talk of a particle following a defined trajectory between measurements. The holon, too, exists in an unanalysable, ambiguous state—the Janus state—which is broken into complementary aspects when we mark the boundary of the holon. We see a holon as either part or whole, but not both; these are complementary, yet incompatible. We can say nothing of the holon before we see either part or whole, renouncing our knowledge of the living system, as it exists prior to our intervention[3]. Bohr's logic of generalised complementarity emerges from the laws of form.

The agencies of measurement and the measured effect have a form which is conspicuous to the human observer, but which cannot be reduced to the behaviour of individual elements of the system. In the conventional interpretation of quantum mechanics, the so-called Copenhagen interpretation, the form of the system is ascribed to some power of the observer's measurement apparatus to collapse the wave function of the elements of the system. Indeed some have suggested that this power lies not in the measuring device, but in the mind of the observer (Wigner, 1970; see also Rae, 1986, chapter 5). In both cases, we are left with the conundrum of how the wave function of the universe could collapse before the existence of observers and their measurements. Wheeler saw the universe before observers as less real, like a 'smoky dragon' (see discussion in Midgley, 1992: chapter 18.) Those who adopt a principle of complementarity tend to reject such metaphysical difficulties and take a phenomenalist stance. Phenomenalism is concerned only with the operations of measurement and leaves open the question of the underlying reality (Harré, 1972: 68-80). Different experimental arrangements can lead to the observation of the electron as a particle and as a wave, but we have no need to enquire further into the nature of the electron. A less orthodox approach is to say that when quantum situations of different forms are possible, a new universe comes into being for each form, only one being actualised in any particular universe (see DeWitt and Graham, 1973; Rae, 1986, chapter 6). These approaches show a certain discomfort with the notion of form, probably because none directly addresses the issue.

In Bohm's causal, indeed morphological interpretation of quantum theory, a quantum

---

[3] I would like to compare the Janus particle in Etter (1998). A quantum system is a system of two linked probabilities, neither of which is itself observable. Measurement of the system amounts to disconnection of the link and the probabilities fall apart into the complementary descriptions of the Heisenberg and Schrödinger equations.

potential is postulated which is dependent on the form of the wave function not on its intensity (see Bohm and Peat, 1989: 88-97; Bohm and Hiley, 1993: 31-32). The particle's trajectory is constrained by the whole form of the quantum potential and the two are considered to belong to different orders of existence, explicate and implicate. Complementary descriptions in terms of explicate and implicate order are required for a full account of the quantum situation (Bohm, 1980: 166).

Bohm's quantum field has much in common with the idea of a morphic fields suggested by Sheldrake (1990, 1995a, 1995b). Morphic fields do not consist of matter or energy, but rather shape matter and energy into particular geometrical patterns. The quantum field for a graphite diffraction grating, for example, shapes the matter and energy of electron particles passed through it into a characteristic diffraction pattern. Even in cases where particulate behaviour is observed, the wave is present, acting as before to guide the motion of the particles. This is Bohm's resolution of wave-particle duality, in terms of a "guiding wave", which is quite unlike any other wave field known to physics. The guiding wave possesses very little energy of its own yet it is able to influence the behaviour of its associated particles.

Sheldrake (1995a) discusses the multiple minimum problem in biochemistry. Proteins fold up in a matter of minutes, assuming only one of many possible minimum energy configurations. If induced to unfold, they will refold again into the normal configuration, avoiding other energetically possible but abnormal arrangements. They are able to reach the same end by a variety of different paths. The total number of possible configurations is enormous (Sheldrake, 1995a: 65). 'It is therefore conceivable that some factor other than energy 'selects' between these possibilities and thus determines the specific structure taken up by the system' (Sheldrake, 1995a: 70-71). It is the morphic field, which brings about this selection. Each morphic field is associated with a particular kind of morphic unit, which it stabilises through a rule of repetition. 'The characteristic form of a given morphic unit is determined by the forms of previous similar systems which act upon it across time and space by a process called *morphic resonance*' (Sheldrake, 1995a: 116-117). Morphic resonance is heterogeneous reproduction and the whole statement is equivalent to the principle of holistic memory. Indeed, Sheldrake (1995b) specifically

32

describes the action of morphic resonance as a kind of organic memory, echoing both Hardy (1965) and Elsasser (1998): '...natural systems, such as termite colonies, or pigeons, or orchid plants, or insulin molecules, inherit a collective memory from all previous things of their kind, however far away they were and however long ago they existed. Because of this cumulative memory, through repetition the nature of things becomes increasingly habitual. Things are as they are because they were as they were...A beech seedling, for example, as it grows into a tree takes up the characteristic shape, structure, and habits of a beech. It is able to do so because it inherits in nature from previous beeches; but this inheritance if not just a matter of chemical genes. It depends also on the transmission of habits of growth and development from countless beech trees that existed in the past' (Sheldrake, 1995b: xvii).

13. TIME AND TIMELESS

Different physiological time scales exist in living things. A mouse, for example, lives at a much faster pace than an elephant. Indeed, physiological time scales change with age, from the fury of youth to the calm of old age. Psychological time scales can change by the emotions. Consider a wonderful play or a film where three hours feel like five minutes, or a boring speech where five minutes feel like three hours.

Bergson makes the distinction between concrete time and abstract or mathematical time (Bergson, 1911: 22). Concrete time is constant creation, where each instant is incommensurable with the last. In abstract time, all times are equivalent. If living time is concrete and embodied then the variations of psychological and physiological time make sense. From an abstract perspective, this makes no sense; in the logic of solid bodies, time does not really flow at all and certainly not at different speeds for different organisms.

The logic of solids—of bodies external to one another and separated in space and time—is the logic of the analytic mode, distinctive of mainstream science. It is a logic of abstract time. In the holistic mode, the unity of a system stands before the separation of parts: it is a unity without unification (Bortoft, 1996). This is a logic of concrete time.

Bohm (1969; Bohm and Peat, 1989) considers that there is a flow of time that is mechanical—a manifest or explicate time—but every so often there are creative periods, where new content unfolds from the implicate, hidden order. In mechanical time, there is a chain of events, where one event determines the next event. Creative change, on the other hand, is "timeless", the origin of a whole new chain of events, incommensurable with the last.

The analytic logic of solids is a good description of the explicate order, the holistic logic that of his implicate order. Whereas for Bohm the implicate order is timeless, for Bergson this is the domain of concrete time. Whether a process appears as in time or timeless depends on whether we look from the abstract or concrete perspective:

Abstract:	time	timeless
Concrete	timeless	time
	analytic	holistic
	explicate	implicate

On the one hand, we have the natural, living process, which is creative and irreversible, to be understood in the holistic mode. On the other hand, we have an artificial or classical process, which is mechanical and reversible, understood in the analytic mode. From the abstract perspective, time is proper to the reversible, artificial process; the natural process appears timeless. From the concrete perspective, time, in its irreversibility, is proper to living things; artificial systems are timeless.

Prigogine (1980) develops a notion of concrete time for irreversible processes, which he calls age. As living things endure, so do they age. Bohm (1987) derives Prigogine's age quantity as an enfoldment parameter. A movement of enfoldment is therefore a movement along an axis of concrete time, or ageing. Such a movement involves a number of repetitive transformations. The cogent moment of time for a living thing grows longer as it ages. So does the rhythm of its life change, solidifying as habits become entrenched.

Think of the history of an invention, such as photography, the bicycle or the motorcar. In the beginning, there are a wide variety of competing designs, which eventually give way to a small number of successful designs. These few designs form the basis of future changes, which are constrained to be much smaller in scope. It is difficult to identify the reason for the survival of the successful few. Gould (1989) describes the evolution of multicellular animals in this way. Testified in the fossils of the Burgess shale, Cambrian there were a large number of disparate body plans in the Cambrian period, which gave way to a smaller number of successful designs. For example, among twenty-five different arthropod designs, only two survived, the chelicerates and uniramians. The most beautiful, complex and common designs became extinct, whereas the rare and specialised continued.

According to Bergson, life is impelled by a creative impetus, an ascending movement, whereas matter is the reverse tendency, a descending movement (Bergson, 1911: 11-12). Matter is life unmaking itself: 'So, from an immense reservoir of life, jets must be gushing out unceasingly, of which each falling back is a world. The evolution of living species within this world represents what subsists of the primitive direction of the original jet, and of an impulsion which continues itself in a direction the inverse of materiality ... In vital activity we see, then, that which subsists of the direct movement in the inverted movement, a reality which is making itself in a reality which is unmaking itself' (Bergson, 1911: 261). The ascending movement takes life to ever more widely differing forms. The descending movement takes matter into ever more regular and repetitive forms. Matter is life grown old.

Sheldrake points out that there must have been time when there were no atoms as we know them: 'Once there were no lead atoms, or sodium atoms, or atoms of any kind at all' (Sheldrake, 1995b: 61-62). There must have been a time when matter had not solidified into patterns we know by the names of these elements. Now any atom of lead is indistinguishable from any other. However, this homogeneity is result of a large number of repetitions in the evolution of the universe: '... these particles have been replicating so long that they are pretty well determined, or fixed in the "cosmic memory"' (Bohm, in Sheldrake, 1995a: 239). In the beginning, all matter was alive, as Peirce said: 'Matter is merely mind deadened by the development of habit to the point where the breaking up of these habits is very difficult' (quoted in Sheldrake, 1995b: 14). Let us think of the early history of the universe as a time of diversity, rather than the unity of the unified field. Two electrons would meet each other and not recognise each other, have a conversation and discover their similarities and differences.

In Elsasser's scheme, the distinction between the homogeneity of matter and the heterogeneity of life is important. We can now see this as a matter of degree rather than kind. Life is still in the vigorous blush of youth; matter has reached a calm uniformity. Elsasser does note that heterogeneous reproduction, even though it involves a creative selection of possible forms, does tend towards repetition: 'What observations show us is that the characteristics of the individual as well as of the species change only very slowly. *Thus it becomes imperative to assume that, in a first approximation, the outcome of creativity is repetition*' (Elsasser, 1998: 154). Species are indeed stable for at least one million years. The possibility of rapid, creative change remains, however. When change does occur, new species emerge very quickly: 'At certain moments in the geological record new species appear that show distinct differences from the older, related ones. This differentiation occurs in a relatively short time as the geological record goes; thereafter the new species maintains its characteristics relatively unchanged for its lifetime, that is until extinction occurs' (Elsasser, 1998: 96-97).

14. NESTED HOLOGRAPHIC SURFACES

Oster and Murray (1989) describe two classes of pattern generation models, chemical prepattern and mechanochemical. From the chemical prepattern viewpoint, either simple chemical gradients are established across tissues or the pattern emerges through 'diffusion-driven instabilities' (Turing, 1952). The latter subclass includes the reaction-diffusion models studied by Prigogine, such as the 'Brusselator' (Prigogine and Lefever, 1968). The mechanical aspects of development, which shape form, are not taken into account in this approach and the identity of the 'morphogens' involved has not been ascertained. From the mechanochemical viewpoint, chemical and mechanical processes interact and are framed in terms of measurable forces and displacements. Goodwin (1990) notes the elusiveness of chemical morphogens and summarises his own work on mechanochemical models, which involve measurable quantities such as the concentration of calcium ions and the viscoelastic strain of the cell membrane.

Both classes of models generate patterns through a combination of activation at short scales and inhibition at long scales (Oster and Murray, 1989; cf. Gierer and Meinhardt, 1972). Models in yet a third class, namely the Lotka-Volterra models of population dynamics, generate pattern in the same way and are therefore morphogenetic (Britton, 1989, 1990). Indeed, Lotka first published his model as a description of the oscillating concentrations of two reacting chemical species (Lotka, 1920). Though activation between species is significant only at short scales, an inhibitory effect will be experienced among species of widely differing scales.

An entity's scale is its position in the hierarchy. The greater an entity's scale, the greater its influence on other entities, and thus the higher its position in the hierarchy. Scale may be defined as 'the period of time or space over which signals are integrated or smoothed to give message' (Allen and Starr, 1982: 18). To illustrate their concept of scale, Allen and Starr (1982: 19) discuss May's (1973) Lotka-Volterra model of the history of resource use in a series of populations (or generations of a given population): 'May's concern is for the influence (messages) that past populations (signal) have upon resources (the holon) at time t. He integrates the signal N using a particular weighting function Q. "The function $Q(t)$ specifies how much weight to attach to the populations at various past times, in order to arrive at their present effect on resource availability." Thus the total effect of past populations on resources [the scale] at time t is

'$\int_{-\infty} N(t') \, Q(t-t') \, dt'$,

'where N = the number of individuals in the past populations.'

May's Q function is an example of a Green's function, where only temporal convolution is considered. The amount of resources available to the present population has the history of resource use of previous generations enfolded within it.

There are a number of previous populations, where contributions of different degrees of enfoldment are combined. The amount of resources available to the present population depends on the total series of generations, on the age of the population. The knock-on effect of more ancient populations on the present population will be greater than the effect of recent populations, thus more ancient populations will filter present resource use more than recent populations. Age is related to scale.

In Gourley and Britton (1996), the inhibition term uses a Green's function to describe how the whole history of predation throughout space and time influences the current behaviour of the prey population. Thus, spatial and temporal convolution are both included. Gourley and Britton (1996: 332) justify their approach as follows: 'Whilst integrodifferential systems tend to be rather complicated in appearance, all we have done essentially is to recognise that time delays should be included in the term representing intraspecific competition for resources for the prey species, and that the assumption of motion (through diffusion) means that any time delay term should be nonlocal in space as well as in time. As a consequence, we have obtained a variety of solution behaviours which reflects phenomena such as animal aggregation, population cycles and the motion of aggregations as observed in nature. We therefore claim that nonlocal effects play a very important role in pattern formation, and that our model is more realistic than the usual type of reaction-diffusion system used to model predator prey interactions in which the species can diffuse.' The richest models use Green's functions to capture the nonlocal, holistic order of morphogenesis.

Bohm make use of Green's functions to describe the movement of unfolding and enfolding that takes place in quantum processes (Bohm, 1980: 160; Bohm and Peat, 1989: 175-179; Bohm and Hiley, 1993: 354-355). The form of the wave function $\Psi(x',t')$ is related to its form at a later time $\Psi(x,t)$, by a Green's function $Q(x - x', t - t')$, such that

$$\Psi(x,t) = \int Q(x - x', t - t')\ \Psi(x',t')\ dx'$$

The value of the wave function $\Psi(x,t)$ is the sum of contributions over the whole range of values x' at time t', weighted by Q. The region near x is in communication with regions from all over space at other times, enfolding the information contributed by them. Information contributed from each region near x' will unfold into the whole space x, filtered by the factor $Q(x - x', t - t')$.

Let us consider the picture of hierarchy introduced by Kron (1963), as a series of tears. Tear a system by removing a layer of components, namely the intersection network, at the interface between adjacent subsystems. Bowden (1990) shows how Kron's picture is equivalent to Huygens principle in the reinterpretation of Jessel (1962). Information about any subsystem is held in holographic form at its surface, that is, at the intersection. All that an observer needs to know about a torn subsystem is the information on the surface enclosing that subsystem. Similarly, all an observer within a torn subsystem needs to know about the outside world is on the surface. A holon is an interface between its parts and the rest of the universe, a holographic surface through which information enters and departs. The signals emerging from the internal dynamics of the torn subsystem pass through its surface. A holon is the surface screen of a subsystem, upon which an image of the dynamics unfolds. The most succinct description of a subsystem is the evolution of the image of the subsystem projected onto its surface.

Take a system and make a series of tears, disconnecting subsystems step by step. A series of tears is a series of transformations of the system matrix of the form $E' = MEM^{-1}$: 'Such a succession of transformations was referred to by David Bohm as an "ordering or enfolding", and by Jessel and Resconi as a Logical System...' (Bowden, 1998). Thus, given a frame of reference, E, the transformation or metamorphosis M turns E into a different frame of reference E' (Bohm, 1980: 165-166). Marking a holon specifies a particular frame reference. The level of the analysis given by the mark is the choice of a particular degree of tearing, a particular degree of enfoldment. E' is enfolded with respect to E, and two are complementary yet incompatible, since an observer cannot adopt both scales simultaneously.

If we base the transformation M on an enfolding parameter, representing successive steps, then quantum movement emerges naturally. $E' = MEM^{-1}$ becomes equivalent to the Schrödinger's description of quantum transitions: '... Schrödinger's equation can be thought of as specifying the evolution of (a series of) tearings ... ' (Bowden, 1998; after Hiley, 1995). Abstract time *t* in Schrödinger's equation has been replaced by an enfolding parameter (as originally proposed in Bohm, 1969). A series of such transformations, $E' = MEM^{-1}$, is an iteration over the levels of the hierarchy. According to von Baer's laws, an organism iterates through its hierarchy of types as it develops. We therefore have the identical structure of order and process in both quantum physics and biological development:

1. In quantum physics
   a. The underlying order of the quantum process, captured by Huygens principle, is a nested hierarchy of holographic surfaces.
   b. The movement of a quantum process, given by the Schrödinger equation, is an iteration over this hierarchy of holographic surfaces.
2. In biological development
   a. The underlying order of the developmental process, captured in morphological classification, is a nested hierarchy of holographic surfaces.
   b. The movement of a developmental process, given by von Baer's laws, is an iteration over this hierarchy of holographic surfaces

The movement of the morphological process, whether quantum or biological, is timeless from the abstract perspective. From the concrete perspective, it is an ageing, or enduring. A biological classification is an informative summary of morphological data, in its most economical form, namely a holographic representation. The most informative summary takes the form of a binary tree (Mickevich and Platnick, 1989), which is also the optimal means to store data holographically (Bowden, 1994).

The discovery of hierarchies of holographic surfaces in biological development and quantum physics makes sense in the light of a recent proposal called the holographic principle. According to this principle, the world is 'a network of holograms, each of which contains coded within it information about the relationship between the others' (Smolin, 2000: 178). Any surface is a channel of information between observers: any surface may be treated as a holon. 'In such a world, nothing exists except processes by which information is conveyed from one part of the world to another. And the area of a screen—indeed, the area of any surface in space—is really nothing but the capacity of that surface as a channel of information. So, ... space is nothing but a way of talking about all the different channels of communication that allow information to pass from observer to observer. And geometry, as measured in terms of area and volume, is nothing but a measure of the capacity of these screens to transmit information' (Smolin, 2000: 177-178). In other words, the world is a hierarchy of holons.

REFERENCES

Alberch, P. (1982) Developmental constraints in evolutionary processes. In: Bonner, J. T. (ed.) *Evolution and Development*, pp. 313-332. Springer-Verlag, Berlin.

Alberch, P. (1991) From genes to phenotype: dynamical systems and evolvability. Genetica 84: 5-11.

Allen, T. F. H. and Starr, T. B. (1982) *Hierarchy: Perspectives in Ecological Complexity*. University of Chicago Press, Chicago, London.

Appel, T. A. (1987) *The Cuvier-Geoffroy Debate: French Biology in the Decades Before Darwin*. Oxford University Press, New York.

Arnold, S. J., Alberch, P., Csanyi, V., Dawkins, R. C., Emerson, S. B., Fritzch, B., Horder, T. J., Maynard Smith, J., Starck, M. J., Vrba, E. S., Wagners, S. P. and Wake, D. B. (1989) How do complex organisms evolve? In: Wake, D. B. and Roth, V. L. (eds.) *Integration and Evolution in Vertebrates*, pp. 403-433. Wiley, New York.

Bateson, W. (1894) *Material for the Study of Variation: Treated with especial regard to discontinuity in the origin of species*. Macmillan, London.

Bateson, P.[P. G.] (1988) The active role of behaviour in evolution. In: Ho, M.-W. and Fox, S. W. (eds.) *Evolutionary Processes and Metaphors*, pp. 191-207. Wiley, Chichester.

Bergson, H. (1911). *Creative Evolution*. Macmillan, London.

Bishop, M. J. and Thompson, E. (1986) Maximum likelihood alignment of DNA sequences. *Journal of Molecular Biology* 190: 159-165.

Bohm, D. (1969). Further remarks on the notion of order. In Waddington, C. H. (ed.) *Towards a Theoretical Biology 2: Sketches*, pp. 41-60. Edinburgh University Press, Edinburgh.

Bohm, D. (1980) *Wholeness and the Implicate Order*. Routledge and Kegan Paul, London.

Bohm, D. (1987) The implicate order and Prigogine's notion of irreversibility. *Foundations of Physics* 17: 667-677.

Bohm, D. and Peat, F. D. (1989) *Science, Order and Creativity*. Routledge, London.

Bohm, D. and Hiley, B.J. (1993) *The Undivided Universe: An Ontological Interpretation of Quantum Theory*. Routledge, London.

Bortfoft, H. (1996) *The Wholeness of Nature: Goethe's Way of Science*. Floris, Edinburgh.

Bowden, K. (1990) On general physical systems theories. *International Journal of General Systems* 18: 61-79.

Bowden, K. (1994) Hierarchical tearing: an efficient holographic algorithm for system decomposition. *International Journal of General Systems* 23(1): 23-37.

Bowden, K. (1998) Huygens' principle, physics and computers. *International Journal of General Systems* 27(1-3): 9-32.

Britton, N. F. (1989) Aggregation and the competitive exclusion principle. *Journal of Theoretical Biology* 136: 57-66.

Britton, N. F. (1990) Spatial structures and periodic travelling waves in an integro-differential reaction-diffusion population model. *SIAM Journal on Applied Mathematics* 50: 1663-1688.

Cairns-Smith, A. G. (1982) *Genetic Takeover*. Cambridge University Press, Cambridge.

Darwin, C., 1859[1968] *On the Origin of Species by Means of Natural Selection, or the Preservation of Favoured Races in the Struggle for Life*. Murray, London. reprinted by Penguin, London, edited with an introduction by J. W. Burrows.

Dawkins, R. (1982) *The Extended Phenotype*. Freeman, Oxford.

De Witt, B. S. & Graham, N. (1973). *The Many-Worlds Interpretation of Quantum Mechanics*. Princeton University Press, Princeton.

Elsasser, W. M. (1998) *Reflections on a theory of organisms: holism in biology*. John Hopkins University Press, Baltimore and London.

Etter, T. (1998) Process, System, Causality, and Quantum Mechanics: A Psychoanalysis of Animal Faith. SLAC-PUB-7890.

Geoffroy Saint-Hilaire, E. (1818) *Philosophie Anatomique*. Paris.

Ghiselin, M. T. (1976) The nomenclature of correspondence: a new look at "homology" and "analogy." In: Masterton R. B., Hodos W. and Jerison H. (eds.) *Evolution, Brain and Behaviour: Persistent Problems*, pp. 279-314. Lawrence Erlbaum, Hillsdale, New Jersey.

Gierer, A. and Meinhardt, H. (1972) A theory of biological pattern formation. *Kybernetika* 12: 20-39.

Goguen, J. (1971) Mathematical representation of hierarchically organized systems. In Attinger, E. (ed.) *Global Systems Dynamics*, pp. 112-128. Karger, Basel.

Goodwin, B. C. (1990) Structuralism in biology. *Science Progress* 74: 227-244. Blackwell, Oxford.

Goodwin, B. [C.] (1994) *How the Leopard Changed its Spots: The Evolution of Complexity*. Weidenfeld and Nicholson, London.

Gould, S. J. (1977) *Ontogeny and Phylogeny*. Belknap Press, Cambridge, Massachussetts.

Gould, S. J. (1989) *Wonderful Life: The Burgess Shale and the Nature of History*. Hutchinson Radius, London, Sydney, Auckland, Johannesburg.

Gourley, S. A. and Britton, N. F. (1996) A predator-prey reaction-diffusion system with nonlocal effects. *Journal of Mathematical Biology* 34: 297-333.

Griffiths, B. (1989) *A New Vision of Reality: Western Science, Eastern Mysticism and Christian Faith*. Collins, London.

Hardy, A. (1965). *The Living Stream: A Restatement of Evolution Theory and its Relation to the Spirit of Man*. Collins, London.

Harré, R. (1972) *The Philosophies of Science*. Oxford University Press, Oxford, New York.

Hennig, W. (1966) *Phylogenetic Systematics*. University of Illinois Press, Urbana.

Hiley, B. J. (1995) The algebra of process. In Borstner, B. and Shawe-Taylor, J. (eds.) *Consciousness at the Crossroads of Cognitive Science and Philosophy*, pp. 52-67. Imprint Academic, Thorverton.

242

Jardine, N. (1970) The observational and theoretical components of homology: a study based on the morphology of the dermal skull roof in rhipidistian fishes. *Biological Journal of the Linnean Society* 1: 327-361.

Jardine, N. and Jardine, C. J. (1967) Numerical homology. *Nature*, London 216: 301-302.

Jessel, M. (1962) *Contribution aux Théories du Principe Huygens et de la Diffraction.* Thesis for Doctorate of Physical Sciences, University of Paris.

Kauffman, S. A. (1969) Metabolic stability and epigenesis in randomly constructed genetic nets. *Journal of Theoretical Biology* 83: 215-246.

Kauffman, S. A. (1970) Behaviour of randomly connected genetic nets: binary element nets. In: Waddington, C. H. (ed.) *Towards a Theoretical Biology* 3: Drafts, pp. 18-37. Edinburgh University Press, Edinburgh

Kauffman, S. A. (1983) Developmental constraints: internal factors in evolution. In: Goodwin, B. C., Holder, N. and Wylie, C. C. (eds.) *Development and Evolution,* pp. 195-225. Cambridge University Press, Cambridge.

Kauffman, S. A. (1992) *The Origins of Order: Self-Organization and Selection in Evolution.* Oxford University Press, New York.

Kluge, A. G. (1991) Boine snake phylogeny and research cycles. *Miscellaneous Publications of the Museum of Zoology, University of Michigan* 178: 1-58.

Koestler, A. (1967) *The Ghost in the Machine.* Hutchinson, London.

Koestler, A. (1974) Beyond atomism and holism. In: Lewis, J. (ed.) *Beyond Chance and Necessity*, pp. 61-72. Garnstone, London.

Kron, G. (1962) *Diakoptics: The Piecewise Solution of Large Scale Systems.* MacDonald, London.

Lankester, E.R. (1870) On the use of the term homology in modern zoology. *Annals and Magazine of Natural History Series* 6, 34-43

Lotka, A. (1920) Undamped oscillations derived from the law of mass action. *Journal of the American Chemical Society* 42: 1595-1599.

McCabe, H. (1987) *God Matters.* Chapman, London.

Manthey, M. (1998) A combinatorial Bit Bang leading to quaternions. arXiv:quant-ph/9809033 v1.

Margulis, L. and Sagan, D. (1995) *What is Life?* Simon and Schuster, New York.

44

Mickevich, M.F. and Platnick, N. I. (1989). On the information content of classifications. *Cladistics* 5: 33-47.

Midgley, M. (1992). *Science as Salvation*. Routledge, London

Nelson, G. J. 1978. Ontogeny, phylogeny, paleontology, and the biogenetic law. *Systematic Zoology* 27: 324-345

Nelson, G. J. (1989) Cladistics and evolutionary models. *Cladistics* 5: 275-289.

May, R. M. (1973) Time-delay versus stability in population models with two or three trophic levels. *Ecology* 54: 315-325.

Oster, G. F. and Alberch, P. (1982) Evolution and bifurcation of developmental programs. *Evolution* 36: 444-459.

Oster, G. F. and J. Murray. Pattern formation models and developmental constraints. *Journal of Experimental Zoology* 251:186-202.

Pattee, H. H. (1978) The complementarity principle in biological and social structures. *Journal of Social and Biological Structures* 1: 191-200.

Patterson, C. (1988) Homology in classical and molecular biology. *Molecular Biology and Evolution* 5: 603-625.

Prigogine, I. and Lefever, R. (1968) Symmetry breaking instabilities in dissipative systems II. *Journal of Chemical Physics* 48(4):1695-1700

Prigogine, I. (1980) *From Being to Becoming*. Freeman, San Francisco.

Rae, A. (1986). *Quantum Physics: Illusion or Reality?* Cambridge University Press, Cambridge.

Raff, R. A. (1996) *The Shape of Life: Genes, Development and the Evolution of Animal Life*. University of Chicago Press, Chicago and London.

Riedl, R. (1977). A systems-analytical approach to macroevolutionary phenomena. *Quarterly Review of Biology* 52, 351-370.

Rieppel, O. C. (1988) *Fundamentals of Comparative Biology*. Birkhauser Verlag, Basel.

Rieppel, O. C. (1994) Homology, topology, typology: the history of modern debates. In: Hall, B. K. (ed.) *Homology: the Hierarchical Basis of Comparative Biology*, pp. 63-100. Academic Press, San Diego.

Roth, V. L. (1988). The biological basis of homology. In C. J. Humphries (ed.) *Ontogeny and Systematics*, pp. 1-26. British Museum (Natural History), London.

Salthe, S. N. (1985) *Evolving Hierarchical Systems: Their Structure and Representation*. Columbia University Press, New York.

Salthe, S. N. (1993) *Development and Evolution: Complexity and Change in Biology*. MIT Press, Cambridge, Massachussetts, and London.

Semon, R. (1921) *The Mneme*. Allen and Unwin, London.

Sheldrake, R. (1990) *The Rebirth of Nature: The Greening of Science and God*. Century, London.

Sheldrake, R. (1995a) *A New Science of Life: The Hypothesis of Morphic Resonance*. 3rd edition. Park Street Press, Rochester.

Sheldrake, R. (1995b) *The Presence of the Past: Morphic Resonance and the Habits of Nature*. 2nd edition. Park Street Press, Rochester.

Simon, H. A. (1962) The architecture of complexity. *Proceedings of the American Philosophical Society*. 106: 467-482.

Simon, H. A. (1973) The organisation of complex systems. In: Pattee, H. H. *Hierarchy Theory: The Challenge of Complex Systems*, pp. 1-28. Brazilier, New York.

Smolin, L. (2000) *Three Roads to Quantum Gravity*. Weidenfeld and Nicolson, London.

Spencer-Brown, G. (1969) *Laws of Form*. Allen and Unwin, London.

Tennant, N. W. (1986) Reductionism and holism in biology. In: Horder, T. J., Witkowski, J. A. and Wylie, C. C. *A History of Embryology*, pp. 407-433. Cambridge University Press, Cambridge.

Turing, A. (1952) The chemical basis of morphogenesis. *Philosophical Transactions of the Royal Society of London Series B* 237. 37-72.

Van Valen, L. M. (1982) Homology and causes. *Journal of Morphology* 173: 305-312.

Varela, F. J. (1979) *Principles of Biological Autonomy*. Elsevier North Holland, New York.

von Baer, K. E. (1828) *Über Entwickelungsgechichte der Thiere. Beobachtung und Reflexion*. Vol. 1. Bornträger, Königsberg.

Waddington, C. H. (1957) *The Strategy of the Genes*. Allen and Unwin, London.

Wagner, G. P. (1986) The systems approach: an interface between development and population genetic aspects of evolution. In: Raup, D. M. and Jablonski, D. (eds.)

245

Patterns and Processes in the History of Life, pp. 149-165. Springer-Verlag, Berlin.

Wagner, G. P. (1989a) The origin of morphological characters and the biological basis of homology. *Evolution* (Lawrence, Kansas) 43: 1157-1171.

Wagner, G. P. (1989b) The biological homology concept. *Annual Review of Ecology and Systematics* 20: 51-69.

Wagner, G. P. (1995) The biological role of homologues: A building block hypothesis. *Neues Jahrbuch der Geologischen und Paläontologischen Abhandlung* 195: 279-288.

Wagner, G. P. and Altenberg, L. (1996) Complex adaptations and the evolution of evolvability. *Evolution* 50: 967-976.

Wagner, A., Wagner, G. P. and Simillion, P. (1994) Epistasis can facilitate the evolution of reproductive isolation by peak shifts: a two-locus two-allele model. *Genetics* 138: 533-545.

Wigner, E. P. (1970). Epistemological perspective on quantum theory. In C. A. Hooker (ed.) *Contemporary Research in the Foundations and Philosophy of Quantum Theory*. Reidel, Dordrecht and Boston.

Williams, R. J. (1956) *Biochemical Individuality*. John Wiley, N.Y., reprinted by Univ. of Texas Press, Austin, Texas.

Self-reference, the Dimensionality and Scale of Quantum Mechanical Effects, Critical Phenomena, and Qualia.

Peter Marcer*, Edgar Mitchell**, Walter Schempp***
*55 rue Jean Jaures, 83600 Frejus, Var, France
aikidopeter@aol.com - http://www.bcs.org.uk/cybergroup.htm
**Edgar Mitchell, Institute of Noetic Sciences, PO Box 540037, Lake Worth, FL.
33454,USA, Fax: +1 561-641-5242, edgarmitchell@msn.com
***Lehrstuhl für Mathematik I, University of Siegen, D-57068 Siegen, Germany
schempp@mathematik.uni-siegen.de

Abstract
Self-reference, the postulated key to a more complete understanding of quantum mechanics, is shown to be a necessary mathematical basis for an evolution of all that exists in relation to a self-created quantum cosmology. The initial act of this self-creation - a critical phenomenon where the material phase transitions give rise simultaneously to mass and the strong, electro-magnetic, weak properties of matter in agreement with those of the standard model of elementary particle physics - is shown to concern 3+1 dimensional Lorentzian space/time and Einstein's general relativity. Similarly subsequent acts giving rise to entirely novel material phase transitions and properties of matter, as predicted by renormalization group theory for which K.G. Wilson received the Nobel Prize, may include, evidence is presented, those of self-aware, possibly conscious, living systems.
Keywords: self-referential quantum systems, geometric phase, phase conjugation, quantum holography, critical phenomena

1 Introduction

Quantum mechanical state vectors are arbitrary up to a constant phase factor. Yet, as Berry[1989] showed, the gauge invariant relative phases of a state vector constitute a new class of quantum observables, called the geometric/Berry phase, quite distinct from those, which are the eigenvalues of some quantum mechanical operator [Resta 1997]. Any interpretation consistent with the quantum formalism, which is universal i.e. capable of describing any physical behavior, quantum or classical [Deutsch 1985], is therefore a valid one in some phase domain. The large body of often heated argument over much of the last century, continuing today, as to which interpretation is to be preferred, can therefore decide nothing definitively so long as it is based strictly on the formalism alone. A boundary condition essential to the correct solution of any problem must be included, and in the case of self-reference can be defined as a mapping of the whole quantum field onto itself i.e. as a field automorphism. Such self-reference therefore necessarily encompasses the whole phase domain so as to include each and every valid interpretation in its own sub-domain, consistent with the arbitrariness of phase, and, of course, the formalism. That is to say, it constitutes a universal model of quantum mechanics, that, as a universal model of a theory (in the language of sets), has, it is known [Erhlich 1986], a unique birthordering or birth-order field automorphism. This unique birthordering can therefore be identified with the evolution of the whole hypothesized self-referential quantum cosmology. One, such as can arise, as will be shown, from some form of degenerate physical instability, or which mathematically could arise in a Godelian manner as has been envisaged, for example, by Hofstadter [1979].

In support of this thesis of a self-referential quantum cosmology, other known self-referential quantum mechanical models are therefore examined and compared, in particular, those of :-

1) the Berry/geometric phase and its relationship to quantum chaos [Berry 1986], which, like chaos, must arise as a consequence of boundary conditions and where, in the case of chaos, self-reference can take the form of self-similar fractal systems,

2) quantum holography (QH) [Schempp 1992], where phase conjugation defines self reference such that the image of any 3 dimensional spatial object coincides with the object itself, and

3) Kenneth Wilson's renormalization group methodology [Wilson 1983] for the determination of the critical phenomenon.

These examinations show:-

1) that the postulated self-referential cosmology is in excellent agreement with the current understanding of the standard model of elementary particle physics, so as to be able to account for existence on all appropriate scales throughout the universe, of the strong, electromagnetic, weak and gravitational properties of matter as all arising spontaneously and simultaneously as a consequence of a critical phenomenon or initial unstable critical point. In particular it is shown in contradiction to the generally held view in physics that quantum theory and general relativity are incompatible, that in fact, the quantizations of mass, electromagnetic, strong, and weak charge in relation to the Rowlands/Cullerne [1999; 2001] extension of the standard model of elementary particle physics are exactly those that ensure such compatibility!!

2) that this critical phenomenon is the first resonant event in an unending incremental process of phase conjugate adaptive resonance, which, as quantum holographic measurement with reference to the cosmological reference frame produces an historical record or history enabling the postulated cosmological evolution. Thus the cosmos may be said to be self-reproducing or "cloning" itself adaptively, ie is self-organizing, and

3) citing previous research, that

a) DNA and its associate life-forms, for example, the simplest living prokaryote cells [Marcer and Schempp 1997a], can be postulated to be highly complex examples of other self-referential sub-systems, operating in accordance with the same quantum physical principles, ie by DNA-wave computation [Gariaev et al. 2001]/quantum holography [Marcer and Schempp 1996], including

b) those self-referential self-aware life-forms, such as ourselves, which maybe described as conscious [Pribram 1991; Marcer and Schempp 1997b ;1998; Marcer and Mitchell 2001].

All provide further evidence in confirmation of the self-organising evolutionary process [Marcer and Dubois 1992] from the Self-Creation to the creation of the self [Marcer 1996].

2 The Renormalization Group Approach to Critical Phenomena

In 1982, Kenneth Wilson was awarded the Nobel Prize for his use of renormalization group methodology in relation to critical phenomena [Anderson 1982]. Experimently well validated, its mathematical basis, the repeated self-referential mapping of the quantum Hamiltonian of the particular material onto itself so to determine that material's stable and unstable critical fixed points/attractors, established a universal means for calculating material phase transitions. It is a quantum theoretic methodology which employs a rescaling/renormalization procedure P utilizing an arbitrary 3 dimensional spatial lattice [Wilson 1983], such as will be seen later, QH also employs based on the 3 parameter Heisenberg nilpotent Lie group G.

Such critical fixed points thus determine all the possible physical properties, noumena and qualia of materials. It maybe concluded therefore that, since all material properties, noumena and qualia, are a consequence of quantum mechanical effects, only in up to 3+1 dimensions as Wilson's methodology [1983] also proves, that we live in a quantum mechanical and not a classical universe. Further it follows that noumena and qualia are only subjective in the sense that they concern measurement with reference to a local measurement standard. That is to say, that in relation to measurement in any self-referential sub-frame of the universe, it is possible to establish an arbitrary measurement standard i.e. the traditional laboratory standard, for example. This is only possible, however, because in the reference frame of the universe as a whole, defined as all that exists, the quantum mechanical state vector is determined only up to a fixed arbitrary constant phase factor. But it must be remembered, in quantum mechanics, that all local measurement standards and corresponding fixed "arbitrary" constant phase factors, cannot be divorced one from the other and from those of the universe as a whole. That is to say, it is requirement of quantum mechanics that all measurements and measurement standards compose a single consistent set, and be considered as objective. For in the proposed self-referential quantum cosmology not only will entirely novel material properties result from the novel material phase transitions continually taking place as the result of repeated self-reference, but such self-referential processes will also ultimately establish the local measurement standards against which these novel material properties are measured. This argument therefore establishes a sense, self-organizational self-reference in any sub-frame, in which this hypothesized cosmology can be considered anthropomorphic, see section 5.2.

In this connection, as already cited Wilson [1983] proved, that while the corresponding classical field equations (to their quantum counterparts) can usually be applied on scales large compared to the Planck length, care is essential as this cannot always be said to be the case, as is still often assumed. That is, the earlier assumption of Landau (whose calculations were indeed contradicted by experimental findings in relation to the Ising effect) and, more recently those of Tegmark, both purportedly showing that quantum mechanical effects only concern atomic scales, are under the circumstances to which Wilson's methodology applies, false in up to 3+1 dimensions [Wilson 1983].

Such circumstances also concern the fact that the mathematical lattice rescaling procedure P fundamental to Wilson's renormalization group methodology for the determination of material phase transitions corresponds with that used in Schempp's quantum holography (QH) [1992] described in terms of the 3 dimensional Heisenberg Lie group G. Thus, the processes of QH, which, for example, provide an experimentally validated mathematical foundation for the workings of magnetic resonance imaging (MRI) machines and synthetic aperture radars [Schempp 1998; 1986; Binz and Schempp, 2000a and b], are, in principle, a physical means to realize Wilson's lattice rescaling procedure P, so as to show :-

i) the nature, dimensionality and scale of quantum mechanical macroscopic effects in relation to the quantum holographic models to be described or cited, of an inflationary cosmology, elementary particle physics, and the living world, and

ii) that the boundary condition of self-reference can be identified :-

a) from considerations of Berry phase [Manini 2001], with a totally degenerate zero energy point,

b) from considerations of Wilson's [1983] theory of critical phenomena, with an unstable fixed point/universal attractor, and

c) with a universal saddle point determined in terms of the Golden Number [Marcer 1992] (see Figure I),

so as to provide an explanation of the hypothesized cosmological evolution.

(a) then says that such an evolution would remarkably be one of entirely geometric-topological origin taking place in the potential landscape of the Hamiltonian parameter space [Lloyd 2001; Manini 2001] rather than being, as is usually supposed, of dynamic origin. This would explain why, as we all aware, there is quite literally "no time like the present". For now there need be no Schrodinger dynamic evolution of the wave function (see section 6), only an incremental 'process' of morphological natural selection, akin to Darwinian evolution, in that whole potential landscape. What one of us [Mitchell and Williams 1996] has called "The Way of the Explorer". Thus change takes the form of material phase transitions relative to an initial phase transition suggesting a resonant model, such that the self-referential systems and subsystems to be described, bootstrap themselves into existence as critical phenomenona. It would also, as a universal model of a universal theory [Deutsch 1985], provide a 'Platonic' explanation for the undue effectiveness of mathematics in quantum physics or vice verse an explanation of the quantum physical realizability of mathematics.

The notion that self-reference in quantum mechanics, a universal theory, defines a universal model of the whole quantum field emergent from a universal saddle point/singularity, is therefore in line with Chapline's [1999] conjecture "Is theoretical physics the same thing as mathematics?". His basic argument shows that quantum mechanics, which offers a natural approach to the vector quantization needed in pattern recognition [Kohonen 1988], can, in its Wigner-Moyal formulation, indeed be interpreted as canonical holographic method for solving pattern recognition problems (as indeed can QH! [Schempp 1992 ; Marcer and Schempp 1998]). This leads him to conclude

i) that the pattern recognition capabilities of the human brain are responsible for " the unreasonable effectiveness of mathematics in relation to physics", and

ii) that the program for the unification of physics is intimately related to Langlands' program for the corresponding unification of mathematics. This program, postulating that the previously supposed independent branches of mathematics actually in fact constitute a related whole, is now nearly proven and has just been extended to include function fields [Mackenzie 2000].

Such conclusions are also in accord with Wheeler's [1986] hypothesis of "the meaning circuit" that while physical laws are described by "algorithmic" means, such algorithms cannot be executed without recourse to the physical processes those laws specify.

3 Phase Conjugation

Phase conjugation, where the image of an object coincides with the object itself, is an experimentally validated condition of self reference in quantum mechanics. In use, for example, as the basis of the spin echo image measurement control techniques in magnetic resonance imaging (MRI) [Schempp 1998; Binz and Schempp 2000a,b], it is the necessary condition for incremental phase conjugate adaptive resonance in QH specified in terms of the 3 dimensional Heisenberg Lie Group G [Schempp 1992]. It can therefore be postulated to define a self-referential cosmology as a quantum holographic phase conjugate adaptive resonant whole :-

i) where the whole and each of the objects or phase conjugate quantum mechanical sub-systems has a coincident quantum object space or self, and

ii) where such selves concerning observable gauge invariant phases of the quantum state vector or Berry phase, are therefore not just an epiphenomena, as spin echo measurement techniques employed in MRI demonstrate.

Such a phase conjugate cosmology (as all that exists) must therefore begin with the initial act of quantum holographic phase conjugate adaptive resonance, which takes place the cosmological reference frame. This model is therefore in excellent agreement with Wilson's renormalization group methodology determining the universal nature of material phase transitions. For this methodology also employs, as already mentioned, the repeated self-referential mappings of, in this case, a quantum Hamiltonian onto itself, so as to select the particular material's stable and unstable critical fixed points, and shows that quantum mechanical effects determining such fixed points, are significant only in up to 3+1 dimensions.

This says:-

a) that the continuum laws of classical mechanics may not apply in macroscopic spatial dimensions in the neighborhood of such critical fixed points; for example, where water exhibits material phase transitions (such as ice or steam) so that the classical equations of hydrodynamics [Wilson 1983] no longer hold. Another example of the failure of classical macroscopic continuum laws, is the radiation law, as its divergence proves. For this divergence led Planck to the discovery of his now well proven quantum radiation law, the necessity for Planck's constant, and to the discovery of quantum mechanics itself. Furthermore, it is again evidence of a microscopic quantum mechanical effect having consequences even on the cosmological scale, and

b) that, in these circumstances, most likely quantum holographic effects do apply, since these are, in principle, a physical means to realize the lattice rescaling procedures P that Wilson's methodology employs. For example, at the unstable critical/saddle point of water/steam there is indeed a "holographic" mixture of bubbles of steam containing droplets of water and vice versa, on all scales down to the atomic.

(b) is further confirmed by the fact that quantum holography is Lorentz invariant (can be interpreted as holding in up to 3+1 dimensions consistent with Wilson's findings) and is based on the mathematics of the 3 parameter Heisenberg nilpotent Lie group G, matrix representation

$$
\begin{matrix}
1 & x & z \\
0 & 1 & y \\
0 & 0 & 1
\end{matrix}
\qquad \text{written as (x,y,z) for convenience}
$$

such that the Haar measure of G is the Lebesgue measure $dx \otimes dy \otimes dz$ of the underlying differential manifold R^3 where $\otimes$ stands for tensor multiplication, so that (x,y,z) are indeed three spatial measures.

In the postulated cosmology, such material phase transitions would not only determine all the physical properties, noumena and qualia, but it can inferred would give rise to the cosmology itself, through a unstable critical fixed point, such as a event where phase conjugate adaptive resonance takes place. Further Wolfram [1984] has shown that such critical fixed points or attractors are of four basic types, consisting of, point, periodic, strange chaotic and computer universal. Thus the cosmological models under discussion namely those concerning the Berry/geometric phase, quantum holography, and Wilson's universal methodology for the determination of critical phenomena, can be identified respectively with

a) the unfolding of an infinitely degenerate state or q point,

b) an initial and infinite sequence of phase conjugate adaptive resonant events, and

c) with, by inference from Wolfram, a quantum computer universal attractor and the associated sequence of quantum computational behaviors,

such that (a) says, see section 6, an historical record, its Berry phase, is maintained in terms of phase, and where in the case of (c) the maintenance of this historical record by means of phase carries the implication that the attractor is quantum holographic, in line with the earlier postulate that Wilson's 3 dimensional spatial lattice rescaling procedure is realized by quantum holography.

That is to say, all three concern an essentially universal unstable fixed saddle point i.e. one between stable fixed points, where further evidence in support of all these being one and the same comes from

a) the feature of universal degeneracy. For this is also a characteristic of QH, which concerns up to a unitary isomorphism, infinite dimensional irreducible linear unitary representations of the Schrodinger type of G, the 3 dimensional Heisenberg nilpotent Lie group, and

b) experimentally validated electro-weak theory in elementary particle physics in terms of the Weinberg/Salam angle. For this angle defines a change of phase $\Delta\theta$ of the reference frame at an unstable critical fixed point, in relation to the interaction from

(i) the unstable weak particles Bo and Wo, into

(ii) the stable electromagnetic photon γ and and its heavy neutral analogue Zo,

such that $\sin(\Delta\theta) = 1/\sqrt{5}$ [Close, 1982]

However, Dubois and Resconi [1992] have shown that there exists a critical fixed point S specified in terms of the Golden Number as a critical parameter, at which such a change of phase $\Delta\theta$ as cited by Close (that of the Weinberg/Salam angle?), is the result of a unimodular unitary and therefore by inference a quantum operation (see Figure II). That is to say the critical fixed point S, could indeed relate to electro-weak theory, long thought likely to provide the basis of such an evolution, through such interactions, for example, as fission and fusion. Further Dubois and Resconi's evidence of a unimodular unitary connection between classical and quantum mechanics, is supported by of the self-similar/fractal/holographic/wave nature of the interface observed in 2 dimensions at the computer generated boundary of the Mandelbrot set. In this connection it is also of particular note [Feigenbaum 1978] that many periodic systems, such as noisy oscillators, fluid flows, and biological populations, etc, which go through critical points and stable regions, show a parallel series of characteristic time periods T, 2T, 4T, 8T, ..and that the limit to such a series is aperiodicity, which mathematically manifests itself as chaos.

4 A Further Key to Understanding Critical Phenomena?

A further key therefore to understanding critical phenomena may be, remarkably, Riemann's Zeta function, identified by Berry [1986] with quantum chaos and now known from the work of Connes [Klarreich 2000] to specify a quantum mechanical system. This function, a means of turning all the integers n, or as Euler showed, all the primes p into another number via the complex amplitude $z = x + iy$, was the subject of a hypothesis by Riemann in 1859, still unproven, that all its non-trivial zeros lie somewhere on the real line $x = \frac{1}{2}$. The amplitude and phase of z therefore show that this famous hypothesis concerns a quantum wave phenomenon with a spectrum of fixed points defining fixed phases on this real line. That is, it can be postulated to define all the gauge invariant relative phases or Berry phase of some quantum state vector (up to some arbitrary constant phase factor), where all these spectral points are fixed points in relation to critical phenomena. A testable hypothesis of this paper is therefore, that the Zeta function concerns Wilson's [1983] experimentally validated use of the renormalization group procedure defining material phase transitions, such as liquid to solid, etc. That is, the critical fixed points (of Zeta) define properties of matter, noumena /qualia, where these, the renormalization group methodology says, concern the symmetry properties of groups. This would provide an irreversible mechanism for evolution in terms of all the unstable fixed points and symmetry breaking, such that physical degrees of freedom of the free energy F become phase unlocked at the unstable fixed points of the evolution. It can then be asserted that all the zeros on the real line x = ½ , correspond to the fermionic states of spin ½ to which the Pauli exclusion principle applies. That is to say the postulate is that the zeros of the Zeta function define the phase conditions of fermionic indistinguishability/degeneracy where systems of fermions may act like a boson such as happens, for example, in low temperature superconductivity in relation to electrons when they form degenerate Cooper-electron pairs. This assertion is in agreement with the fact that this phenomenon of superconductivity only happens below some critical temperature, and is therefore indeed a material phase transition in accordance with the precepts of Wilson's methodology [1983] and its findings, in relation to quantum mechanical effects, described in terms of critical lengths/scales, etc, in dimensionality d = 1,2,3 or 4. It is in line with examples of the Berry/geometric phase in quantum mechanics, well known before Berry's work, which concern the rotations of a spinor. For technically the factor distinguishing integer and half integer spinors is related to the 1:1 and 2:1 representations of the 3 dimensional rotation group [Manini 2001]. It points to non-trivial topological properties underlying the relation between vector quantities and adiabatic parameters q in relation to the Berry phase, which concern, for example:-

i) either, fields such as, for example, the external magnetic field in relation to low temperature superconductivity, or

ii) some internal degrees of freedom of the system Hamiltonian H under investigation, where these maybe treated as "slow" classical variables, affecting adiabatically the "fast" quantum dynamics of the other degrees of freedom. Here "slow" means that the parameters q change only by small amounts, ie there is smooth dependence of H on the parameters q. Otherwise changing q from one point to another can lead to a totally new and unrelated eigensystem.

Item (ii) can therefore be interpreted as saying that the three spatial degrees of freedom (x,y,z) concern such "slow" classical variables, below some critical parameter which can therefore be postulated to be "the velocity of light", so that below this velocity or critical fixed point, quantum locality as opposed to non-locality applies in accordance with generalized Lorentz invariance. That is to say, above such a critical fixed point, not only would these spatial degrees of freedom lead to totally new quantum eigensystems, but their spatial character below this critical point could be regarded as a quantum physical property like those of mass, spin, charge, etc, as being a consequence of cosmological evolution. Such an interpretation then says :-

(a) that such "spatial" degrees of freedom correspond to quantum mechanical as well as classical properties,

(b) that this is in good accord with phase conjugate adaptive resonance in QH, where the condition of phase conjugation specifies points on the light cone and therefore the same critical fixed point concerning the "the velocity of light" c,

(c) that it would allow an extension of the standard model of the families of leptons and quarks, such as that proposed by Rowlands and Cullerne [1999]. For (b) does indeed concern the two symmetrical algebras of 4 vectors with real vector units **i**, **j**, **k**, and imaginary scalar i, and the quaternions with imaginary vector units *i, j, k* and real scalar 1, on which their model uniting respectively the symmetry properties of space/time and charge/mass (where charge now includes strong, electromagnetic and weak) is based. This would, not only, as already argued here, explain all the properties of mass, charge, space and time as critical phenomena, but say that mass/charge is the totally new quantum eigensystem appropriate to time/space, when these may no longer be treated as "slow" classical variables. That is to say, the velocity of light c appropriate to special relativity in relation to Lorentz invariance, now appears, in the role of a critical fixed parameter, separating the local (classical) from the non-local in quantum mechanics. Thus in this proposed self-referential cosmology of a self-created universe as a critical phenomenon, the Rowlands /Cullerne model defines the nature of 3+1 space/time structural (holographic) stability, where

i) evidentially the least complex neutral space-time stable units concerning all these properties of mass and the strong, electromagnetic and weak charges are those of neutral hydrogen and helium, with 1 proton and 2 protons respectively in relation to the unstable weak nuclear reactions governing fission and fusion respectively, while the remainder in relation to such circumstances concern the stable and unstable isotopes of the periodic table, and

ii) similarly the cosmic time/space evolution of individual quantum fields in respect of mass and charge relates to their coupling constants. For these, it is known, are also an expression of the unstable critical fixed points, that concern, for example, gravitationally, $\cong 10^{38}$ unit hydrogen or proton masses; strong, 3 unit quarks (defining the baryons); electromagnetic, 137 units of Coulomb charge. These unit numbers are of particular significance in relation to the ANPA model of elementary particle physics known as the Combinatorial Hierarchy or Program Universe (see [Pierre Noyes 1999] for a recent in a long series published in the ANPA Proceedings often cited here], where as here, the emergence of Lorentzian space/time is a fundamental consequence following from the precepts of the Hierarchy, as first discovered by Bastin and Kilmister [1954].

iii) in relation to such neutral units of mass, the space/time 4 vector behavior is that an invariant mass scalar, or mass geodesic in 4 dimensions. This therefore conforms to the precepts of Einstein's theory of general relativity, as can also be proven in QH using Lie transformational theory, since QH is defined, as above, in terms of the 3 dimensional Heisenberg nilpotent Lie group. Furthermore it can now be inferred in relation to electromagnetic charge, that the behaviour of such fixed charged units must also conform to that of general relativity, as this is known to be the case in relation to the Klein Kalutza equation. Thus, the Rowlands/Cullerne model tells us that units of mass/charge including the zero units such electromagnetic quanta, correspond to null geodesics or sources/sinks of such 4 vector Lorentz invariant general relativistic space/time fields, so that in contradiction to the generally held view in physics that quantum theory and general relativity are incompatible, in fact the quantizations of mass, electromagnetic, strong, and weak charge in relation to the Rowlands/Cullerne extension of the standard model of elementary particle physics are exactly those that ensure such compatibility!! In these domains therefore spatial curvature and matter/charge would be the antithetic quantities, which cancel each other out, rather than, as is usually supposed, those of matter and anti-matter which are, of course, transformable into energy. That is, space/time curvature and matter/charge can now be postulated to be the mechanism to explain how this postulated self-referential universe is enabled to create itself from an initial instability or unstable critical point, in terms QH would imply, of an incremental process of phase conjugate adaptive resonance. This requires the simultaneous creation of mass and space or their corresponding simultaneous destruction on various cosmological scales at such a critical point in accordance with Rowlands/Cullerne. Similarly Mach's equivalence principle in relation to mass and inertia in accordance with his global precept that existence of any particular mass in the universe is consequence of the existence of all the others masses, then follows as a consequence of the antithetic nature of mass/energy and time/space, and the fact that the Rowlands/Cullerne model says the mass is a non-local quantum mechanical property. These conclusions receive further support by the fact that Rowlands and Cullernes' [2001] generalization of the Dirac equation is nilpotent and can be expressed in terms of quantum creation and annihilation operators, and that spin and helicity in accordance with the accepted quantum precepts are also implicit in their model. A further conclusion since QH is specified in terms of the 3 dimensional Heisenberg nilpotent Lie group must therefore be that since Lie transformational theory and its methodologies are a means to determine 3 dimensional spatio-temporal invariants, that Lie groups, systems and their prolongations also constitute solutions compatible with general relativity and quantum mechanics. Such Lie transformational systems have been extensively used by Hoffman [1989] to model structure in the brain and the processes of perception and thought. Hoffman's little known work can therefore, here, be strongly hypothesized to be accurate, valid models of thought, the brain and neural structure warranting much more extensive study, since they are based on the stability criterion for spatio-temporal matter, as described here, that must also apply in all living systems and in particular in actual brains, as indeed should those of DNA.

Correspondingly the arbitrary constant phase factor in relation to geometric phase can be considered as the "ground state" of a cosmology, of which the Zeta function specifies in relation to spin/fermionic behaviour the critical fixed points, considered as the cosmology's eigenlevels (and gauge invariant phases) so as to specify all its material phase transitions. Thus this whole cosmology, like the hydrogen atom, is described by an infinite spectrum of eigenlevels, and can be pictured in the same way [Klarreich 2000]. But any cosmology, defining a universe in terms of its dictionary meaning "of all that exists", demands a "ground state", that cannot itself be measured, since there is nothing further to measure it against. That is to say, such a cosmos behaves self-referentially with respect to measurement. A fact known to be experimentally the case in relation to quantum vacuum phenomena such as those of the Lamb shift and the Casimir effect [Puthoff 1990].

This hypothesis of a self-referential cosmology is also in agreement with the hypothesis of Berry [1986], that there exists a quantum mechanical system of an unknown energy function/Hamiltonian without time reversal symmetry, whose eigenvalues are defined by the zeros of Riemann's Zeta function. Such an energy function with an arbitrary constant phase factor or un-measurable ground state, might also explain the supposed phenomenon dark matter, which some cosmologists, on the basis of the latest astronomical observations, claim is in need of explanation [Caldwell and Kamionkowski 2001].

5 Living Systems

5.1 Models for the Basis of Life

It has been mentioned earlier in section 3, that in passing through phase transition points, water is marked by quantum mechanical effects/quantum coherent states on all scales from the atomic up to some correlation length. Thus at both the critical points concerning the gas/liquid and liquid/crystal (snow) phases of water, there will exist droplets on all scales containing quantum coherent water within which quantum self-interference and spontaneous phase conjugation [Noboli 1985;1987] will take place. That is to say such droplets as quantum resonant cavities would provide the conditions necessary for the quantum wave functioning of DNA as proposed independently by Marcer and Schempp [1996; 1997b] and Gariaev group [2001], where the latter paper presents some of the Gariaev group's experimental evidence and computer simulations in support of their theoretical thesis that such DNA-wave computation/quantum holography is the basis for life.

Further evidence in support of this hypothesis is that it fits in a coherent and practical way with the currently existing scientific hypotheses and evidence, that recognizable life : -

a) began near the volcanic fissures in the ocean bed, where the simpler unstable critical point of the gas/liquid state of water is sustained, so as to foster, it can therefore be hypothesized, the formation of single celled prokaryote organisms and their chemistry as proposed see (d) below,

b) was enabled to develop into its complex many celled Eukaryote forms at the unstable critical point of the liquid/crystal (snow) phase during the correspondingly sustained period for which the geology of the recently hypothesized "Snowball Earth" theory now provides substantial supporting evidence. The many celled forms, rather than the single cell forms can be hypothesized to arise in this particular phase transition point as a consequence the more complex self-similar/holographic nature of the quantum coherence that must exist there as indicated by the universal fractal nature of snow flakes in relation to this unstable critical point,

c) would be generally sustained on sunlit water surfaces of all scales, oceans, seas, lakes, ponds, pools, puddles, down to drops. For such water surfaces facilitate quantum holographic transduction between the electromagnetic and the acoustic frequency domains, as Gariaev and his collaborators [2001] have demonstrated to be the case, during their investigations into wave bio-computation in DNA. Such transduction (of energy from the electromagnetic to the acoustic frequency domain leading to dynamical stable material structures) could therefore be hypothesized as the basis of photosynthesis and the evolution of chlorophyll for example. And it must here be hypothesized to govern the entire variety of functioning established by surface receptors between the outside and the inside of living cells.

d) all the recent evidence for optimally controlled quantum signal induced chemistry [Rice1992; Dahleh et al. 1990; Schleich 1999; Leichtle et al. 1998; Patel 2000] for example, as an alternative to standard thermodynamically controlled chemistry /"cooking". For example, the use of computers to teach lasers to control molecules, so as to optimize chemical reactions, has already been demonstrated in the laboratory [Judson and Rabitz 1992]. It constitutes the new possibility by means of coherent quantum signaling for the evolutionary development of optimally controlled chemical reactions such as are often found in living systems, and points to the need to reassess, for example, the 1952/53 experiments of Miller and Urey into the origins of life, where within a closed flask, unstructured electric discharges through a 'primordial Earth atmosphere' for many days produced a soup of the basic amino-acids important in living processes, but nothing more.

e) the fact that such material phase transitions not only produce new and previously unknown physical properties, but also concerns the free energy F at critical temperatures T. Such critical temperatures characterize many complex life forms, and lead to the expectation that life-forms, such as ourselves, based on critical fixed material phase transitions as hypothesized here, would become critical temperature self-regulating, so as to optimized the working and use of their free energy F, and so as to be able to function as quantum coherent wholes, rather than classical mechanisms, such as it is still generally assumed, by both molecular biologists and biologists that living systems are.

Indeed this fact could even be the unique factor regulating the appearance of the property – noumena/qualia of human consciousness; i.e. that it has, as is indeed observed, its own critical temperature, etc, which characterizes its human emergence, and optimal functioning.

It might be objected that such critical temperatures only occur, in principle, in the thermodynamic limit in a system with an infinite number of degrees of freedom. However, this in indeed what quantum holography with its infinite dimensional irreducible unitary linear representations of the Schrodinger type of G, in principle, has.

5.2 The Nature of Self-Referential Conscious Observers

If in a self-referential quantum holographic subsystem, an object were an observer capable of making observations [Marcer and Schempp 1996; 1997; Marcer and Mitchell 2001], these observations/measurements would, it has been shown have to be phase conjugate. That is, from the perspective of their own self-referential frame, such observers would perceive other objects, where they are actually located outside their own embodiment in 3 spatial dimensions, which is essential to survival and exactly the nature of human perception. Similarly, as has also been shown, the result of quantum measurements of such a observer's perceptions (its local Berry phase) constitute a generalized quantum holographic record that can be used :-

i) to define the human observer's experience ie the observer's perceptions, since such experience is indeed how each of us measures ourselves and our actions against some reference frame, be it that of the world/universe as a whole or some role model, and
ii) to define both the observer's awareness of that world/universe and conversely of its own bodily (and mental) self-awareness, ie the observer's own embodiment or body from the perspective of its own self-referential frame.

Thus human consciousness must, by implication from (i) and (ii) and further levels of self reference in regard to the human observer's own reference frame, be a very personal, i.e. one from the perspective of its own unique reference frame and history of experience. It includes in this model however the awareness of the human observer's actual quantum self or will, defined as the observer's own free (physical and mental) energy (this is however ultimately inseparable from that of the Universe as a whole!). For example, the mental free energy, which we all self-acquire naturally as a child (what we truly observe when a child is being willful), that is used to exert and then control or partially control our physical free energy and later our mental/thought processes themselves [Marcer and Schempp 1996]. That is to say how the human self controls its brain implies that brain itself has an neural object image or mental self, which we call the mind, which can be used to control the brain's quantum neural embodiment, and is used consciously as when, for example, starting to learn to drive a car, or in some act of great courage or folly, when such conscious control can be used to indeed override all the human being's established experience or norms, mental or physical. This prediction that the human organism has two principal self-reference frames, one physical and one mental associated respectively to its entire physical and neural embodiments, in respect to its physical and mental wholeness/health, is one for which Stecker [2001] has produced demonstrative and simple experimental evidence of their physical separation. The process of the spatial separation or evolution of mind frame or self from the whole body frame or Self, can therefore be postulated to have indeed taken place, as man's ancestors began walking on two legs, and can be seen in this light as a prelude to the emergence of human consciousness, as we know it. This model therefore postulates human consciousness to be a noumena/qualia of living systems that arises as the result of a higher level of self-reference now reached by cosmological evolution in relation to the Earth Biosphere and perhaps even in relation to that of the Cosmos as a whole, i.e. it is a quantum material phase transition, and an inevitable emergent property of such an evolution.

6 A Illustrative Mathematical Model of the Desired Cosmological Boundary Conditions

> Having eliminated every possible solution to a problem,
> That which remains, however improbable must be the truth.
> Sherlock Holmes

The mathematical model, below, uses Schrodinger equation to illustrate that the boundary conditions always essential to a correct solution could indeed in this case be remarkable and be identified from the known considerations :-

A) of Berry/geometric phase [Manini,http] with the totally degenerate quantum state of zero energy, or q point, and correspondingly

B) of QH [Schempp, 1993] with a quantum vacuum Bargmann-Fock emitter/ absorber model expressed in terms of annihilations and creation operators.

The postulate proposed is that the Hamiltonian H is zero in the Schrodinger equation for the state vector ψ considered to apply to the Universe as a whole, so that

$$ih\partial\psi/\partial t = H\psi = 0$$

There can therefore be no Schrodinger evolution of dynamic origin and this time invariance ensures that there is quite literally "no time like the present" just as we all experience it.

However it does not preclude, considerations of the Berry phase say, a cosmological evolution of entirely geometric-topological origin [Lloyd 2001], as is also the nature of our experience. For ψ is now a complex constant $a \in T$ the complex torus group, and a standing wave. That is,

$$\psi = a = \exp(i\theta) = z/|z|$$

where z is any complex number, since normalization of ψ requires that

$$\psi\psi^* = \sin\theta \sin\theta + \cos\theta\cos\theta = 1$$

where $\psi = \sin\theta + i\cos\theta : \psi^* = \sin\theta - i\cos\theta$

It therefore follows that the phase θ corresponds to the Berry parameter/angle in the Berry parameter space. Thus θ which specifies an arbitrary constant phase factor, may take any continuum value to satisfy the normalization, and so ψ defines a totally degenerate state, where

(i)   the degeneracy would ensure a non-trivial loop in the Berry parameter space and measurable gauge invariant phases of the state vector ψ, so that there exists observable Berry phases θ,

(ii)   these observable phases point to non-trivial topological properties between vector quantities and adiabatic parameters q, and

(iii)   the θ space with the degenerate θ points removed is infinitely multiply connected – an astonishing geometric-topological concept, allowing θ to be continually updated, considerations of Berry phase [Resta, 1997; Manini 2001], say, by :-

a) how long the system has been away from its initial state,

b) where in three dimensional space it travelled, and

c) what other quantum mechanical states were visited on route

so that θ constitutes a complete history or historical record of the system's evolution and

(iv)   this degeneracy of ψ allows θ to change discontinuously by arbitrary amounts, yet normalization shows that all solutions are equivalent up to a unitary isomorphism. An example in optical holography described in terms of a process u/|u| concerns the sudden change of phase known as the Gouy effect [Schempp 1992]. In QH this arises from the hidden symmetries of the metaplectic group Mp(1,R) which is group describing the automorphisms of

        G and forms a twofold covering of the symplectic group Sp(1,R). It can therefore be seen as a renormalization,

(v)   further ψ can always be normalized, so in this cosmology the fundamental problem of renormalization is solved.

ψ may also :-

(a) act as the reference wave in relation to QH, performing the function of the ultimate measurement standard in regard to the quantum holographic measurement process, and

(b) serve as a diffraction grating/filter in relation to holography in regard to the 1933 Dirac/Kapitza postulate recently validated [Bucksraum, 2001]. Noting that such standing waves have two intensity peaks per cycle.

Thus ψ specifies an infinite dimensional parameter space standing wave set, which in QH concerns up to a unitary isomorphism, unique infinite dimensional irreducible linear unitary representations of the Schrodinger type of G, where the equation for normalization above shows, there is complete phase entanglement. Such complete phase entanglement thus confirms that :-

(i)   since QH is Lorentz invariant [Binz and Schempp 2001] there will be both the spatial (and implicitly the temporal coherence) (indicative of the mathematical signature $\{+,+,+, - \}$) necessary in QH for full wave-front reconstruction,

(ii)   that in QH specified in terms of the 3 dimensional Heisenberg Group Lie Group G(x, y, z), the spatial measures x, y, z, can be regarded as three spatial fundamental degrees of physical freedom, which in relation to the Berry phase may be treated approximately as "slow" classical variables, as already postulated. That is, these measures x,y,z are indeed true quantum mechanical and not just classical variables and so could concern the mathematical signature $\{-,-,-, +\}$ in relation to quantum non-locality. This is confirmed by the facts that in QH there is both a retarded and an advanced standing wave set, and phase conjugate adaptive resonance specifies coordinates where the 3 dimensional object image and that of the object coincide and so takes place on the Minkowski light cone itself,

(iii)   that coupled circle maps, which are able to model chaotic oscillations more efficiently than ordinary (i.e. not incursive or hyperincursive) differential equations, could therefore be used to more generally describe θ. These maps are a tool to describe both synchronisation and adaptation/learning by Hebb-type rules [Bauer and Nartienssen 1991]. For example, in a model where one such mapping represents the phase dynamics of one system (a neuron in the brain, for instance) or a group of neurons, it has been observed that, depending on the coupling strength, different maps show correlated or uncorrelated behaviour, while the autocorrelation function remains flat as is expected for a chaotic signal. Another example would therefore be the fundamental gauge fields of physics (general relativity, the non-Abelian electro-weak and chromo-dynamic quantum fields, etc). It says that the corresponding coupling constants (the gravitational, electromagnetic, weak, strong, etc) or "strengths", represent evidence of correlated or uncorrelated behaviour, as is generally postulated to happen in the course of any postulated cosmological evolution.

Correspondingly in QH, the postulated cosmology would :-

(i) take place by spontaneous phase conjugate adaptive resonance,[Noboli 1985; 1987] in bounded systems, which the cosmos/universe defined as all the exists, can be assumed to be,

(ii) be described [Schempp 1983] through the linear Schrodinger representation U of G as a quantum vacuum Bargmann-Fock emitter/absorber model expressed in terms of annihilation/creation operators, a, a* , where the number states $|n(k)\rangle$, which are the quantum states occupying the mode k, are the eigenstates of the number operator $N(k) = aa^*$ and $[a, a^*] = \pi$ is the bosonic commutation relation, and

(iii) be described as a Lie transformational system, which in terms of its Lie diffeomorphism, or differential mapping with a differential inverse, confirms the conclusions reached concerning the geometric/topological nature of its behaviour and its renormalizability.

That is to say, in QH, where the phase θ is the quantity of physical significance, a repeated cycle of adaptive phase conjugate resonance describes the means by which the cosmology evolves. This results from the fact that θ adaptively maintains a complete history or historical record of the cosmology from the postulated totally degenerate zero energy quantum vacuum state, which existed before the initial spontaneous phase conjugate adaptive resonance, and which will partially continue to exist so as to initiate each following cycle, such that :-

(i) the system/cosmology can never return to its initial state so satisfying the Third law of Thermodynamics,

(ii) in each phase conjugate adaptive resonant cycle, QH shows that entropy acts as a quantum holographic information metric [Zurek 1989; Coveney, Jessel and Marcer, 1991] so satisfying the Second Law of Thermodynamics,

(iii) this is an adiabatic process appropriate to QH, and the Berry/geometric phases θ such that the First Law of Thermodynamics holds during each cycle,

The concluding inference can therefore be that the proposed self-referential cosmology
i) functions as a quantum harmonic oscillator, since it is known that such oscillators are equivalent to an assembly of bosons each having one polarization state, and
ii) that its totally degenerate initial vacuum state is a totally squeezed state, since it known that oscillations in a photon (boson) distribution of squeezed states and interference in phase space concerns the fact that a single mode of the electromagnetic field in a number state is equivalent to a harmonic oscillator with dimensionless co-ordinates p and q such the trajectories are circles with radius $\sqrt{2}(m+1/2)$ traversed in a clockwise direction and such that the area $2\pi($ in units of h) are defined by an inner

radius √2m and an outer radius √2(m +1), establishing the connection with coupled circle maps and complete phase entanglement.

Acknowledgements: The authors wish to thank the editor of the CASYS 2001 Proceedings, Daniel Dubois for many seminal and valuable discussions both in relation to the content of this paper and over past years.

References

Anderson P.W. 1982 The 1982 Noble Prize in Physics, Science 218 19 November 763-764.

Bastin E.W. and Kilmister C.W. 1954 The Concept of Order 1. The Space-Time Structure, Proceedings of the Cambridge Philosophical Society, 50, Part 2, 278-286.

Bauer M. and Nartienssen W. 1991 Coupled Circle Maps As a Tool to Model Synchronisation on Neural Networks, Network 2, 345-351.

Berry M.V. 1989 The Geometric Phase, Scientific American, December, 26-32.

Berry M.V. 1986 Reimann's Zeta Function: a model of quantum chaos, Springer Lecture Notes in Physics 263, 1-17, Quantum Chaos and statistical nuclear physics, editors Seligman T.H. and Nishioka H., Springer, Berlin.

Binz E. and Schempp W. 2000a Creating Magnetic Resonance Images, Proceedings of the Third International Conference on Computing Anticipatory Systems, International Journal of Computing Anticipatory Systems, 7, 223-232.

Binz E. and Schempp W. 2000b A unitary parallel filterbank approach to Magnetic Resonance Tomography, American Institute of Physics Proceedings 517, of the Third International Conference on Computing Anticipatory Systems, editor Dubois D. August 9-14, 1999 Liege Belgium 406-416.

Binz E. and Schempp W. 2001 Quantum Hologram and Relativistic Hodogram: Magnetic Resonance Tomography and Gravitational Wavelet Detection, American Institute of Physics Proceedings 573 of the 4th International Conference on Computing Anticipatory Systems, editor Dubois D. 98-131; section 9, 118-120.

Bucksbaum P.H. 2001 Particles driven to Diffraction, Nature 413, 13th September, 117-118.

Caldwell R.R. and Kamionkowski M. 2001 Echoes of the Big Bang, Scientific American, January, 28-33.

Chapline C. 1999 Is Theoretical Physics The Same Thing as Mathematic? Elsevier Physics Reports, 315, 95-105.

Close F. 1982 The Cosmic Onion, Heineman Educational Books, 117.

Coveney P.V. Jessel M. and Marcer P, 1991 Huygens' Principle and computability, Speculations in Science and Technology, 14, 3, 203-210.

Dahleh M. Pierce A.P. and Rabitz H. 1990 Optimal Control of Uncertain Systems, Physics Review A, 42,3, 1st August 1065-1079.

Deutsch D. 1985 The Church-Turing principle, and the universal quantum computer, Proceedings of the Royal Society of London, A400, 97-117.

Dubois D. and Resconi G. 1992 Hyperincursitivity A new mathematical theory, Presses Universitaires de Liege, Chapter VI, section 6, 6.4.

Ehrlich P. 1986 The Absolute Arithmetic and Geometric Continua, Proceedings of the Philosophy of Science Association, 12, 237-246.

Feigenbaum M.J.1978 Quantitative universality for a class of non-linear transformations, Journal of Statistical Physics, 19,1, 25-52.

Gariaev P. Birstein B. Iarochenko A. Leonova K.A. Marcer P. Kaempf U. Tertishy G. 2001 The DNA-wave Biocomputer Fourth International Conference Computing Anticipatory Systems, Journal of Computing Anticipatory Systems,10, 290-310.

Hoffman W.C. 1989 The Visual Cortex is a Contact Bundle, Applied Mathematics and Computation 32, 137-167. This work is an excellent summary, with many references to papers published by Hoffman as early as mid 60s which began with such papers as "The Neuron as a Lie group germ and Lie product" Quarterly Journal of Applied Mathematics, XXV,4,1968, 423-440.

Hofstadter D.R.1979, Godel, Escher, Bach: an Eternal Golden Braid, Pengiun Books, London.

Judson R.S. and Rabitz H. 1992 Teaching Lasers to Control Molecules, Physics Review Letters, 68, 10, 9th March, 1500-1503.

Klarreich E. 2000 Prime Time, New Scientist, 11th November, 32-36.

Kohonen T. 1988 Self-Organization and Associative Memory, Springer, Berlin.

Leichtle C. Schliech W.P. Averbukh I.Sh. and Shapiro M. 1998, Quantum State Holography, Physics Review Letters 80,7, 1418-1421.

Lloyd S. 2001 Computation from Geometry, Science 292, 1st June, 1669.

Mackenzie D. 2000 Fermat's Last Theorem's First Cousin, Science 287, 4th February, 792-793

Manini 2001 http://www.sissa.it/~manini/berryphase.html Berry's geometric phase: a review,03/05,1-9.

Marcer P. 1992 Order and Chaos in DNA – the Denis Guichard Prizewinner: Jean-Claude Perez, Kybernetes, 21,2, 60-61.

Marcer P. 1996 From the Self-Creation to the creation of the self, Proceedings of the 18th annual meeting of the Alternative Natural Philosophy Association (ANPA), Wesley House, Cambridge, editor K.Bowden, 172-189, contact is via anpa-discussions-subscribe@yahoogroups.com

MarcerP. and Dubois D. 1992 An outline model of cosmological evolution, Proceedings 13th International Congress of Cybernetics, Namur, Belgium, 24-28th August Symposium VII New Concepts in Cybernetics, 161-164.

Marcer P. and Schempp W. 1996 A Mathematically Specified Template for DNA and the Genetic Code, in terms of the physically realizable Processes of Quantum Holography, Proceeding of Greenwich (University) Symposium on Living Computers, editors Fedorec A. and Marcer P. 45-62.

Marcer P. and Schempp W. 1997a The Model of the Prokaryote Cell as an Anticipatory System Working By Quantum Holography, Proceedings of the 1st International Conference on Computing Anticipatory Systems, Liege, Belgium, August 11-15, editor Dubois D. 307-313.

Marcer P. and Schempp W. 1997b Model of the Neuron Working by Quantum Holography, Informatica 21,519-534.

Marcer P. and Schempp W. 1998 The brain as a conscious system, International Journal of General Systems, 27, 1/3, 231-248.

Marcer P. and Mitchell E. 2001 What is consciousness?, The Physical Nature of Consciousness, editor Philip Van Loocke, 145-174, Advances in Consciousness Research series, John Benjamins B.V., Amsterdam.

Mitchell E. and Williams J 1996 The Way of the Explorer. G.P.Putnam & sons, New York.

Noboli R.1985 Schrodinger Wave Holography in the Brain Cortex, Physical Review A 32,6, 3618-3626.

Noboli R. 1987 Ionic Waves in Animal Tissue, Physical Review A 35,4, 1901-1922.

Patel A. 2000 Quantum Algorithms and the Genetic Code, Proceedings of the Winter Insitute of Quantum Theory and Quantum Optics, 1-13 January, S.N. Bose National Centre for Basic Sciences, Calcutta, India.

Pierre Noyes H. 1999, Program Universe and Recent Cosmological Results, Proceedings of the 20th annual meeting of the Alternative Natural Philosophy Association (ANPA), Wesley House, Cambridge, editor K.Bowden, 192-214, contact is via anpa-discussions-subscribe@yahoogroups.com

Pribram K.H. 1991 Brain and Perception: Holonomy and Structure in Figural Processing. Lawerence Eribaum Associates, New Jersey.

Puthoff H. 1990 Everything for Nothing, New Scientist, 28, July, 52-58.

Resta R.1997 The Geometric Phase, Europhysics News,28,19.

Rice S.A. 1992 New Ideas for Guiding the Evolution of a Quantum System, Science, 258, 16th October, 412-413.

Rowlands P. and Cullerne J.P. 1999 A derivation of particle structures and the Dirac Equation from fundamental symmetries, Proceeding of the 20th annual meeting of the Alternative Natural Philosophy Association (ANPA), Wesley House, Cambridge, editor K.Bowden,155-191. contact is via anpa-discussions-subscribe@yahoogroups.com

Rowlands P. and Cullerne J.P. 2001, Nilpotent Representations of the Dirac Algebra, Proceeding of the 22th annual meeting of the Alternative Natural Philosophy Association (ANPA), Wesley House, Cambridge, editor K.Bowden, 99-106.

Schempp W. 1986 Harmonic Analysis on the Heisenberg Group with Applications in Signal theory, Pitman Notes in Mathematics Series 14, Longman Scientific and Technical, London.

Schempp W. 1992 Quantum Holography and Neurocomputer Architectures, Journal of Mathematical Imaging and Vision, 2, 279-326.

Schempp W. 1993 Bohr's Indetermincy Principle in Quantum Holography, Self-adaptive Neural Network Architectures, Cortical Self-organisation, Molecular Computers, Magnetic Resonance Imaging and Solitonic Nanotechnology, Nanobiology 2,109-164.

Schempp W. 1998 Magnetic Resonance Imaging, Mathematical Foundations and Applications, John Wiley, New York.

Schleich W.P. 1999 Sculpting a Wavepacket, Nature 397, 21st January, 207-208.

Stecker C.A. 2001, Anatomy of Anticipation, American Institute of Physics Proceedings 573, of the Fourth International Conference on Computing Anticipatory Systems, editor Dubois D. August 2000, Liege Belgium, 638-651.

Wheeler J.A. 1986 Physics as Meaning Circuit: Three Problems, Frontiers of Non-equilibrium Statistical Physics, editors Moore G.T. and Scully M.O. Plenum Press, New York.

Wilson K.G. 1983, The Renormalization Group and critical phenomena, Reviews of Modern Physics, 55,3, July, 583-600.

Wolfram S. 1984 Universality and complexity in cellular automata, Physic 10D, Preface and 1-35.

Zurek W.H. 1989 Thermodynamic cost of computation, algorithmic complexity, and the information metric, Nature, 341, 14th September, 119-124.

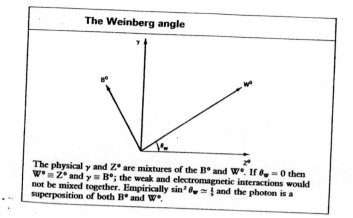

The Weinberg angle

The physical γ and Z^o are mixtures of the B^o and W^o. If $\theta_w = 0$ then $W^o \equiv Z^o$ and $\gamma \equiv B^o$; the weak and electromagnetic interactions would not be mixed together. Empirically $\sin^2 \theta_w \simeq \frac{1}{5}$ and the photon is a superposition of both B^o and W^o.

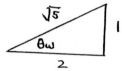

The determinant of the Sierpinski matrix, for example, is equal to -1

$$Det \begin{vmatrix} 1 & 1 \\ 1 & 0 \end{vmatrix} = -1$$

which means an unimodular operator.

$$\begin{vmatrix} 1 & 1 \\ 1 & 0 \end{vmatrix} \begin{vmatrix} x \\ y \end{vmatrix} = \begin{vmatrix} x+y \\ x \end{vmatrix}$$

$$x^2 + y^2 = 1 \quad (x+y)^2 + x^2 = 1$$

$$i.e. \quad x = \frac{2}{\sqrt{5}} \quad y = -\frac{1}{\sqrt{5}}$$

Example 1 :

$$\begin{vmatrix} 1 & 1 \\ 1 & 0 \end{vmatrix} \begin{vmatrix} x \\ y \end{vmatrix} = \begin{vmatrix} x+y \\ x \end{vmatrix}$$

$x=1 \quad 1 \quad 2 \quad 3 \quad 5$

$y=o \quad 1 \quad 1 \quad 2 \quad 3 \quad ...$

$\lim \frac{x}{y} \to L$

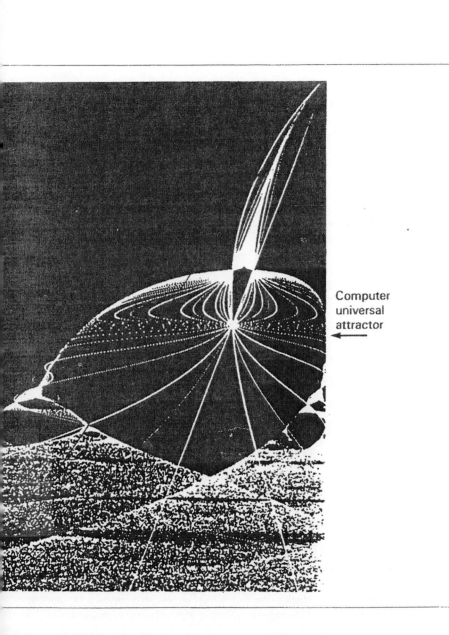

Computer
universal
attractor

DERIVING PLANCK'S CONSTANT FROM: ITS DIMENSIONAL PECULIARITIES, REALISTIC FLUID MODELS AND LARMOR'S RADIATION LAW - "This May Signal Its Rejection as a Fundamental Constant of Quantum Mechanics"- Dirac, 1963

William M. Honig,
Curtin University, Science & Engineering Div.,
Perth, Western Australia

Direct Mail Address: W, Honig,
P.O.B. 361, So. Perth, 6151, Western Australia

E-mail: rhonigw@cc.curtin.edu.au

The dimensional peculiarities of Planck's constant and a realistic phenomenology give a physically realistic interpretation of Planck's Constant. On this basis, Planck's Constant is derived from Larmor's Radiation Law. A clue to a realistic meaning for the fine structure constant is also suggested.

Key Words: Photex, Photex-pair, photon, dimensional designations, realistic pictures of physical reality, discrete electromagnetic fields, inconsistent logics.

1. INTRODUCTION

The subject of this paper has been presented previously but in an abbreviated and incomplete form which made comprehension very difficult [1]. The graphic simplicity of the physically realistic phenomenology developed over the past 15+ years is summarised here to immediately aid the reader's understanding. It would have been irritating, discourteous, and indifferent to direct the reader instead to dig out the 15+ year sequence of papers and especially the realistic illustrations, which have been presented. The importance of this subject to interested readers unfamiliar with a realistic phenomenology further justifies this procedure. Interested readers will, thus, be able to read this paper with the realistic pictorials at hand and without having their patience severely tried (references are given).

In Scientific American (May '63) P.A.M. Dirac made some surprising comments [2]. He had doubts about the future of the Uncertainty Principle and Quantum Mechanics (implied) and on the nature of Planck's constant, which are clearly expressed (at age 60) when he was close to the prime of his powers. The crux of his argument is quoted here:

"There are some fundamental constants in nature: the charge of the electron (e), Planck's constant, h, divided by 2π, designated h-bar, (η), and the velocity of light, (c). From these fundamental constants, one can construct a number that has no dimensions: the number $\eta c/e^2$. That number is found by experiment to have the value 137 or something close to 137.... .

The physics of the future, of course, cannot have the three quantities, η, e, and c all as fundamental quantities. Only two of them can be fundamental, and the third must be derived from these two. It is almost certain that c will be one of the two fundamental ones. The velocity of light, c is so important in the four-dimensional picture, and it plays such a role in the special theory of relativity, correlating our units of space and time, that it has to be fundamental. Then we are faced with the fact that of the two quantities η and e, one will have to be fundamental and one will be derived. If η is fundamental, e will have to be explained in some way in terms of the square root of η. It seems most unlikely that any fundamental theory can give e in terms of a square root, since square roots do not occur in basic equations. It is much more likely that e will be the fundamental quantity and that η will be explained in terms of e^2. Then there will be no square roots in the basic equations. I think one is on safe ground if one makes the guess that in the physical picture we shall have at some future stage, e and c will be fundamental quantities and η will be derived.

If η is a derived quantity instead of a fundamental one, our whole set of ideas about uncertainty will be altered. Now, η is the fundamental quantity that occurs in the Heisenberg uncertainty relation connecting the amount of uncertainty in position and in momentum. This uncertainty cannot play a fundamental role in a theory in which η itself is not a fundamental quantity. I think one can make a safe guess that uncertainty relations in their present form will not survive in the physics of the future."

This is part of my motivation for deriving Planck's constant. The fall of Planck's constant as a fundamental constant, however, should also have to imply the fall of Quantum Mechanics itself. The derivation of Planck's constant has to be on a different basis than Quantum Mechanics. The different basis adopted is realistic in nature. This derivation is a 3-step process:

1. The peculiarities of the dimensions of Planck's constant are discussed, which is a necessity for the derivation of Planck's constant, which is step 3, below.

2. A brief view of the newly developed realistic but unfamiliar phenomenology must be presented which is both descriptive and pictorial. This introduces the reader to the phenomenology which has been developed, and upon which much of the work is based. Many references explain this in detail.

3. Larmor's electromagnetic dipole radiation law is then used with the above to derive Planck's constant in its dimensionally correct form.

Section 2 - Dimensional Peculiarities of Planck's constant, Section 3 - A Capsule View of the Realistic Phenomenology, and Section 4 - Planck's Constant: Derivation from Larmor's Radiation Law, of this paper discusses each of the 3 steps above.

This work started with a search for a realistic logic for Quantum Mechanics (QM), separately for Special Relativity (SR), and for realistic views of physical reality and non-euclidean geometry culminating in the development of a realistic fluidic phenomenology [3-25]. In this work, emphasis has been on developing the realistic phenomenology. This is a necessity, because it has been neglected/forbidden by the tenets of SR/QM for the past 75 years.

It has been shown[3-25] how a realistic phenomenology eliminates conundrums and supports microscopic fluid models in Physics. It is based on a microscopic continuous two-fluid superposed + and - charged plenum. Operational invariance of SR is retained.

Progressive versions and developments of all this work with several other inclusions have appeared [1-26]. A recent book and its review [3, 4], later versions of these concepts, many of their details and a three-part article[7, 8, 9] are referenced. Both late and early versions of these ideas[1-25] are also listed. The sixteen Figures in Section 3, below give the vital pictorial views of the realistic phenomenology.

2. DIMENSIONAL PECULIARITIES OF PLANCK'S CONSTANT

We start with the simple and realistic expression defining the energy of the photon:

$$E = h f \qquad\qquad (1)$$

where E is the energy of the photon, f is frequency in cycles per second and h is energy per [cycle per second]. If energy is expressed in electron volts (eV) then h is 4.14×10^{-15} eV/[cycle/second]. We use these particular terms because they are convenient for the physically realistic ideas to be presented. It is instructive to peruse the stop-action pictures of dipole radiation as first given by H. Hertz (Fig. 1). It is for an electron, say, which is accelerated back and forth in the vertical direction and generates a sequence of EM field configurations as shown. One might term these a continuous sequence of toroids, which start out, as toroidal 'smoke rings' in space. They then continuously deform into the well-known kidney-shaped EM field patterns while moving radially from the electron at the speed of light, c.

It is well known that Eq. 1 must refer to a minimum energy. It also emphasised that the speed of EM energy must always be as given by SR as the speed of light. Although in a confined cavity of the proper shape standing waves can be set up, this is merely the consequence of waves moving in opposing directions at the speed of light. All of our empirical experience thus, with EM energy is that there are no physical exceptions to its velocity as c. We now introduce the idea of an EM rest frame, which is a non-physical rest frame and is conceptual only [13, 18, 25]. Even the Hertz pictures and all other such EM figures are indeed pictures of such EM rest frames because the pictures are stationary. The symbols f and h in Eq. (1) above, indeed contain the dimensions: cycles per second, as they should since EM energy can only be experienced as motion at the velocity, c. This is a tenet of Special Relativity which has long been considered obvious but is also supported by the Michealson-Morley and many other experiments. Why then bring in the concept of an EM rest frame? Its great value lies in the fact that the Planck Equation, Eq. (1), should also refer to the same EM energy, E, in such a peculiar rest frame. The symbol f which is in cycles per second in Eq. (1), in a physical rest frame, must change to cycles alone in the EM rest frame. The time dimension should be removed or in clearer language, it must be suppressed in the EM rest frame. This is because there is no motion or no time dimension in the EM rest frame. The dimensional meanings for quantities in Physics have been usually treated as a minor and obscure subject; often used but seldom discussed. The most common use for the suppression of a dimension lies in the treatment of η (h-bar) where

$$\eta = h / 2\pi. \tag{2}$$

and where, following the usual dimensional designations just given for h one should get

$$\eta = h / 2\pi \text{ is in energy per [radian per second].} \tag{3}$$

Converting the energy to electron volts this becomes 0.658×10^{-15} eV per [radian per second], which clearly follows from the above. The unusual step, however, which presently exists both for h and for η, is their use in QM where the dimension: cycles or radians are suppressed!

Thus: $h = 4.14 \times 10^{-15}$ eV-seconds or generally dimensions of h is energy-time. (4)

and $\eta = 0.658 \times 10^{-15}$ eV-seconds or generally dimensions of η is energy-time. (5)

It is sometimes argued that cycles or radians are not properly dimensions and results in QM also show that these Eqs. (4, 5) are successfully used in QM, so that these "dimensions" can be treated in this way. In addition, it often said that the suppression of the dimensions is permitted because radians or cycles are never used so that the necessity for their inclusion does not exist. We agree in this last case because their successful use in QM justifies this. Dimensions, however, are quantitative entities which can be either continuous or discrete but there should be a necessity for their inclusion; which should be all that is needed. For future new advances to appear such a freedom for dimensions should exist. We suppress time in the EM rest frame because of its usefulness in what follows and because time is never used in this rest frame.

We define here the designation h, for the particular rest frames in terms of subscripts:

$$h_{emrf}, \ h_{prf} \tag{6}$$

where emrf is the electromagnetic rest frame and prf is the physical rest frame. The dimensional designation for these rest frames are as given above. The absolute numerical value, however, of these rest frames are identical, thus:

$$|h_{emrf}| = |h_{prf}| = 4.14 \times 10^{-15} \tag{7}$$

In a complete sense $\quad h_{prf} \;=\; 4.14 \times 10^{-15}$ eV per cycle per second, $\qquad$ (8)

and $\qquad\qquad\qquad\qquad h_{emrf} = 4.14 \times 10^{-15}$ eV per cycle $\qquad$ (9)

Similar arguments can also be made for η using Equations like Eqs. (3 to 9).

3. A PREVIEW OF LATER SECTIONS

The realistic significance of the above and many details will be discussed further in later sections. The implications of Eq. (9) are astonishing. This starts with Eq. (1) which is a minimum energy. Together with the Hertz's pictures, Figure 1, which displays continuous cycles of dipole EM energy, the result is that each cycle of minimum EM energy is 4.14×10^{-15} eV. Arrival at this conclusion, which will be discussed further, is also bolstered by the fact that what we are considering here is the simplest electron motion that generates EM radiation. This is for electrons in, say, rectilinear motion with acceleration and deceleration in these directions which generate the perpendicular EM dipole waves. The Hertzian picture, Figure 1, shows a never-ending procession of dipole waves. The new attitude taken here will be for will be for each single EM half-cycle of the Hertzian picture of Fig.1 taken separately. These are for single discontinuous half-cycles, each of which of which is called the photex. It will also be useful to discuss 2 such contiguous entities which will be called the photex-pair. This will consist of two sequential identical EM field distributions (except for the opposite directions of each half cycle's fields).

Eds. Note: Figure 1 should be put here, approximately

This prompts the further conclusion that the half cycle is a more fundamental entity than the cycle. Figure 2 contrasts the continuous dipole radiation EM fields with that of only one discontinuous discrete half cycle of dipole radiation. It also implies that each half cycle of such dipole radiation will have a minimum energy which is half that of the cycle or 2.07×10^{-15} eV. Each such discontinuous entity will be named: **'photex'**, and will always be a half cycle. They can naturally be generated in pairs: one for acceleration and one for deceleration of the generating electron in, say, an electron collision. In this case, a rebounding droplet electron in a collision will first decelerate until its incident velocity reaches zero at the collision point. It then accelerates in the reverse direction reaching its incident velocity and energy but minus the energy of 4.14×10^{-15} eV of the **'photex-pair'** which is emitted in a rebounding collision. Figure 3 pictures the details of such collisions with a rigid microscopic wall merely for purposes of clarity. This, can be replaced with a collision with another electron instead; the realistic case.

Eds. Note: Figure 2 should be put here, approximately

Dividing Eqs. (8, 9) by 2 gives each expression in terms of the photex (a half cycle is a photex):

$[h_{prf}] / 2 = 2.07 \times 10^{-15}$ eV per half cycle per second or eV per photex per second,

$[h_{emrf}] / 2 = 2.07 \times 10^{-15}$ eV per half cycle or eV per photex.

The final surprising statement in is: We have now a realistic model which is a half cycle discrete dipole EM field distribution. Finite assemblies of these can be the wave trains that De Broglie had often hoped for and discussed [26]. The use of continuous EM radiation has here been demoted, providing now for discontinuous (discrete) EM phenomena: like the photex or finite assemblies of them.

4. A CAPSULE VIEW OF THE REALISTIC PHENOMENOLOGY

The items given below show the reader how wide the realistic approach must be. This section provides details of a developing phenomenology which are indeed necessary to understanding the realistic basis of this paper. It may be skipped on a first reading by those who wish to see the details of the Planck constant derivation which is given in section 4.

All the 16 Figures are displayed here in serial order to give the reader the full graphic flavour of the realistic approach. This non-verbal and pictorial sequence of all the Figures provides the reader with the broad direct realistic basis, which is discussed in detail in the text. We think this is the easiest way to introduce the realistic approach of this paper. Merely supplying a list of scattered references to the realistic figures is an obstacle which disadvantages earnest readers, who in the main, would not be terribly familiar with the realistic ideas presented here

These figures are of paramount importance in a realistic theory such as is presented here. The adherents to QM have usually forbidden literal pictures of physical reality or at least denigrated and obscured them. This is because of the importance of the abstract approach in QM. The appearance of Schrodinger Equations, for example, is always repeated in QM papers and texts. In a realistic theory, illustrations are meant to be literal representation of physical reality and as such have a similar importance as the equations of QM have and should appear or reappear as often. In a realistic theory these pictures actually represent physical reality and give a view of physical reality which is simpler and clearer than the conceptions of QM. Repetition of such figures should be as prevalent in papers based on a realistic approach as are the abstract equations and concepts of QM.

The realistic approach features the following:

1. Pictorial literal views of physical reality are shown most of them self-explanatory, see Figs. 1-16.

2. No piecemeal reconstruction of standard SR or QM, both must change together.

3.   Relativistic invariance is retained based on Builder/Ives/Lorentz literal rest frame fluidic distortions [27], [28], see Fig. 6.   This shows that our physical rest frame does not change with velocity for internal observers, whereas these changes will be evident to observers in the absolute rest frame (the rest frame of the universe).

4.   The present standard versions of SR/QM are each globally inconsistent and locally consistent[22].

5.   Particle and electromagnetic EM wave models are to be constructed from a dual fluidic plenum.

6.   This plenum consists of positive and negative charged microscopically continuous fluids. The quiescent (and neutral) plenum is the superposition of these two fluids, with each fluid density equal to that of the classical electron, see Fig. 3.

Eds. Note: Figure 3 should be put here, approximately

7.   Variations in the fluid densities and their velocity fields are then constructed for particle and wave models.   The electric and magnetic fields derive from the fluidic properties.   Each model must consist of globally equal positive and negative charge distributions from the original plenum and with localised polarised charge flow fields and a net global velocity field of zero.

8. This makes antiparticles possible by reversing fluid model charge densities and velocity fields.

9. Details of the electron fluid droplet model are shown in Figs. 4 and 5. In Fig. 4 both the positive and negative densities are arranged as shown.   Fig. 5 shows that the internal negative fluid of the electron droplet rotates as a rigid body, with no curl in that fluid, and with an equatorial velocity

Eds. Note: Figures 4 and 5 should be put here, approximately

of c. The positive fluid which remains after the spherical negative fluid droplet is gouged out in the plenum, is necessary to provide the external field of the electron droplet. Its circumferential flow has curl external to the droplet and provides for magnetic interaction with the droplet core.

10. Discussion and references are made[3], [7], [8], [9] for a spinning spherical droplet model of a fluidic electron. In a realistic operational version of SR, the spherical droplet becomes a spinning discoid with an angular momentum vector in the direction of motion. Like a flying spinning pancake, it flattens with increasing velocity in the direction perpendicular to its motion.

Eds. Note: Figure 6 should be put here, approximately

As its velocity increases towards the light velocity, c, in the absolute rest frame this 'pancake' reaches a radius of infinity and the whole rest frame is destroyed, see Fig. 6.

11. In Fig. 7, The Tennis Ball Sequence is shown. It is for the suggested generation of Photex pairs at each collision of the droplet electron rebounding endlessly between 2 rigid walls (but in a practical case between image or real electrons). This is similar to an endlessly rebounding tennis ball

Eds. Note: Figure 7 should be put here, approximately

between two rigid walls. This can be for realistic and practical case of an initial electron kinetic energy of 1-20 electron volts. Deceleration-to-zero collisions of the electron droplet with a wall generate single half wave dipole EM field distributions (a propagating 'smoke ring', i.e., a photex) and a similar one on reversal and electron acceleration from the wall. This is a photex pair. The detailed pictorial character of this come from their dissection from the continuous case, Fig. 1.

Hertz drew this in the 1880s to show continuous EM dipole emission by an electron in rectilinear deceleration and acceleration, see Figs. 2, 7 for pictures and comment on discrete EM waves.

12. A finite number of these entities would then constitute a finite wave train eliminating the present need for the mathematical Fourier functions which extend infinitely in space and time. Alternately these functions can still be used together with window functions to isolate discrete half wavelength portions (or photexi) portions of infinitely extended Fourier waveforms.

13. The space-time continuum is the pictorial arena for realistic phenomena. Figs. 8 and 9 show two experimental situations illustrating this. As has and will again be shown, the generation of the

Eds. Note: Figure 8 and 9 should be put here, approximately

photex and the photex-pairs are done by droplet electron rebounding collisions. This decrements the electron droplet kinetic energy by energies of the about 4×10^{-15} eV for each photex pair or each rebound event. One sees then in Fig. 8 that if, say, a 50 eV electron kinetic energy is incident upon a set of repelling planes between which it bounces, then after about 0.25×10^{15} such bounces the electron would lose about 1 eV of kinetic energy and is the basis for experiments.

The interesting isolated electron experiments of Dehmelt have revealed that the lifetime of an electron in his apparatus have durations of about two weeks. The electron in these experiments is in rapid circular motion due to the imposed magnetic fields. Fig. 9 shows the decomposition of this motion into two perpendicular vector components. This thus reduces the circular motion to two back and forth rebounds for each vector and there would inevitably be an ongoing reduction into in the kinetic energy of the electrons via the photex-pair emission scheme given above. These photex-pair considerations resulted in values of lifetime close to those, which were measured.

Correspondence with Dehmelt about this revealed that he worked with Cohn-Tannoudji who was able to derive these lifetimes from standard QM considerations and he thus needed no inputs from a realistic theory. We have shown that this behaviour is always possible when using an inconsistent theory like QM[22]. This is no surprise since we show that the axioms of QM can be taken as inconsistent [22]. It is well-known that an inconsistent theory literally permits any theorem to be derived/proven. Dehmelt's basic work is given[29] with electron lifetime results[29].

14. The energy, E, required for setting up the varying fluidic charge densities and velocity fields of a model is the agency for the creation of the mass, m, of that model via $E = mc^2$. All of the electron mass has been derived from it fluid model, see item 21 below. A mu meson mass might be modelled on the hydrodynamic flow of the well-known Hills spherical vortex, see Fig. 10. This can be done to check if the charge-flow regime of Fig. 10 needs an energy a few hundred times that of the assembly energy of the droplet electron. If so the [mu meson]/droplet electron mass ratio can be realistically justified. A similar charge flow geometry may also exist for the heavier mesons. In this case, Fig. 10 could to be modified by squeezing in several additional modes of toroidal flow inside the same sphere of Fig. 10.

Eds. Note: Figure 10 should be put here, approximately

Protons may come from more complicated flow and charge regimes, for, say, a spherical droplet with variations containing charge and flow modes that can change in the radial, azimuthal, and conical angle (R, θ, φ) directions, see Fig. 11, a suggestive sketch for this. In this case, it is easy

Eds. Note: Figure 11 should be put here, approximately

to see that the assembly of such higher order charge-flow modes would easily require a lot more energy that than the simpler rotating electron droplet model. This may easily give via proton/electron fluidic assembly energy ratios like the mass ratio, 1846, which experiment provides. Quarks and the other exotically named nuclear objects can thus correspond to the different spatial spherical modes shown. In Fig.11 the alternate 60 degree angular regions could consist of opposing charged fluids. This alternation could then supply a mechanism for the gross neutrality of the model. This could explain the closeness of the masses of proton and neutron and with a shell of polarised fluid upon the underlying structure of the neutron, will give a proton model. Anti-protons would then consist of opposite charge and flow regimes to that of the proton.

15. It has been shown[15, 16] that when the Quantum Potential in its D'Alembertian form is equated to ηω then it results in a version of the Schrodinger Equation. These equations also apply in a clear way to the tennis ball sequence, Fig. 7 with its non-linear generation

of photexi/photex pairs giving the EM wave equation from the Laplacian form of the Quantum Potential.

16.   The fluidic point of view also permits a natural view that each half wavelength toroidal EM field distribution can be taken in a realistic sense as a nonlocal discrete entity. This object, the photex, obviously appears, in a realistic sense as non-local. Thus, like a ripple on a pond it is in many places at once. The toroidal photex has the radial motion at the speed, c. It can also be made to appear to an appropriate observer as a local object. In this case, it can appear as a (local) sphere or with a radial gauge shrinkage, as a canonical particle. Either way a finite number of these entities would still constitute a wave train. These discrete objects eliminate the Fourier space-time infinitely extended functions (see latter part of next item).

17.   A Helmholtz essay[30] and an engraving by Escher[31] supply a basis for a realistic view of Non-Euclidean space which permits extensions of rest frames to give both a realistic view of the non-local and local photex.

With the aid of Escher's Fig. 12 the Helmholtz essay on rest frames with Euclidean coordinates is given pictorial meaning in which the images in a spherical mirror are discussed.

Eds. Note: Figure 12 should be put here, approximately

Helmholtz shows that the hand which is in Euclidean space for the local observer (with its surroundings) is also reflected in the mirror in such a way that the image in the mirror also seems to the observer in the mirror to be the same as that seen by the Euclidean observer. The famous Escher print[31], "Hand with Reflecting Sphere", was drawn in 1935. Sixty- Five years earlier, in 1870, Helmholtz wrote about this in the paper[30], "On the Origin and Significance of Geometrical Axioms". The graphic relevant discussion, is here reproduced:

"Let me first remind the reader that if all the linear dimensions of other bodies, and our own, at the same time were diminished or increased in like proportion, as for instance to half or double their size, we should with our means of space perception be utterly unaware of the change. This would also be the case if expansion or contraction were different in different directions, provided our own bodies changed in a like manner, [also for rotation].

Think of the image of the world in a convex mirror. The common silvered globes set up in gardens give the essential features. A well-made mirror of moderate aperture represents the objects in front of it as apparently solid and in fixed positions behind its surface. But the images of the distant horizon and the sun in the sky lie behind the mirror at a limited distance, equal to its focal length. Between these and the surface of the mirror are found the images of all the other objects before it, but the images are diminished and flattened in proportion to the distance of their objects from the mirror. Yet, every straight line or plane in the outer world is represented by a 'straight line' or 'plane' in the image.

The image of a man measuring with a rule a straight line from the mirror would contract more and more the farther he went from the surface of the sphere. With his shrunken rule, however, the man in the image would count out exactly the same number of centimetres as the real man. And in general all geometric measurements of lines or angles made with regularly varying images of real instruments would yield exactly the same results as in the outer world, all congruent bodies would coincide on being applied to one another in the mirror as in the outer world, all lines of sight in the outer world would be represented by 'straight' lines of sight in the mirror.

In short, I do not see how men in the mirror are to discover that their bodies are not rigid solids and their experiences not good examples of Euclid's axioms. But if they could look out upon our world as we can look into theirs, without overstepping the boundary, they must declare it to be a picture in a spherical mirror and would speak of us just as we speak of them. If two inhabitants of the different worlds could communicate with one another, neither, as far as I can see, would be able to convince the other that he had the true, the other the distorted relations."

In fact, as above, neither observer can convince the other that his own world is not Euclidean. This matter has far reaching consequences, particularly since one can via such views map the doubly-connected space of the photex toroid to a space where this becomes a singly connected sphere in which can be located the canonical local particle. Such a mapping from a toroid to a sphere appears to be mathematically impossible because of the singularities which exist for such mappings. In a fluidic practical sense the singularities can be mapped to portions of space which can be infinitely distant or with infinitely small energies so that their affects are negligible.

Fig. 13 shows most of such a mapping. First, one can mathematically slice open the toroid and straighten it out so that it looks like a cylinder. This is the first sketch at the top of Fig. 13. The axis of the cylinder is then shrunk to a point in such a way that the cylindrical surface assumes the

Eds. Note: Figure 13 should be put here, approximately

shape of a sphere; this is subject to a condition that the distance from the center point of the axis shrinkage to the surface of the cylinder, finally becomes a constant, which is the radius of the sphere. At this point, a radial shrinkage of the spherical radius reduces the sphere to the canonical point. The poles of the sphere, s and s', are the locations for the two singularities of the mapping and may be neglected in a practical sense if vanishingly small fluidic energies are associated with them. One can, of course map in the opposite direction, from local particle to non-local toroid.

18. In Fig. 14 is shown a sketch of the shedding of a toroid photex by a droplet electron, which must occur each time the droplet moves into or out of a rebound. This rolling up of

Eds. Note: Figure 14 should be put here, approximately

the toroidal vortex can be given by a winding or curling number[20] also shown in this Figure. This parameter requires a deeper insight into toroidal vortex generation, probably derived from parameters of the droplet electron, See part 5 of Final section.

The import of the fine structure constant, α, can also be suggested by the content of this paper. It can be shown how the canonical value of α is only assumed to be dimensionless. The discussion of dimensionality given in section **2** shows that its purely numerical value occurs because of the suppression of cycles or radians in h or η, something which is eminently supportable up till now but which does not hold for the postulated electromagnetic rest frame introduced in that section. If radians or cycles are reintroduced then the dimensions of α^{-1} which is 137.037...... has the dimensions: per cycle or per radian. This leads directly to the content of Figure 14. Since the introduction of relevant dimensions is now possible according to the discussion of dimensionality given in section **2,** the winding or the curling number of a spherical vortex (a photex) can now be inserted into the dimensions of α^{-1} . It has the dimensions: vortex-winding number per cycle or per Photex pair. Figure 14 is now seen as a picture of spherical vortex development. A Reference to such phenomena is given in the last lines of section **4.**

19. The sketch in Fig. 15 presents a realistic mechanism for the double slit experiment. This has been presented mainly to show the great variability which fluidic phenomena can

Eds. Note: Figure 15 should be put here, approximately

provide. Electrons rebounding from the slit mask generate photex pairs of the right wavelength and frequency so that their propagation through the slit the via Huygens' principle places the photex or photex pair EM energy in the region where this EM flux can combine and act in straightforward ways to guide those electrons which actually go though the slit, to generate the effects which are seen in this experiment.

20. Apropos of the item above, a presentation has appeared which derives all the mass of the electron[1] from its fields (usually called EM mass). This has been criticised because it merely
shows the great variability of fluids which can be tailored to fit almost anything. This then will have no great importance unless and until many more theoretical fluidic results are forthcoming which receive experimental confirmation or have clear heuristic values.

21. Fig. 16 shows an even more fanciful sequence for the capture of a free electron by a singly ionised nucleus. Since not much work has been done on this, only the general idea is presented. The

Eds. Note: Figure 16 should be put here, approximately

electron is shown as a spinning droplet in rectilinear motion which deforms and finally becomes a bubble in atomic capture surrounding the nucleus. This provide a realistic reason for the lack of radiation from orbital electrons; they are not radiating because they are bubbles or cavities surrounding the nucleus.

22. This paper and the ideas proposed have been solely concerned with QM/SR. No proposals are made for explaining gravity or the General Theory of Relativity (GTR). The only gravitational implication lies in item 15 where $E = mc^2$, says that this equation should be used to find the mass of fluid models by first finding the energy needed for the fluid model assembly. It does thus imply that a mechanism might be found for gravitation and GTR somewhere in the fluid models. Although no work has been done on this, a connection may exist in the phenomena of the oppositely charged fluids. In the '20s, Tonks & Langmuir showed "Plasma oscillations" existed in neutral ionised gases and in the atmosphere, which were indeed found.

Thus, something like "plenum oscillations" of the dual fluids might exist in the fluid models.

This could be a mechanism for gravitational waves and/or mass?

23. Finally, with more relevance to this paper, the realistic approach has made it possible for the first time to actually derive Planck's constant, h (or h/2) in its dimensionally correct form and directly from Larmor's radiation formula and the physical properties of the photex.

5. PLANCK'S CONSTANT: DERIVATION FROM LARMOR'S RADIATION LAW

The relations below with their usual meanings will be used freely in what follows to simplify various expressions:

$$E = \eta\omega, \qquad \lambda f = c, \qquad \omega k = c \qquad \eta = h/2\pi. \qquad (10)$$

In the second relation above, λ is wavelength (in cms per cycle) and k is the wave number, $2\pi/\lambda$, where f is frequency (in cycles per second) so that c would be in cms/second since the dimension: cycle, will algebraically cancel out. We find first the relationship between h/2 and the other well-known fundamental constants. Starting with the fine structure constant, α :

$$\alpha = e^2 / (4 \pi \varepsilon_0 c \eta) = 1/137 \qquad (11)$$

Solving for η : $$\eta = e^2 / 4 \pi \varepsilon_0 c \alpha \qquad (12)$$

Subst. (11) in (12): $$\eta = e^2 (137) / 4 \pi \varepsilon_0 c \qquad (13)$$

Subst. (10) in (13): $$h = e^2 (137)(2\pi) / 4 \pi \varepsilon_0 c \qquad (14)$$

As previously explained, the photex is the more fundamental entity and it is characterised by h/2:

Thus from Eq. (14): $\qquad h/2 = e^2 [137 \pi] / 4 \pi \varepsilon_0 c$ $\qquad\qquad$ (15)

or $\qquad\qquad h/2 = [e^2 / 4 \pi \varepsilon_0 c] [430.4]$ $\qquad\qquad$ (16)

The Eqs. (15 or 16) will be compared with the forthcoming result of operating on the Larmor radiation law. This law is given by Sommerfeld [32] as:

Total instantaneous energy radiated per unit time:

$$S = e^2 [(acceleration)^2] / 6\pi\varepsilon_0 c^3 \qquad\qquad (17)$$

This represents the instantaneous power. We first postulate the 'tennis ball' motion of Figure 7. This motion of the electron is needed for the half cycle (photex) generation when the moving electron is being decelerated from its incident speed to a velocity of zero at the wall after which it reverses direction and then accelerates away from the wall opposite to the direction of its incident motion. As discussed, for each such deceleration-acceleration situation, one photex pair is emitted. It consists of two adjacent photexi 'smoke rings'. The (acceleration) [2] term in Eq. (17), therefore, can apply to two photexi or a photex-pair and nothing else; no time continuous function is to be used. The function of time for the position of the radiating electron will be given by a single discrete sine wave cycle. For each photex this is a half cycle sine wave cycle.

We first treat the case of the photex pair. We need to get from the Larmor law, the expression for h as energy per cycle per second in the physical rest frame and carry along the expression for energy per cycle in the EM rest frame. Finally, these are converted to expressions for the half cycle which can be compared with the h/2 expression of Eq. (16). The Larmor law of Eq. (17) is slightly modified:

$$S = [e^2 (time \ summation \ of \ a^2)] / [6 \pi \varepsilon_0 c^3] \qquad\qquad (18)$$

which has the units: energy/time and the 'a' term above is the acceleration.

We approximate the collision process of the electron droplet with a wall by assuming a stationary electron undergoing sinusoidal motion about a stationary point. This is approximately what the electron encounters in the repulsive electric fields of Fig. 8. We do this because there is no present detailed theory realistically covering electron collision processes. Hertz, however, and many others more than 100 years ago assumed such motion when deriving the dipole EM energy emitted by an electron in sinusoidal motion. They got from this, sinusoidal EM dipole energy field distributions. Even in the realistic case we should expect to get the same sort of EM fields either discretely or continuously as in Figs. 1 and 2 (See further discussion in 2nd paragraph after Eq. (31)). Although the electron motion is as in Figure. 7, a one cycle of simple sinusoidal function replaces this only for the collision process of deceleration and acceleration which results in a photex pair (2 half cycles). The discontinuous half cycle sinusoid will be used because we are trying to find the energy of the 'photex' half sinusoid. Thus, with A as the amplitude of the electron motion, in the direction x:

$$x = A \sin \omega t, \tag{19}$$

times the window function, which encloses a single half sinusoidal cycle.

The velocity of electron, v is: $dx / dt = v = \omega A \cos \omega t$ \hfill (20)
again, inside the single half sinusoidal cycle.

The acceleration of the electron, a is: $a = d^2x / dt^2 = dv / dt = -\omega^2 A \sin \omega t$ \hfill (21)
again, inside the single half sinusoidal function. It is noted that x, v, and a functions are all equal to zero at the edges of the single half cycle sine wave or the single full cycle sine wave. There are no discontinuities in these functions.

Finally: \hfill $a^2 = \omega^4 A^2 \sin^2 \omega t$ \hfill (22)

and for a photex or half the time average of $a^2 = \omega^4 A^2 [1/2]$ \hfill (23)

This is because the time summation of $\sin^2 \omega t$ for a half cycle sine wave is $[\pi/2]$, see reference[33], but this must be divided by the time interval π to result in the factor $[1/2]$ in (23). This links (23) to a half cycle(photex), and (23) will carry a link to a full cycle(photex pair); both are followed henceforth.

[The integration of a single half cycle of sin squared divided by the single time interval π is what is meant by time summation.] \hfill (24)

Since we are integrating only one half cycle of a $\sin^2$ term, S, therefore, becomes:

$$S = [e^2 \ (\text{time summation of } a^2)] / [6 \ \pi \ \varepsilon_0 \ c^3] \tag{25}$$

It is because of the single half cycle time summation above that the word cycle appearing henceforth should refer to half cycles. This somewhat ambiguous nomenclature below emphasises the similarity in dimensionality changes both for the half cycle (the photex) and the cycle (the photex pair).

Continuing: \hfill $S = [e^2 \ \omega^4 A^2] [1/2] / [6 \ \pi \ \varepsilon_0 \ c^3]$ \hfill (26)

The units of S are power or energy/second or eV per second. This could also be written, as energy per second/cycle although the word cycle has been superfluous and suppressed, is needed now.

The task now is to try to convert S which has the units energy-cycles/second into a measure, say, T which has the units energy per cycle in the physical rest frame or energy per cycle in the EM rest frame. It should be evident upon study that if S is multiplied by $1/f^2$ it becomes the proper T for the appropriate rest frame. Thus, the dimensional modification sequence for this is:

1. S has the dimensions: energy per second per cycle (or energy-cycles per second) in the physical rest frame (here cycle is restored) or energy-cycles in the EM rest frame; where time is suppressed.

2. $[1/f]$S now has the dimensions energy in the physical rest frame; or energy-seconds in the EM rest frame, but with time suppressed here the units for $[1/f]$S in the EM rest frame become: energy.

3. $[1/f^2]$S has the dimensions energy per cycle per second in the physical rest frame; however $[1/f]$S in the EM rest frame could be energy per cycle per second. In this last case, it has been shown above that time can be suppressed in the EM rest frame, so that this last case becomes energy per cycle.

4. Finally, $[1/f^2]$S has the dimensions energy per half cycle per second in the physical rest frame; or energy per half cycle in the EM rest frame.
(All 4 items above and all discussion below is taken with the word cycle replaced with half cycle.)

We carry out the algebraic simplification of T, assuming the physical rest frame is used. We also know that we can switch to the EM rest frame at any time. Starting with the initial value of T:

$$T = [1/f^2] [S] = [1/f^2] [e^2 \omega^4 A^2] [1/2] / [6 \pi \varepsilon_0 c^3] \tag{27}$$

$$T = [e^2 / 4 \pi \varepsilon_0 c] [1/f^2] [\omega^4 A^2/c^2] [1/1.5] [1/2] \tag{28}$$
$$= [e^2 / 4 \pi \varepsilon_0 c] [(2\pi)^4 f^4 A^2/ f^2 c^2] [1/3]$$
$$= [e^2 / 4 \pi \varepsilon_0 c] [(2\pi)^4 A^2 f^2 / c^2] [1/3]$$
$$= [e^2 / 4 \pi \varepsilon_0 c] [A^2 /\lambda^2] (2\pi)^4 [1/3]$$

Finally: $\quad T = [e^2 / 4 \pi \varepsilon_0 c] [A^2 /\lambda^2] [519.54] \tag{29}$

The intervening steps between (28) and (29) above are provided to clarify the reduction to (29).

Now, the last factor of Eq. (29), 519.54, should be compared to the last factor, [430.4], of Eq. (16). In Eq. (29) it is 21% higher than in Eq. (16). To this accuracy, the proof is compete that h/2 and thus h can be derived from the dimensional, realistic phenomenology, and Larmor's Law applications in this paper. All this is true provided that the $[A^2 / \lambda^2]$ factor in (29) is equal to one. We cannot reasonably deduce much more than this. However, playing with these numbers a bit: suppose that the factor $[A^2 / \lambda^2]$ is equal to about 0.8, then the proof becomes quite accurate. This could be because we have only used the approximations of (27) through (29) and there is no theory for the fine details of the electron collision process that generates the photexi. Falling back on the equating of $[A^2 / \lambda^2]$ to one makes:

$$A = \lambda \qquad (30)$$

Falling back on some dubious arm waving one might be able to modify the factor $[A^2 / \lambda^2]$ so that:

$$A = \lambda / 2 \qquad (31)$$

This is not much help in trying to read some deep meaning into a relationship between A and λ. A, is the half amplitude of the sinusoidal displacement function, Eq. (19,) which was some sort of approximation to the actual realistic displacement. 'A' might be between .5 and 1.0 times λ is a possibility. It also points to the fact that there may be another unknown factor in the expressions (27) through (29) that may someday be replaced with a clearer realistic explanation of the collision process. One is tempted to look at the Wyler work in the early '70s, which Robertson ably summarised[34]. The realistic physical process discussed in that paper provides a possibility for the usefulness of Wyler's work. It should also be mentioned that A.O. Barut[35] discussed the need for a similar interpretation of Larmor's law in 1978 as in Eq. (8) but found no justification for it in standard QM.

Added remarks must be made about the use of Larmor's radiation law and the use of the sine function for the representing the behaviour of the electron with Eqs. (19) - (22) when it enters into collisions as per the Tennis Ball sequence of Figure 7. First, Hertz and later many others gave the electron the vertical sinusoidal motion shown in Figure 1 from which they then derived the emitted dipole sinusoidal EM fields. It was a necessity that the electron interaction with the wall or more realistically with an actual electron would result in sinusoidal EM fields. Very little has been done on the microscopic details of electron collisions, probably because such work also falls under the QM bans on microscopic representations. Work has been done on the details of macroscopic collisions[36] of many different kinds of balls. Unfortunately none of this material appears to be useful. The repulsive force between two electrons coming to a collision have indeed been cited by Panofsky[37] but with no detail or quantitative treatment given. The simple-minded approach of Eqs (19-21) used here obviously does not tell the full story. This is evident because: (1) the measured and theoretical values of Planck's constant still differ by about 20% and (2) because the details of the electron droplet collision cannot be realistically replaced by the simple-minded physical sinusoidal motion of a quiescent electron droplet about a fixed point.

285

Here the example cited above of an electron in a retarding and reversing field shown in Figure 8 and section 14 of part 3 above is relevant. The electron progresses through ever-greater reversing fields where the sequence of its realistic relativistic dimensional change can easily be calculated. Upon velocity reversal, the dimensions can also be calculated. These actions might be used to find the parameters of the generated Hertzian photexi[39]. Thus, the something more which is needed and the missing elements of the collision process could be able to decrement the derived magnitude of Planck's constant by this 20%.

The next section (items 5 and 6) show the usefulness of the derivation of Planck's constant of this paper.

5. FINAL REMARKS AND THE IMPORT OF THIS PAPER

This derivation is exact in providing the dimensionally correct form for h or h/2 (although numerically the result differs by about 21% from the required value). This appears to be the first indication that h or h/2 is derivable from a fluidic electron model in a vortex shedding situation and relates well to the Dirac comment. Physically this may provide a sea of photexi each with energies of about 10^{-15} eV that gives a realistic explanation for uncertainties due to myriads of photexi expanding throughout the universe. This will, demote, of course, the uncertainty principle by providing realistic random EM phenomena as causes of uncertainties and space chaos.

The ideas presented here and elsewhere[3-25] possess physically realistic and heuristic qualities which come from the fluid models. It appears to establish a physically realistic process for the derivation of h or h/2 and can explain the generation of EM dipole fields by vortex-shedding behaviour of droplet electrons.

The expanding 'smoke rings' of EM energy (the photex EM model) provides a discontinuous discrete EM model. It further provides an obviously non-local but realistic model for EM energy (the photex), as described in many of the references and in Item 17 of Section 3. The canonical photon here can be pictured as a mathematical convenience rather then a single particle as it is now taken (see below).
It is useful to give at least a partial discussion of the significance of some of the matters which have been presented. Itemising in no particular order:

1. The use of two space fluids to represent an ether permits a visually simple mechanism to portray the emission of EM waves. It is similar to the hydrodynamic phenomenon: the shedding of hydrodynamic vortices. It further permits these discontinuous chunks of EM radiation (like 'smoke rings') to exist in a realistic and natural way.

2. The energy of particles, waves, etc., can be estimated from fluid models and via $E = mc^2$ its complete mass equivalent can be found. In this way the masses of fundamental particles can be tied to
modes of charge density and flow. It thus provides a realistic view tying the increasing mass of heavier particles to increasingly complicated modes of charge and flow fields.

3. The explanation of the photon can via the realistic approach given here be taken as mathematic models consisting of myriads of photexi. Usually the instantaneous emission of a photon by an atom liberating an electron can be explained in a realistic way as follows: the liberated electron leaves an atom with a kinetic energy, E. and a velocity, v. Up to now the energy is taken via the Planck relation as a particle (a photon) which is instantly generated and then goes its own way. In the realistic approach given here the De Boglie relation: $p = mv = \eta\ k$ has an important relevance. Here p is the electron momentum, mv, m is the mass of the electron and v is its velocity, η is $h/2\pi$, where h is Planck's constant, and k is the wave number of EM radiation or $2\pi/\lambda$ and finally it is easily shown that λ is the wavelength for the photon of frequency f.

Assume that a good portion of an Avogadro's number of atoms are undergoing electron emission of the same kind and so according to QM would all liberate photons, of the same energy hf, and the same frequency f. Referring back to the realistic section 12 where the Tennis Ball Sequence of electron collisions is discussed: electrons with a specified velocity v will generate photex pairs with the requisite wavelength corresponding to the energy E as above. Since Avogodro's number is about 10^{23} and since about 10^{15} collisions will generate about 1 eV of EM energy, then the same number of collisions which may take as little as 10^{-15} seconds or even less depending on the number of atoms participating in the reaction. Thus, many more atoms than 10^{15} could generate total photex energies of 1-50 eV in very short times of less than, say, 10^{-6} or 10^{-9} seconds. In this way, myriads of photexi can be quickly generated and can serve as realistic models for the canonical photons which are now demoted to the status of mathematical though somewhat convenient fictional constructs.

In hydrodynamics, Karman and others have discussed the behaviour of cylindrical vortex sheets of alternately distributed rotation. It appears that such hydrodynamic phenomena are self-organising and stable. Lamb has described this[38]. It is suggested here that photex toroids may behave in a similar fashion but much theoretical work on this remains to be done. This again supports de Broglie's idea of finding a way to make finite EM wave trains (of photexi)

.
4. Still with application to the realistic item 12 of section 3 where the Tennis Ball Sequence of electron collisions is discussed: One can from easily develop from this a realistic physical meaning for the Uncertainty principle:

$$(p\ x - x\ p) \text{ is greater than or equal to } \eta. \qquad (32)$$

If one starts with sketch 2 of Figure 7, assume the electron moves to the right at a speed v. After the rebounding collision in sketches 4 and 5 the electron is moving left and has lost an amount of energy corresponding to the energy of a photex pair (about 10^{-15} eV). The values of x in both terms of (32) above can be taken as identical. Their difference corresponds to the value of h (in the EM rest frame) and so (32) above now acquires a physically realistic meaning. It is the decrement in the energy of the rebounding electron droplet (suppressing the 2π in η of Eq. 32 above).

5. In recent years, I had come to the conclusion that QM can never be disproven because it is an inconsistent theory and by the well-known rules of logic, such theories can be used to prove literally anything[22]. Thus no matter what empirical phenomena a realistic theory could provide; the above argument seemed unassailable. It explains the tenacious nature of QM and is a very powerful basis for the continuing validity of QM. Only recently have I come to see there may be one exception to this rule. The exception lies in the Dirac argument which is given at the beginning of this paper. This argument states that the derivation of Planck's constant (presumably via some sort of non-QM method like the realistic arguments proposed here) will cause the fall of Planck's constant as a fundamental constant. I presume that QM will also fall to be replaced by a theory with a realistic basis as has here been discussed. This argument of Dirac's, however, also bans QM from supplying any proof of its own of the derivation of Planck's constant. This is because such an argument argues against itself; an impossible situation which is much stronger than a merely inconsistent theory and also because no adherent to QM would argue against its own validity.

6. Finally, the very existence for the derivation of Planck's constant which has been given here is in itself a proof or at least a confirmation of the validity of the photex concept since the energies of photexi confirm its physical meaning as given here as the minimum energy of a half wave dipole EM field configuration.

Endnotes

The titles of explanatory papers are listed here. These titles show clearly the purposes of the papers and provide a good introduction to the reader of a deeper understanding (via these papers themselves) of the realistic phenomenology. The numbers below are not in serial order because they are the reference numbers for these titled papers only. The numbers below are from the 'References' section given further on, where the data on the location of these papers can be found. Book titles are in the 'References' section.

1. "Deriving Planck's Constant & the Complete Self-Energy of the Electron from Dual Charged Fluid Models"
2. "The Evolution of the Physicist's Picture of Nature"
5. "A Triad of Axioms for Realistic Versions of STR/QM: Inconsistent Logics, Escher Non-Euclidean Geometries, and Charged Fluids"
6. "Logical Organisation of Knowledge with Inconsistent and Undecidable Algorithms Using Imaginary and Transfinite Exponential Number Forms for Non-Boolean Fields"
7. "An Electromagnetic World Picture, Part I, Massless Dual Charge Fluids for Modelling Vacuum Space, Fundamental Particles, & Electromagnetic Waves"
8. "An Electromagnetic World Picture, Part II: Planck's Constant, a Discrete Wave Model: the Photex, a Physical Model for the QM Hidden Variable"

9. "An Electromagnetic World Picture, Part III: Subjectivity of Space, Relative Metrics, and the Locality-Nonlocality Conundrum"
10. "Minimum Photon 'Rest Mass', From Planck's Constant & Discrete Electromagnetic Waves"
11. "Godel Axiom Mappings in Special Relativity & Quantum Electromagnetic Theory"
12. "Relativity of the Metric"
13. "Photex Rest Frames and Null Geodesics"
14. "Quaternionic Electromagnetic Wave Equation and a Dual Charge-Filled Space"
15. "Realistic Fluid Models for h & for de Broglie Waves, & Wave Equations from the Quantum Potential" and the paper, "Erratum"
16. "Wave Equations from Laplacian and D'Alembertian Quantum Potentials"
17. "Physical Models for Nonlocal Particles, Hidden Variables, and All That"
18. "On the Physical Meaning of Planck's Constant, h, From a Realist Sub-quantum Theory"
19. "Transfinite Ordinals as Axiom Number Symbols in Quantum and EM Wave Functions"
22. "Local Consistency and Global Inconsistency from 'Hegelian Realistic' Version of QM/STR"
23. "Direct Calculation of h and the Complete Self Energy of the Electron From Fluid Models"
24. "Phenomenology of a Subquantum, Realistic, Relativistic Theory"
25. "On the Physical Meaning of Planck's Constant, h, From a Realistic Subquantum Theory"
27. "Ether and Relativity" and "The Constancy of the Velocity of Light"
30. "On the Origin and Significance of Geometrical Axioms"
31. "Hand with Reflecting Sphere"
34. "Wyler's Expression for the Fine Structure Constant α"
35. "The Creation of a Photon: A Heuristic Calculation of Planck's Constant η of the Fine Structure Constant, α." the related paper is, "The Zitterbewegung and the Einstein 'A' Coefficient of Spontaneous Emission"

References

1. Honig, W.M., Physics Essays, **8**, 260-263, 1995.
2. Dirac, P.A.M., published in Scientific American, May 1963, Reprinted in *Mathematics in the Modern World* , pp. 242-243, see also pp. 239-247, Freeman & Co., San Francisco 1968.
3. Honig, W. M., (a)*Non-Standard Logics and Non-Standard Metrics in Physics*, World Scientific Publishing, Singapore, London, USA, 1995, ISBN 981-02-2203-3 (hc) $33 USD, ISBN 981-02-2251-3 (pbk) $23 USD.
4. A. Bitsakis, Book Review of Reference 3a above, Physics Essays, **10**, 174-176, 1997.
5. Honig, W.M., To appear in Physics Essays, 2001
6. " , IEEE Trans. in Knowledge and Data Engineering, **5**, No. 2, 190-203, 1993.
7. " , Physics Essays, **4**, 583-590, 1991.
8. " , Physics Essays, **5**, 254-261, 1992.
9. " , Physics Essays, **5**, 514-525, 1992.
10. ", Foundations of Physics, **4**, 367-380, 1974.

11. ", Foundations of Physics, **6**, 37-57, Feb. 1976.

12. ", Foundations of Physics, **7**, 549-572, 1977.

13. " Int. Jour. Theor. Physics, **15**, 673-676, 1976.

14. ", Lettere al Nuovo Cimento, **19**, 137-140, 28 May 1977.

15. ", Physics Essays, **11**, 166-179, 1998 also Physics Essays, **11**, 474, 1998.

16. ", Physics Essays, **11**, 600-608,1998.

17. ", *Problems in Quantum Physics*, 120-147, World Sci. Pub. Singapore, 1988:
    '87 Gdansk Conf. Procs.

18. " , *Problems in Quantum Physics*, 575-581, World Sci. Pub., Singapore 1988. Proceedings of the '87 Gdansk Conference.

19. ", Int. Jour. Theor. Physics, **15**, 87-90,1976.

20. ", *The Quantum and Beyond*, pp. 262-264, Philosophical Library, Inc., 200 W. 57 St., N.Y.,N.Y., 10019, USA, 1986. (hc) ISBN-8022-2517-9, $30 USD and (sc) $24 USD.

21. " , Editor, *Quantum Uncertainties*, Proc. of NATO Conference, 1986, Univ. of Bridgeport, USA: 3 papers by Honig, published by Plenum Press, 1987, ISBN 9971050-449-9.

22. " , Physics Essays, **12**, No. 3, 1999.

23. " , Proc'd'gs the Conference, Frontiers of Fundamental Physics, at Olympia, Greece, Sept. 1993, in *Frontiers of Fundamental Physics*, Eds. M. Barrone & F. Selleri, Plenum Press, 1994.

24. " , Conference Proceedings, Trani, Italy, Sept.'92, *Waves & Particles in Light and Matter*, Eds. A. van der Merwe & A. Garuccio, pp. 527-539, Plenum Press, 1994.

25. " , *Problems in Quantum Physics*, pp. 575-581, World Scientific Publishing, Singapore & N.Y., (1988), the Proceedings of the '87 Gdansk Conference of the same title.

26. De Broglie, L., *Non-Linear Wave Mechanics*, Elsevier, Amsterdam, 1960.

27. Builder, G., Aust. J. Physics, **11**, 279-297, and Aust. J. Physics, **11**, 457-480, 1958.

28. Prokhovnik, S.J., *The Logic of Special Relativity*, Cambridge Univ. Press 1967 and *Light in Einstein's Universe*, Kluwer Press, 1985, see refs. to Ives' work.

29. Dehmelt, H., Scientific American, Aug.,1980. Cohen-Tannoudji, P.R.L., 67-70, 1985.

30. Newman, J.R, *World of Mathematics*, Vol. 1, 661-662, 642-668, Helmholtz essay: "On the Origin and Significance of Geometrical Axioms", (as written in 1870), Simon & Schuster, New York, 1956. This was illustrated by Escher 65 years later[29].

31. Escher, M.C., *The Magic Mirror of M.C.Escher*, see p. 74, "Hand with Reflecting Sphere", (drawn in1935), Tarquin Pubs., England, 1985.

32. Sommerfeld, A., Electrodynamics, Vol. 3, p. 151, Eq. 24, Academic Press, N.Y. 1964.

33. Stegun, A., *Handbook of Mathematical Functions*, p. 78, Eq. 4. 3. 141, Dover 1964.

34. Robertson, B., "Wyler's Expression for the Fine Structure Constant α", PRL, **27**, 1545-1547, 1971.

35. Barut, A.O., Z. Naturforsch., **33a**, 993-994 (1978). Another related paper appeared in *Old and New Questions in Physics, Cosmology, etc.*, Plenum 1983, Edited by van der Merwe.

36. Cross, R., Am. Jour. Physics, **67**, 222-227, 1999; see its many references and one by Auerbach citing a H. Hertz paper in 1882 on the subject.

37. Panofsky, W.K.H., Classical Electricity and Magnetism, 257-260, Addison-Wesley, 1962

38. Lamb, H., *Hydrodynamics*, see index under Karman, Dover Publications, 1945.

290

39. Batchelor, G. K. , *An Introduction to Fluid Dynamics*, 588-593, Cambridge Univ. Press, 1967.

Put the followingText Under the Illustrations

Figure 1. Hertz's Continuous Dipole EM Wave Sketches

Figure 2. (a) Continuous Hertzian Dipole Waves. (b) The single Photex, a discrete EM Dipole Half-cycle wave.

Figure 3. The Two-Fluid Model for Quiescent Vacuum Space.

Figure 4. Electron Droplet Model. Cutaway of (- , +)Charge Distribution.

Figure 5. 3 - D Cutaway of Electron Spherical 2 - Fluid Model.

Figure 6. Cross Section of Spherical Electron and its Fields Showing Their Motional Distortion in Absolute and Co-moving Rest Frames.

Figure 7. Tennis Ball Sequence. Electron Inelastic Collisions with Walls or Image Electrons Causing Photex-Pair Generation. Each photex field distribution is contained within the dark curved lines as shown n Figure 4b. Dotted areas are the (+) external fields of the droplet electron causing its electric and magnetic fields. The EM photex and all EM fields are formed from these fluids. The oval and half oval clear areas are the internal (-) fluids of the droplet electrons. The deformation of the electron spherical droplet to an oval is an exaggerated view of its shape according to the realistic STR versions of Builder-Ives-Lorentz.[27, 28]

Figure 8. Double - wall rebound experiment.

Figure 9. Dehmelt isolated electron lifetime experiment.

Figure 10. Hill's spherical vortex as mu meson model.

Figure 11. Suggested proton fluid model.

Figure 12. Escher print, "Hand with reflecting sphere". A realistic picture showing how a non - Euclidean space looks. Both the observer with his hand showing and the man in the reflection think that they are living in a flat Euclidean space. Each thinks that the other man is living in a spherical non - Euclidean space. Helmholtz discussed this very situation 65 years before Escher drew this picture.

Figure 13. Mapping a toroidal vortex to a cylinder to a sphere and finally to a particle via a radial gauge shrinkage.

Figure 14. Photex vortex fluidic generation - vortex shedding by a droplet electron.

Figure 15. Double slit experiment - EM photex pair wave generated at electron collision point with barriers/slits to form the interference patterns.

Figure 16. Suggested atomic capture sequence. The malleability of the electron is shown. The bubble enclosed electron is a realistic view that my resolve many puzzles about atomic electrons. The photex as a moving spherical field distribution is shown at the right end of sketches 9 and 10. In this figure charge polarities are not directly specified.

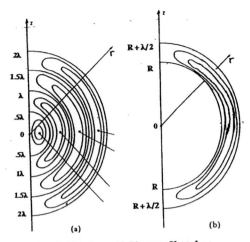

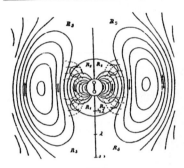
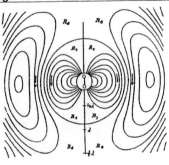

Figure 1. Usual Dipole and Photex Sketches.
  a. Usual Dipole Radiation(only 4 half waves shown).
  b. Photex Field (single half wave).

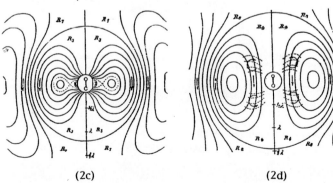

(2a)

(2b)

(2c)

(2d)

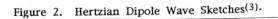

Figure 2. Hertzian Dipole Wave Sketches[3].

292

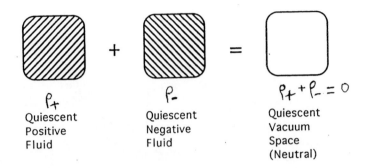

ρ_+ ρ_- $\rho_+ + \rho_- = 0$

Quiescent
Positive
Fluid

Quiescent
Negative
Fluid

Quiescent
Vacuum
Space
(Neutral)

Figure 3.   The 2-Fluid Model for Quiescent Vacuum Space

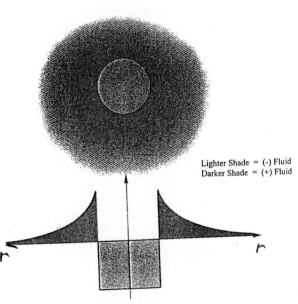

Lighter Shade = (-) Fluid
Darker Shade = (+) Fluid

Figure 4.   Charge Distribution -
Cutaway of Electron Spherical Fluid Model

293

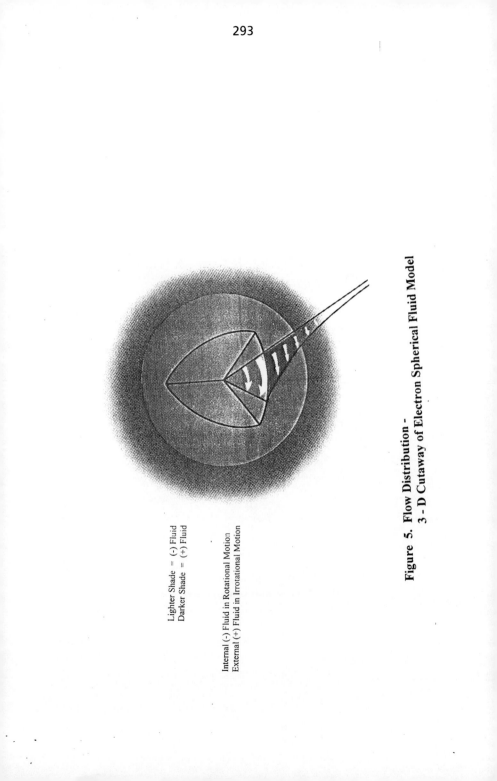

Lighter Shade = (-) Fluid
Darker Shade = (+) Fluid

Internal (-) Fluid in Rotational Motion
External (+) Fluid in Irrotational Motion

**Figure 5. Flow Distribution -
3 - D Cutaway of Electron Spherical Fluid Model**

In Absolute Rest Frame

In Comoving Rest Frame

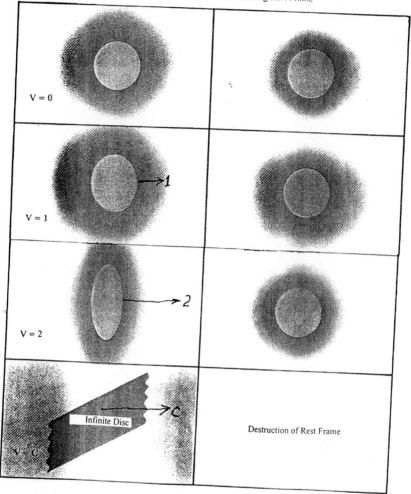

Figure 6. Cutaway of Spherical Electron - Motion
in Absolute and Comoving Rest Frames

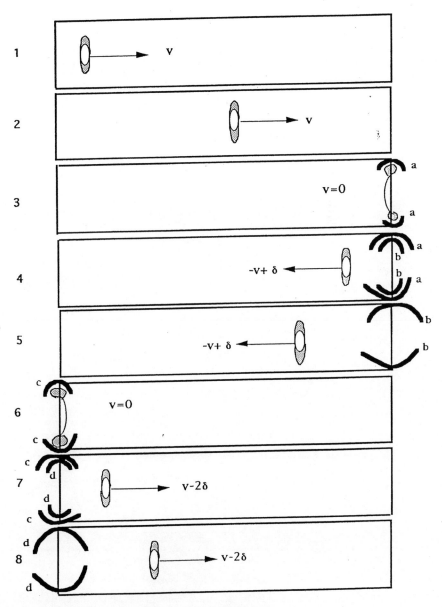

Fig. 7. Tennis Ball Sequence. Electron inelastic collisions with walls or image electrons cause photex pair generation. Each photex field distribution is contained within the dark curved lines as shown in Figure 4b. Dotted areas are the (+) external fluids of the droplet electron causing its electric and magnetic fields. The EM photex (and all EM fields) are formed from these fluids. The oval and half-oval clear areas are the internal (-) fluids of the droplet electron. The deformation of the spherical electron droplet to an oval is an exaggerated view of its shape according to the realistic STR versions of Builder-Lorentz-Ives [27, 28]

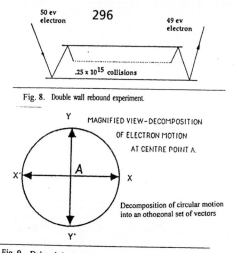

Fig. 8. Double wall rebound experiment.

Y

MAGNIFIED VIEW-DECOMPOSITION
OF ELECTRON MOTION
AT CENTRE POINT A.

X'   X

A

Decomposition of circular motion
into an othogonal set of vectors

Y'

Fig. 9. Dehmelt Isolated Electron Lifetime

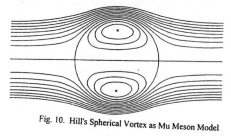

Fig. 10. Hill's Spherical Vortex as Mu Meson Model

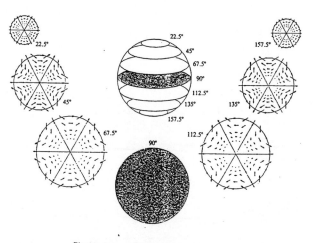

Fig. 11. Suggested Proton Fluid Model

Fig 12

298

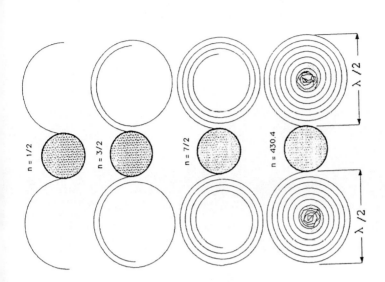

Fig. 14. Photex Fluidic Generation - Vortex Shedding by a Droplet Electron

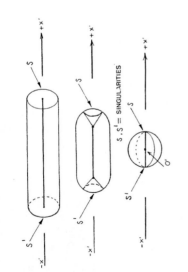

S, S^1 = SINGULARITIES

Fig. 13. Mapping Toroidal Photex to a Cylinder to a Sphere and finally to a particle via a radial gauge shrinkage

299

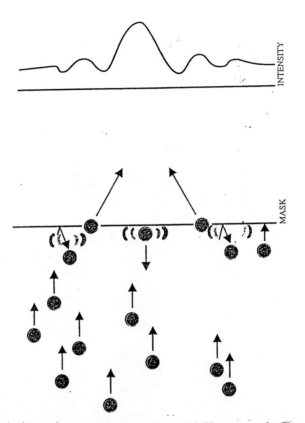

Figure 15. Double Slit Experiment - Electromagnetic Photex-Pair Wave generated at Electron Collision With Barriers/Slits is What Deflects the Electrons going Through the Slits to Form the Interference Patterns.

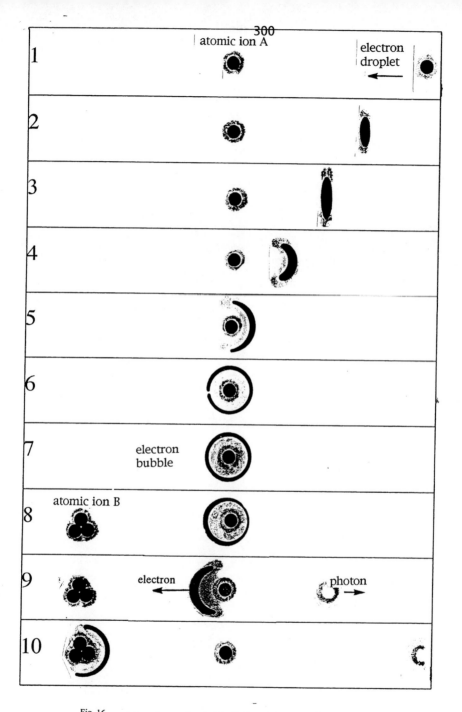

Fig. 16. Atomic Capture Sequence. The malleability of the electron is shown. The bubble-enclosed atom is a realistic view which may resolve many puzzles about atomic electrons. The photon as a moving spherical field distribution is shown at right end of sketches 9 and 10.

In this Figure Charge Polarities
Are Not Directly Specified

International Journal of Theoretical Physics, Vol. 18, No. 7, 1979

2 3 0 4

On the Physical Interpretation and the Mathematical Structure of the Combinatorial Hierarchy[1]

Ted Bastin

12, Bove Town, Glastonbury, Somerset, England

H. Pierre Noyes

Stanford Linear Accelerator Center, Stanford University, Stanford, California 94305

John Amson

The Mathematical Institute, The University of St. Andrews, Scotland

and

Clive W. Kilmister

Department of Mathematics, King's College, University of London, England

Received March 5, 1979

The combinatorial hierarchy model for basic particle processes is based on elementary entities; any representation they may have is discrete and two-valued. We call them *Schnurs* to suggest their most fundamental aspect as concatenating strings. Consider a definite small number of them. Consider an elementary creation act as a result of which two different Schnurs generate a new Schnur which is again different. We speak of this process as a "discrimination." By this process and by this process alone can the complexity of the universe be explored. By concatenations of this process we create more complex entities which are themselves Schnurs at a new level of complexity. Everything plays a dual role in which something comes in from the outside to interact, and also serves as a synopsis or concatenation of such a process. We thus incorporate the observation metaphysic at the start, rejecting Bohr's reduction to the haptic language of common sense and classical physics. Since discriminations

[1]Work supported by the Department of Energy under contract number EY-76-C-03-051.

occur sequentially, our model is consistent with a "fixed past–uncertain future" philosophy of physics. We demonstrate that this model generates four hierarchical levels of rapidly increasing complexity. Concrete interpretation of the four levels of the hierarchy (with cardinals $3, 7, 127, 2^{127} - 1 \approx 10^{38}$) associates the three levels which map up and down with the three absolute conservation laws (charge, baryon number, lepton number) and the spin dichotomy. The first level represents $+$, $-$, and $\pm$ unit charge. The second has the quantum numbers of a baryon–antibaryon pair and associated charged meson (e.g., $n\bar{n}, p\bar{n}, p\bar{p}, n\bar{p}, \pi^+, \pi^0, \pi^-$). The third level associates this pair, now including four spin states as well as four charge states, with a neutral lepton–antilepton pair ($e\bar{e}$ or $\nu\bar{\nu}$), each pair in four spin states (total, 64 states)—three charged spinless, three charged spin-1, and a neutral spin-1 mesons (15 states), and a neutral vector boson associated with the leptons; this gives $3 + 15 + 3 \times 15 = 63$ possible boson states, so a total correct count of $63 + 64 = 127$ states. Something like $SU_2 \times SU_3$ and other indications of quark quantum numbers can occur as substructures at the fourth (unstable) level. Breaking into the (Bose) hierarchy by structures with the quantum numbers of a fermion, if this is an electron, allows us to understand Parker-Rhodes' calculation of $m_p/m_e = 1836.1515$ in terms of our interpretation of the hierarchy. A slight extension gives us the usual static approximation to the binding energy of the hydrogen atom, $\alpha^2 m_e c^2$. We also show that the cosmological implications of the theory are in accord with current experience. We conclude that we have made a promising beginning in the physical interpretation of a theory which could eventually encompass all branches of physics.

1. INTRODUCTION: GENERAL PRINCIPLES OF THE COMBINATORIAL HIERARCHY

In this section we are concerned with the basic principles of our combinatorial model of basic physical interactions. This theory was presented at two successive conferences on "Quantum Theory and the Structures of Time and Space" at Tutzing (Bastin, 1976b). We shall compare and contrast our own principles with the central position in those conferences as a convenient and brief way to present the relation of our theory to the basic principles of the quantum theory, since we may regard the central position established at Tutzing as the most coherent existing attempt to establish foundational principles for current quantum theory.

The combinatorial hierarchy model was originally developed (Bastin, 1966) as an attempt to base physics on a single binary process called "discrimination." Sets of "columns" containing only the existence symbols 0, 1 closed under this operation are then viewed as new entities, and the process is repeated. In this way we generate a hierarchy of four levels of rapidly increasing complexity. Although the explicit representation of this hierarchy is not unique, the scheme itself is, as we demonstrate in this paper. Tentative contact with experiment can be made by specific interpretation of the representations, and structural features familiar in the study of elementary particle physics emerge, including some well-known numerical results. This theory is essentially intended as a conceptual underpinning of the existing formalism of the quantum theory.

The central idea at the Tutzing conferences was a theory of *Ur*'s—basic, discrete, two-valued entities. The claim made by the *Ur* theorists (see particularly von Weizsäcker's 1978 paper) has been that if finitism is firmly and clearly enough embraced, then something very like the usual quantum theoretical formalism can be sustained as a consistent theory and the paradoxes and other perplexities avoided.

A different position has been maintained by Finkelstein (1969, 1977, 1979), who accepts the finitist part of the *Ur* program but considers that further innovation in basic principles is necessary. He adopts a process philosophy, thinking that the elementary discrete constituents of nature must have a principle of concatenation, and that this principle, whatever it may be, must tell us a good deal about the interrelations of the classical and the quantum worlds.

Our theory accords with Finkelstein's demand for innovation beyond the finitist assumption; we adopt the general direction of his "process," or sequential concatenating conjecture. We present a definite model within the class specified by his conjecture, and can claim experimental backing for our model. Our model is distinct from quantum mechanics; it might become equivalent to the latter under special conditions. Some results that would normally be thought to be dependent upon quantum mechanics as a complete theory appear in our model at a more general stage than that at which we make contact with the special case of quantum mechanics. We discuss below how some recent work of Finkelstein's (1969, 1977, 1979) might allow such contact to be made.

The historical origins of the quantum theory concerned the experimental discovery of discreteness and an attempt to explain it using a continuum conceptual framework (we may consider that the Planck radiation formula was a striking experimental ratification of a theoretically arbitrary mathematical imposition of discreteness). Early quantum theory hardly claimed to be explanatory; the modern form of the theory has usually been seen as a successful reconciliation of the continuous and the discrete, and therefore as a satisfactory explanation of the latter. However, in view of the continuing unease with the conceptual foundations of the theory, it seems as appropriate today as it ever was to enquire (a) wherein the explanation lay, and (b) how successful it was. It is sensible to carry on our enquiry in the context of any of the traditional *Gedankenexperimente* (two-slit experiments, photon-splitting experiments, photon correlation experiments such as have been imagined by a sequence of theorists going back to Einstein, Podolsky, and Rosen).

As everybody knows, quantum theory has maintained that there is a distinct class of things in the universe called measurements or observations and that different rules apply to these from those that apply to interactions in which the acquisition of knowledge is not involved. In one way or another use is made of this principle to justify the importation into the formalism of a discrete principle. As everybody also knows, this principle has never produced peace of mind, even though the great thinkers of the quantum theory have concentrated their attention upon it. Consider, for example, the recent essay by Wheeler and Patton (1977). We shall refer to these arguments as the "observation metaphysic."

In Bohr's attempt to achieve an understanding of the observation metaphysic, an absolutely central part was played by his (Bohr's) insistence that all theoretical formulations had to be interpreted through the massively consistent and pervasive language which was at once classical physics and the common sense world. Bohr though it inconceivable that any underpinning or revision of this language using conceptual entities less evident to the senses was conceivable, practicable, or desirable. Indeed, his philosophy made a virtue of the necessity of this position.

In the *Ur* theory this position of Bohr's has been abandoned, though it would not be true to say that the "observer metaphysic" has gone with it. What has happened is that as a result of their finitist presupposition the *Ur* theorists have been able to present the conventional quantum theoretical view of measurement as a merely technical development free from its paradoxical characteristics, at the expense of a profound innovation in the application of probability to the quantum picture. The actual alternatives at any quantum process are finite, and the continuum of states out of which the measurement process picks one are in a different category, being "possibilities."

We, too, postulate entities that would be disallowed by Bohr's form of operationalism. We are equally concerned to find a comprehensible and still profound replacement for the "observation metaphysic," and claim to find it in the *individual* process.

Let us imagine a universe containing elementary entities which we may think of as our counterparts of the *Urs*. To avoid confusion we will amend the terminology and call them *Schnurs* (German for "string")—a term that appropriately suggests computing concepts, in a way that represents their most fundamental aspect of concatenating strings. The Schnurs are discrete, and any representation they may have is two-valued. Consider a definite small number of them. Consider an elementary creation act as a result of which two different Schnurs generate a new Schnur, which is again different. We speak of this process as "discrimination." By this process, and by concatenations of this process, alone can the complexity of the universe be explored. It is also necessary that a record of these discriminations and resulting creations be kept as a part of the structure defined by the Schnurs; otherwise there is no sense in saying that they have, or have not, been carried out. Hence we consider a new lot of Schnurs, which consist of concatenations of creation processes preserving the discriminate structure explored by the original Schnurs. The members of the new class are themselves constituents of the universe and are also free to take part in the creation or discrimination process, and to map up to higher or down to lower levels. This last requirement is the stage at which the necessity becomes clear for a reflexive or recursive aspect to our model, which in current quantum theory takes the form of the "observation metaphysics." The construction of a hierarchy of new levels of Schnurs is necessary to obtain an approximation to a physical continuum; by means of it we can ultimately speak of a physical entity in a background of other physical entities in accordance with the requirements of common sense. However, it makes no sense to speak of the individual entities except in terms of the part they play in the construction. Everything plays a dual role, as a constituent in a developing process, where something comes in from outside to interact, and as a synopsis or concatenation of such a process where the external interaction becomes subsumed in one new entity.

How can a thing be both aspects at once? We do not think we are able at present to say clearly how it can, and we must let our model, which incorporates this duality, lead us forward without having a complete insight, as earlier theorists had to do in quantum theory. However, we are in a better position than current quantum theory, for we can adopt a strictly process view and insist that we always view the process from one viewpoint—albeit a viewpoint that can, and must, change. Then we are freed from conceptual confusion, and we progress by considering stability conditions under which the limitations of our way of approaching the inescapable duality are compensated. Indeed, we find in the stability of the hierarchy levels a profound condition under which we can be sure of a sort of automatic self-consistency which reflects itself in the properties of quantum objects, and which is the basis of our interpretation of our model.

We do not think it impossible that a mathematical way of thinking will emerge in which the dual function can be comprehended without the device of considering the structure of the universe from one point at which the decision making is occurring. One might revert to a more classical or synoptic mathematics. However, we do not think we can do it at present [though Parker-Rhodes (1978), whose work has played such an important part in our model, and who feels uncomfortable with a process philosophy, is trying to formulate something very similar in terms of a "mathematics of

indistinguishables," which transcends the process aspect]. We would conjecture that if such a conceptual framework ever is discovered, its proper
field of application would be wider than physics, and that the restricted
process view would probably be adequate for physics.

Our view of space–time is *constructive* in the sense that there is one set
of principles that gets us from the Schnurs to whatever approximation to
the continuum of space we decide we need. Our scheme is also constructive in the sense that we require that any mathematical constructions that
are needed to specify the attributes of any physical things, including the
space continuum, shall also be so derived. In this sense the *Ur* theory is not
constructive, and we have found our vital objection to it in this lack of
constructivity. This use of the term "constructive" is stringent. We are,
however, using it as in its *locus classicus*, Brouwer's theory of mathematical
intuition (which also stimulated the development of intuitionist logic).

Brouwer's basic concept is that of the free choice sequence. The
formal need for the free choice sequence is to construct the continuum
adequately. For Brouwer, the constructions of mathematics have no absolute quality but are creations of the intellect, whose validity is relative to
the state of mathematical understanding at a given epoch. They play a part
in guiding the development of the free choice sequences. So do other
considerations that we should normally regard as contingent. (An example
of Brouwer's was to make the development of a free choice sequence
depend upon whether, at the particular time in question, four successive
sevens were known to occur in the expansion of π). It would be possible
(and Brouwer was quite open to this suggestion) to regard the totality of
considerations that could influence free choice sequences as including the
contingent behavior of physical systems, in which case the similarity of the
processes in our constructive model and the basic entities with which
Brouwer constructed his universe would be quite close.

It would be fascinating to pursue this connection with Brouwer's
thought, but this cannot be the place. We introduce it at all here only
because it may be felt by some readers that our theory requires a mathematical ontology which is just wrong ; it may reassure the readers to
know that something very like what we propose has been authoritatively
put forward for analogous reasons in the literature of the foundations of
mathematics. The connection is also relevant to our present discussion,
because Brouwer's constructivism has no separate world of mathematical
entities; the difficulty we encounter with the *Ur* theorists is that they allow
themselves the use of continuous mathematical constructions where we felt
that a constructive development should include mathematical entities used
in the theory.

When one has a model for elementary processes one has to reconcile it with the macroscopic awareness of the world as an extended manifold of space and time. This is a large undertaking, which is usually not very explicitly faced. The traditional argument of a correspondence limit is only a small part of the problem for it presupposes that the problem has already been solved for the microscopic entities. Traditionally physicists rely on macroscopic experience to have universal application, and face the resulting confusions piecemeal. The position of the *Ur* theorists is not dissimilar for, as we have seen, they allow themselves to introduce continuum group theory, which then imports the principle of interpretation of extended spaces. We have left ourselves no such loophole, and the problem remains to be tackled.

Finkelstein's process approach also has to face this problem. Two arguments of his are relevant to it: (a) He has shown (Finkelstein, 1969) that the left–right moves of a dichotomous variable on a two-dimensional checkerboard generate, in the limit as the step size goes to zero, the full forward light cone of the Minkowski $(3+1)$-space. (b) Given any partial ordering relation, one can, by a theorem due to Galois, construct a lattice logic. If the lattice logic is that of bra and ket, then a theorem of Birkhoff's allows the construction of Hilbert space from the lattice (Finkelstein, 1979). It is not clear to us that this can meet the whole problem from our point of view; his approach might still end up with the commitment to macroscopic experience that we are trying to avoid. We hope that his treatment will turn out to be relevant to our problem. Certainly the lattice-theoretic result could be very significant in establishing a connection with Hilbert space.

We turn now to another difference between our Schnur theory and the *Ur* theory. This concerns the question whether we locate the reflexive character in the individual *Ur* processes or in statistical assemblages of them. We hold the former view, the *Ur* theorists the latter. The tradition is on our side, even though one is stretching a point in arguing as we have done that traditional quantum theory fails crucially at the point where it has to appeal to an observation metaphysic to introduce the reflexive character of quantum processes and yet claim support from that quarter. Still, the traditional argument that the essential character of quantum processes has to be defined for individual processes is very strong. One is accustomed to having to refute various facile approaches to the foundations of quantum theory by pointing out that the characteristic quantum-observation effect is individual and therefore cannot depend upon a statistical effect. For example, in the photon-splitting experiment, the incident beam can be attenuated to such a degree that the incident photons would have to be treated individually, and therefore could not interfere. Yet interference does take place. This piece of experimental evidence provides a very sharp refutation of any view whose attribution of simple atomic properties to the photons is subject to the restriction that one may consider only statistical distributions of these; von Weizsäcker's distinction between possibility and probability in conjunction with his principle of the finite alternatives allowed by the Ur's is used to explain why the Ur theory is not in this class [J. H. M. Whiteman (1971) introduced a concept that he called *potentiality* to achieve a similar end.] However, this matter is crucial and one feels that the detailed mechanics that makes a statistical effect appear as an individual one should be presented. We think that our model, in which the effect is individual, has a crucial advantage, and that this advantage is a direct consequence of our constructive approach.

In all other respects, we find ourselves in complete agreement with the analysis of the use of probability that von Weizsäcker (1978) has undertaken. Probability is closely related to the concept of time in the quantum physics context. The concept of time that is commonplace in modern philosophical writing, and which owes more to Hume than to any other thinker, seems to be in conflict with a good deal of the thinking of physicists. Starting with Galileo, the time of physicists is based primarily upon the analogy between time "displacement" and displacement in space. Our model has developed partly from discussion that was designed to show that in a discrete approach one might have the advantage of adopting the Humean point of view without outrage to physical theory. Then one could take the past simply as the fixed domain and the future as the domain of uncertainty and of probabilistic inference. This point of view can be tagged "Fixed Past, Uncertain Future" (Noyes, 1975, 1976, 1977).

It is obviously tempting to identify the duality of function of our elementary discriminators or Schnurs with the duality of description in complementarity. Certainly the two are connected, but the connection is not simple, as must be clear from the foregoing discussion of the differences between our view and current quantum theory. Bohr's view of complementary descriptions seems to be very much a special form of a more general philosophy and to have had its special form dictated by the special form in which quantum physics has developed. It is probably safe to say that if one could state the general philosophy without such special reference, it would contain the reflexive or recursive character with which our discussion has been concerned. However, Bohr's philosophy has proved notoriously difficult to state in this bare form in spite of the best efforts of fifty years. We conclude this section by stating what we feel to be the reason for this recalcitrance.

309

In a discrete or finite theory it is not too perplexing to introduce a reflexive philosophy by using a recursive mathematical model, which is what we do. The really perplexing difficulties seem to appear if we associate this reflexive character with an observation imagined against an objectively existing background, as is done in so-called "measurement theory." Two incompatible principles are being appealed to. One principle requires entities in the universe to be constructed using the observation process; the other takes a realist view of them. Not surprisingly, no reconciliation of the resulting perplexities is achieved by studies at a technical level where fundamental principles tend to be assumed rather than discussed.

One question has been avoided till now. In our model the elementary entities have a dual function. One of the dual aspects is analogous to that of an observing system. Do we imagine that this aspect of its dual role would correspond to the quantum theoretical "observation," and if so how would we react to those writers on quantum theory who wish to see something irreducably mentalist in the observation? In reply, we would first observe that we are not compelled to answer this question before we can use our model. We have a model for interactions which are elementary (*Ur*) in the sense that all we know is built up from them, and we have an interpretation for the model in terms of scattering processes. This interpretation does not have to be the only one. We have tacitly assumed that the conditions of high energy are favorable for exhibiting the simplicity of the model and hence the scattering situation. However, under other conditions the interacting entities might even be living organisms with consciousness. The model should still apply. What we absolutely are not either compelled or allowed to say is that the phenomenon of consciousness as a separable ingredient is necessary for the interaction.

2. CONSTRUCTION OF THE HIERARCHY

In this section we develop the specific formalism by which we are implementing the program discussed above, using a very explicit representation of the abstract hierarchical structure. The mathematical structure itself is developed in group theoretic language in the Appendix. Our basic elements are the existence symbols 0 and 1, and our basic mathematical operation is symmetric difference or addition modulo 2: $(0+0=0, 1+0=1, 0+1=1, 1+1=0)$. The symbols are grouped as ordered sets ("columns") of height n $(n=1,2,3,...)$. The comparison between two such columns is called "discrimination." Each column x, whose height we can

310

indicate by writing $(x)_n$ for x, has elements ("discriminators") x_i ($i=1,\dots,n$); thus $x=(x_i)_n$. A column with every element $x_i=0$ is called a "null" column. The basic binary operation of discrimination between two columns x,y of equal height is defined by

$$D_n(x,y)=x+y=(x_i+y_i)_n \tag{2.1}$$

The concept of such discriminators is abstracted from the more familiar idea of discrete quantum numbers, while the discrimination operation itself can be viewed, as we will discuss in another section, as an abstract model of a general scattering ("production") process in which the result of scattering two different systems is a third system that differs from either. Our mathematical model thus describes chains of atomic or elementary processes. Our policy for presenting the theory is first to establish a correspondence between the mathematical model that describes these chains of processes and the familiar structure of quantum numbers. In this way we can first view the mathematical model as providing a classification scheme. The basic dynamics of our theory is represented during the construction of this classification scheme by the concept of *discriminate closure*. We introduce this concept by the following argument.

Starting with columns of a given height, we imagine new columns formed by concatenating a sequence of them. Entities corresponding to the new columns are said to constitute a new level in the hierarchy. There is no difference between the new and the old in logical type; the only difference is that the boundary between the observing system and that which is observed has changed. The great conceptual and mathematical difficulties of such an idea can be handled in one special case, which is therefore of great importance. This case is that in which the entities at the new level represent all combinatorially possible concatenations of entities at the previous level, starting with a given set. Hence we get a *discriminately closed subset*.

A "discriminately closed subset" or DCsS consists of one or more nonnull columns, such that discrimination between any two distinct columns in the set yields a member of the set. Assume that we start from a basis of j linearly independent columns, that is, columns for which no sum of two or more different columns is null. Then there will be 2^j-1 distinct discriminately closed subsets. Symbolizing a DCsS by $\{\ \}$, a basis of two columns a,b gives the three DCsSs $\{a\}$, $\{b\}$, $\{a,b,a+b\}$; a basis of three columns a,b,c gives the seven DCsSs $\{a\}$, $\{b\}$, $\{c\}$, $\{a,b,a+b\}$, $\{b,c,b+c\}$, $\{c,a,c+a\}$, $\{a,b,c,a+b,b+c,c+a,a+b+c\}$. Proof of the general result is immediate either by noting that the number of DCsSs is simply the number of ways we can combine j things $1,2,\dots,j$ at a time, or by

311

induction. The first step in constructing the hierarchy is then to consider the $2^j - 1$ DCsSs so formed as the basic entities of a new level.

The reason for seeking a constructive process of hierarchical nature that yields levels of rapidly increasing (in our case exponentiating) complexity is again abstracted from experience. We have detailed in the first section the reasons why we start from an elementary process (discrimination) which already implicitly contains the "observation metaphysic." There we also explained why, in our view, we adopt a constructive, process-oriented approach. The further requirement that the hierarchy so generated terminate is a basic requirement if we are to retain the principle of finitism. We defer the discussion of the reflexive character of the scheme until it is further developed. That the *combinatorial hierarchy* obtained by starting with columns of height $n = 2$ yields levels of interesting physical structure and sufficient complexity, and terminates at the appropriate level, has been shown previously (Bastin, 1966). We summarize the construction here.

We have seen that, given j linearly independent columns, we can always construct $2^j - 1$ DCsSs at that level. For them to form the basis of a new level, however, they must themselves be representable by linearly independent entities that contain the same information about discriminate closure as the sets themselves. For this purpose we introduce multiplication modulo 2 and matrices because linear operators preserve discrimination. We look for $2^j - 1$ matrices which (a) map each column in one of the subsets onto itself and onto no other column; (b) map only the null column onto the null column, and hence are nonsingular; and (c) are linearly independent. Provided this can be done, and the original basis consists of columns of height n, then the matrices themselves can be rearranged as columns (e.g., by putting one row on top of another by some consistent rule), and will then provide a linearly independent basis of $2^j - 1$ columns of height n^2. Such mapping matrices are easy to find for $n = 2$ (see below). Explicit examples have been found for $n = 3$, 4, and 16 (Noyes, 1978) proving the existence of the hierarchy. A formal existence proof has also been provided (Kilmister, 1978) based on unpublished work (Amson, 1976).

The use of matrix algebra could be misunderstood as implicitly incorporating into the scheme the basic assumptions of linear algebra. In fact, matrix algebra using the symbols 0, 1, discrimination, and multiplication mod 2 is the natural extension of the discrimination idea to incorporate mappings. This can be seen in more formal terms by following the group theoretic discussion given in the Appendix.

We can now present the general situation. We have seen that if at some level l there are $j(l)$ linearly independent columns of height $n(l)$, we can construct immediately $d(l) = 2^{j(l)} - 1$ DCsSs. Provided these can be mapped according to the restrictions given above, they form the basis for a new level with $j(l+1) = d(l)$ and $n(l+1) = n^2(l)$. The process will terminate if $n^2(l) < 2^{j(l)} - 1$ since at level l there are only $n^2(l)$ linearly independent matrices available; clearly this will always happen for some finite n. The situation for $n(1) = j(1) = N$, i.e., when the vectors at the lowest level which span the space are used as the basis, is exhibited in Table I. Thus, perhaps surprisingly considering the simplicity of the assumptions, the hierarchy with more than two levels turns out to be unique. See the Appendix for a more detailed discussion.

Although the cardinal numbers given by the hierarchy are unique, the specific representations used in the construction are not. It is important to understand this clearly because it is a complication in making any *simple* interpretation of the discriminators as representing the presence or absence of particular conventional quantum numbers in an isolated system. This ambiguity is present at the lowest level since for the two basis columns we have three choices: $a = \binom{1}{0}$, $b = \binom{0}{0}$; $a' = \binom{1}{0}$, $b' = \binom{1}{1}$; $a'' = \binom{1}{1}$, $b'' = \binom{0}{1}$. Corresponding to these three possible choices of basis, there are three different sets of mapping matrices. When, as here, the number of independent columns is equal to the height of the columns $(n = j)$, the maximal discriminately closed set (MDCS) contains all the nonnull vectors in the space [here it is $\{\binom{1}{0}, \binom{0}{1}, \binom{1}{1}\}$] independent of the choice of basis; further, the only possible mapping matrix for the MDCS is then the unit matrix. For the first basis, the mapping matrices for $\{a\}$ and $\{b\}$ are $\binom{11}{01}$ and

TABLE I. The Possible Hierarchies Starting from $n(1) = j(1) = N$

l		1	2	3	4	Hierarchy terminates because
$N=2$	$n(l)$	2	4	16	256	
	$j(l)$	2	3	7	127	$(256)^2 < 2^{127} - 1$
$d(l) = 2^{j(l)} - 1$		3	7	127	$2^{127} - 1 \approx 10^{38}$	
$N=3$	$n(l)$	3	9			
	$j(l)$	3	7			$9^2 < 127$
	$d(l)$	7	127			
$N=4$	$n(l)$	4	16			
	$j(l)$	4	15			$16^2 < 2^{15} - 1$
	$d(l)$	15	$2^{15} - 1$			
$N>4$						$n^2(1) < 2^{j(1)} - 1$

$\binom{10}{11}$, respectively. For the second $a=a'$, so that matrix is the same but the mapping matrix for $\{b'\}$ is $\binom{01}{10}$; for the third we note that $a''=b'$ and $b''=b$. Rearranging the matrices as columns then give three different possible bases for the second level of the hierarchy, namely, with the rule

$$\begin{pmatrix} AC \\ DB \end{pmatrix} \to \begin{bmatrix} A \\ B \\ C \\ D \end{bmatrix}$$

$$a_2 = \begin{bmatrix} 1 \\ 1 \\ 0 \\ 0 \end{bmatrix}, \quad b_2 = \begin{bmatrix} 1 \\ 1 \\ 1 \\ 0 \end{bmatrix}, \quad c_2 = \begin{bmatrix} 1 \\ 1 \\ 0 \\ 1 \end{bmatrix}; \quad a_2' = \begin{bmatrix} 1 \\ 1 \\ 0 \\ 0 \end{bmatrix}, \quad b_2' = \begin{bmatrix} 1 \\ 1 \\ 1 \\ 0 \end{bmatrix}, \quad c_2' = \begin{bmatrix} 0 \\ 0 \\ 1 \\ 1 \end{bmatrix};$$

$$a_2'' = \begin{bmatrix} 1 \\ 1 \\ 0 \\ 0 \end{bmatrix}, \quad b_2'' = \begin{bmatrix} 0 \\ 0 \\ 1 \\ 1 \end{bmatrix}, \quad c_2'' = \begin{bmatrix} 1 \\ 1 \\ 0 \\ 1 \end{bmatrix} \tag{2.2}$$

In addition to this ambiguity, there is the further problem that we could have used any other rule for converting the matrices into column vectors, provided only the same rule is used for all three matrices. Thus the ordering of the rows has no significance, and *within* a level the properties of the system under discrimination are unaltered by a permutation of rows in the basis. An important structural property which does emerge, however, is that instead of the basis of three unit columns such as (1000), (0100), (0010), or any linearly independent set constructable on such a basis, at least two of the columns in the basis always contain two ones in the same two rows. This property guarantees that the MDCS (up to a permutation of rows) at the second level will always be

$$\left\{ \begin{bmatrix} 1 \\ 1 \\ 0 \\ 0 \end{bmatrix}, \begin{bmatrix} 1 \\ 1 \\ 0 \\ 1 \end{bmatrix}, \begin{bmatrix} 1 \\ 1 \\ 1 \\ 0 \end{bmatrix}, \begin{bmatrix} 1 \\ 1 \\ 1 \\ 1 \end{bmatrix}, \begin{bmatrix} 0 \\ 0 \\ 0 \\ 1 \end{bmatrix}, \begin{bmatrix} 0 \\ 0 \\ 1 \\ 0 \end{bmatrix}, \begin{bmatrix} 0 \\ 0 \\ 1 \\ 1 \end{bmatrix} \right\} \tag{2.3}$$

Note that the first two rows may always be written as $\binom{1}{1}$ or $\binom{0}{0}$. We shall find this fact significant as a clue to physical interpretation. (Note that "rows" always refers to places in a column even though columns may be printed vertically or horizontally for purely typographical reasons.)

When it comes to constructing mapping matrices for the second level, we cannot use the unit matrix to represent the MDCS given in equation

(2.3) because it maps all 15 possible nonnull columns of height 4 onto themselves, and not just the required seven. The eight columns that must be excluded are of the form $(10xy)$ or $(01xy)$. A nonsingular matrix that has none of these as eigenvectors, but all the columns of equation (2.3), is exhibited in equation (2.4):

$$a\begin{bmatrix} 0 & 1 & 0 & 0 \\ 1 & 0 & 0 & 0 \\ 0 & 0 & 1 & 0 \\ 0 & 0 & 0 & 1 \end{bmatrix}\begin{bmatrix} x \\ x \\ y \\ z \end{bmatrix} = \begin{bmatrix} x \\ x \\ y \\ z \end{bmatrix}, \qquad \begin{bmatrix} a \\ b,c,d \\ e,f,g \end{bmatrix}\begin{bmatrix} x \\ \bar{x} \\ y \\ z \end{bmatrix} \neq \begin{bmatrix} x \\ \bar{x} \\ y \\ z \end{bmatrix},$$

$$\bar{x} - 1 + x, \qquad \begin{vmatrix} a \\ b,c,d \\ e,f,g \end{vmatrix} \neq 0$$

$$b\begin{bmatrix} 0 & 1 & 0 & 0 \\ 1 & 0 & 0 & 1 \\ 0 & 0 & 1 & 1 \\ 0 & 0 & 0 & 1 \end{bmatrix}\left\{\begin{bmatrix} 1 \\ 1 \\ 0 \\ 0 \end{bmatrix}\begin{bmatrix} 0 \\ 0 \\ 1 \\ 0 \end{bmatrix}\begin{bmatrix} 1 \\ 1 \\ 1 \\ 0 \end{bmatrix}\right\} c\begin{bmatrix} 0 & 1 & 0 & 0 \\ 1 & 0 & 1 & 0 \\ 0 & 0 & 1 & 0 \\ 0 & 0 & 1 & 1 \end{bmatrix}\left\{\begin{bmatrix} 1 \\ 1 \\ 0 \\ 0 \end{bmatrix}\begin{bmatrix} 0 \\ 0 \\ 0 \\ 1 \end{bmatrix}\begin{bmatrix} 1 \\ 1 \\ 0 \\ 1 \end{bmatrix}\right\}$$

$$d\begin{bmatrix} 1 & 1 & 0 & 0 \\ 1 & 0 & 0 & 0 \\ 0 & 0 & 1 & 0 \\ 1 & 0 & 0 & 1 \end{bmatrix}\left\{\begin{bmatrix} 0 \\ 0 \\ 1 \\ 0 \end{bmatrix}\begin{bmatrix} 0 \\ 0 \\ 0 \\ 1 \end{bmatrix}\begin{bmatrix} 0 \\ 0 \\ 1 \\ 1 \end{bmatrix}\right\} e\begin{bmatrix} 0 & 1 & 1 & 1 \\ 1 & 0 & 0 & 1 \\ 0 & 0 & 1 & 1 \\ 0 & 0 & 0 & 1 \end{bmatrix}\left\{\begin{bmatrix} 1 \\ 1 \\ 0 \\ 0 \end{bmatrix}\right\}$$

$$f\begin{bmatrix} 0 & 1 & 0 & 0 \\ 1 & 1 & 0 & 1 \\ 0 & 0 & 1 & 1 \\ 0 & 1 & 0 & 1 \end{bmatrix}\left\{\begin{bmatrix} 0 \\ 0 \\ 1 \\ 0 \end{bmatrix}\right\} g\begin{bmatrix} 0 & 1 & 0 & 0 \\ 1 & 1 & 1 & 0 \\ 1 & 1 & 1 & 0 \\ 0 & 1 & 1 & 1 \end{bmatrix}\left\{\begin{bmatrix} 0 \\ 0 \\ 0 \\ 1 \end{bmatrix}\right\} \qquad (2.4)$$

Choosing as a basis the columns (1100), (0010), (0001) we also exhibit six specific mapping matrices which have as eigenvectors only the columns in the six remaining DCsSs. This representation is not unique, since we find that of the 35 possible choices of three columns as a basis, omitting those that are not linearly independent or that are equivalent to others under a permutation of rows, there are 15 alternative choices. However, all of them have more than four descriptors in the three columns, so the choice exhibited is in that sense the simplest.

In order for these seven mapping matrices to form a basis for constructing the $2^7 - 1 = 127$ DCsSs of level III, they must be linearly independent. The linear independence is exhibited explicitly in equation

(2.5), after using a particular rule for rearranging the matrices as columns:

$$\begin{bmatrix} I & A & K & L \\ B & M & G & E \\ O & P & C & F \\ J & N & H & D \end{bmatrix} \rightarrow \begin{array}{c} A \\ B \\ C \\ D \\ E \\ F \\ G \\ H \\ I \\ J \\ K \\ L \\ M \\ N \\ O \\ P \end{array}
\begin{matrix}
a & a+b & a+c & a+d & b+e & b+f & b+c+f+g \\
\begin{bmatrix}1\\1\\1\\1\\0\\0\\0\\0\\0\\0\\0\\0\\0\\0\\0\\0\end{bmatrix}
& \begin{bmatrix}0\\0\\0\\0\\1\\1\\0\\0\\0\\0\\0\\0\\0\\0\\0\\0\end{bmatrix}
& \begin{bmatrix}0\\0\\0\\0\\0\\0\\1\\1\\0\\0\\0\\0\\0\\0\\0\\0\end{bmatrix}
& \begin{bmatrix}0\\0\\0\\0\\0\\0\\0\\0\\1\\1\\0\\0\\0\\0\\0\\0\end{bmatrix}
& \begin{bmatrix}0\\0\\0\\0\\0\\0\\0\\0\\0\\0\\1\\1\\0\\0\\0\\0\end{bmatrix}
& \begin{bmatrix}0\\0\\0\\0\\0\\0\\0\\0\\0\\0\\0\\0\\1\\1\\0\\0\end{bmatrix}
& \begin{bmatrix}0\\0\\0\\0\\0\\0\\0\\0\\0\\0\\0\\0\\0\\0\\1\\1\end{bmatrix}
\end{matrix} \quad (2.5)$$

The explicit choice of mapping matrices, which again is not unique, was again made in such a way as to get the simplest possible basis for level III in which all 16 rows are occupied.

To construct level IV we first find a basic matrix that has any of the 127 vectors that can be constructed from the seven given in equation (2.5), and none of the remaining 128 nonnull columns of height 16 that are not of this form, as eigenvectors. One possibility is exhibited in equation (2.6):

$$\begin{bmatrix}
0&1&0&0&0&0&0&0&0&0&0&0&0&0&0&0\\
1&0&0&0&0&0&0&0&0&0&0&0&0&0&0&0\\
0&0&0&1&0&0&0&0&0&0&0&0&0&0&0&0\\
0&0&1&0&0&0&0&0&0&0&0&0&0&0&0&0\\
0&1&1&0&0&1&0&0&0&0&0&0&0&0&0&0\\
0&0&0&0&1&0&0&0&0&0&0&0&0&0&0&0\\
0&0&0&0&0&0&1&0&0&0&0&0&0&0&0&0\\
0&0&0&0&0&0&1&0&0&0&0&0&0&0&0&0\\
0&0&0&0&0&0&0&0&1&0&0&0&0&0&0&0\\
0&0&0&0&0&0&0&0&1&0&0&0&0&0&0&0\\
0&0&0&0&0&0&0&0&0&0&1&0&0&0&0&0\\
0&0&0&0&0&0&0&0&0&0&1&0&0&0&0&0\\
0&0&0&0&0&0&0&0&0&0&0&0&1&0&0&0\\
0&0&0&0&0&0&0&0&0&0&0&1&0&0&0&0\\
0&0&0&0&0&0&0&0&0&0&0&0&0&0&0&1\\
0&0&0&0&0&0&0&0&0&0&0&0&0&0&1&0
\end{bmatrix}
\begin{bmatrix}a\\a\\a\\a\\b\\b\\c\\c\\d\\d\\e\\e\\f\\f\\g\\g\end{bmatrix}
=
\begin{bmatrix}a\\a\\a\\a\\b\\b\\c\\c\\d\\d\\e\\e\\f\\f\\g\\g\end{bmatrix}
\quad (2.6)$$

One then forms the 127 DCsSs, and finds nonsingular mapping matrices for each of them. This is done by leaving the first six rows of this basic matrix untouched—which guarantees that none of the unwanted columns from the 128 are brought back as eigenvectors—and adding ones one at a time to the remaining structure in such a way as to restrict the eigenvector set. Care must be used not to make the matrix singular and to maintain linear independence. The procedure is straightforward, if somewhat tedious, so the explicit result will not be given here. This empirical procedure thus proves the existence of all four levels of the hierarchy.

3. LEVELS 0, I, II, AND III: BARYONS, MESONS, LEPTONS, AND PHOTONS

In this section we attempt to correlate the mathematical structure developed above with some facts known from elementary particle physics. Because any physical process requires development of the hierarchy through the levels successively, the significant physical magnitude is not the cardinal of each level separately, but rather their cumulative sum, which gives the sequence $3, 10, 137, 137 + 2^{127} - 1 \approx 10^{38}$. Obviously these numbers could be interpreted immediately as the inverse of the superstrong, strong, electromagnetic, and gravitational coupling constants and suggest that in some sense the cumulative levels refer to systems of bosons with increasingly refined definitions of their possible interactions. One way to make this more specific would be to assume that the various systems at each cumulative level all have equal *a priori* probability, and that the probability of "coupling into" any one of them by the characteristic described at that level is therefore the inverse of the corresponding number. We will give this vague idea of coupling more specific content shortly. Further, the fact that the first three levels can be mapped up or down freely, but that any attempt to construct a linearly independent representation of the fourth level with $2^{127} - 1$ DCsSs must fail after $(256)^2$ linearly independent matrices have been selected, suggests that the destabilization of particle systems due to weak decay processes with coupling constant $10^{-5}m_p$ might also emerge from the scheme since $1/(256)^2$ has approximately this value (Bastin, 1966). This requires us to assume that the unit of mass in the scheme is the proton mass, but this is already clear from the initial sequence, since $\sim 10^{-38}$ *is* the gravitational coupling between two protons; the gravitational coupling constant between two electrons is 10^{-44}. Thus we can hope to derive the ratio of the electron mass to the proton mass once the scheme is sufficiently developed.

We are now in a position to state our policy toward the general question of the physical interpretation of the hierarchy so as to be

317

consistent with the identification that has already been made of the basic scheme of cardinal numbers with dimensionless constants. This policy has two aspects. First we have the task of identifying the quantum numbers with configurations in the hierarchy, and secondly, we have to introduce fields corresponding to the quantum numbers, and show that we should expect these fields to have the characteristics that we find in nature. The second task will be coterminous with that of defining an extended space for the particles to be "in." Only the first task is confronted in this section.

We wish to identify places in columns with quantum numbers, and we wish to regard associations of quantum numbers in given columns as *systems* which, under conditions of stability that have yet to be established, will carry over unchanged into stable or unstable particles. For the moment we call them "systems." These ends require us to solve the following problems:

(1) How to get an initial distinguishing characteristic of a column which is available for taking the first step in interpretation in the sense that it cannot be eliminated by choosing a different basis.

(2) How to interpret the interrelations of columns in a set (including of course a DCS) at one level.

(3) How to relate the interpretation of a column at one level with that of columns of different lengths and hence different quantum numbers at another level.

The first step in the solution of these problems is to define *conservation* in respect of a set of properties to each of which a quantum number is conventionally assigned. These are the eight properties (1) of having z component of spin up, (2) of having z component of spin down, (3) of having charge $+$, (4) of having charge $-$, (5) of being a lepton, (6) of being an antilepton, (7) of being a baryon, (8) of being an antibaryon.

It makes things clearer to begin by speaking of properties and only later of the dichotomous variables that can correspond to quantum numbers. The latter require two rows to represent them.

Definition. A quantum number will be said to be *conserved* if the algebraic difference between the number of ones in the corresponding pair of rows of properties is constant *at each step* in the generation process.

The choice of the foregoing definitions (in particular that of the conserved quantities and of their relation to descriptors) embodies a lot of detailed argument whose correctness must be judged by the coherence of the resulting scheme. Moreover the choice of quantum numbers assumes the emergence of discrete quantities through the history of the quantum theory so that the theory is now at a stage that makes it ripe for combinatorialization. Thus in particular the use of the z component of spin as the appropriate quantum number for combinatorialization is obscured

　　　　　　　　　　　　　　　　　　　　　　　　　　　　Bastin et al.

by the spatial idea of spin, but it is becoming more perspicuous as the "helicity state"; we stick to the earlier term.

Our definition of conservation introduces two novelties in principle. One is that of forming the algebraic sum of a set; the other is that of a primitive notion of simultaneity. The two are related since in forming the sum one is making an assertion about what is true collectively of the set *at each step*. The change is considerable since one abandons the principle of individual access in enumeration; although this change is already implicit in the hierarchy construction itself, it is appropriate to introduce it here with the motivation of the very fundamental idea of conservation. It is also at this point that we see the root of an idea of sequential delay that will take us from a purely sequential theory to one with a more conventional space and time. However, having recorded this starting point, we will not attempt to develop it further now.

We notice in the above account that all the structures that are going to be interpretable (dichotomous variables) require representation by *two* rows, so that systems of one row are not given a meaning. This principle already exists as a matter of logical necessity in the hierarchy construction —a correspondence that indicates satisfactory coherence in the theory as a whole. (The level of single elements cannot generate a hierarchy.) It follows that at level II the 4-columns are properly regarded as a pair of pairs.

We now return to the set of problems posed above. To handle the first problem—that of initial interpretation—we first draw attention to the "doubled discriminators" of Section 2, which we have shown must exist in the mapping construction. We note first that this asymmetry is already enough to refute the criticism that since one can always take a minimal basis using only columns of the form

and since row position is arbitrary, no interpretation that depends on relative position of ones can be significant. In fact we cannot always take such a minimal basis; we are therefore justified in beginning our interpretation with a nonminimal basis, and in particular with one in which we have the doubled discriminators which we have shown to be necessary.

The doubled discriminators enable us to develop a notation for putting together two systems, each of which is described by a dichotomous variable; we shall use spin as our first example (Bastin, 1976a). In Table II

TABLE II. Triplet–Singlet System from Two Dichotomic Vectors

Conventional notation				Hierarchy notation			
$S=1$			$S=0$	$S=1$			$S=0$
$S_z=1$	0	-1	$S_z=0$	$S_z=1$	0	-1	$S_z=0$
$\begin{bmatrix}1\\0\\1\\0\end{bmatrix}$	$\dfrac{1}{2^{1/2}}\begin{bmatrix}1\\1\\1\\1\end{bmatrix}$	$\begin{bmatrix}0\\1\\0\\1\end{bmatrix}$	$\dfrac{1}{2^{1/2}}\begin{bmatrix}1\\-1\\-1\\1\end{bmatrix}$	$\begin{bmatrix}1\\0\\1\\0\end{bmatrix}$	$\begin{bmatrix}1\\1\\1\\1\end{bmatrix}$	$\begin{bmatrix}0\\1\\0\\1\end{bmatrix}$	$\begin{bmatrix}0\\0\\0\\0\end{bmatrix}$

we assign the first two rows to indicate spin up or spin down of one system, and the second two rows to refer to spin up or spin down for the other system. The resulting singlet or triplet states are represented in Table II both in the conventional notation using algebraic vectors and in the hierarchy notation using only existence symbols. We see that the descriptive content of the two notations is identical so far as distinguishing the four possible singlet or triplet states goes. We also note that the singlet state is the null column; we can only give meaning to such a state in a richer system with more rows containing nonnull descriptors.

The spin-z state refers to a *single* system of spin $1/2$ (which can be up or down) for which the algebraic notation is $\begin{pmatrix}1\\0\end{pmatrix}$ or $\begin{pmatrix}0\\1\end{pmatrix}$. A singlet/triplet system is either a spin-0 system with one state and a spin-1 system with three states, or the composition of two spin-$1/2$ to give the same result. The conventional notation for the result is given in Table II in comparison with our notation.

We have shown the above identification to be possible and consistent with the idea of conservation; we have not shown it to follow necessarily from the existence of doubled descriptors. The latter demonstration requires a new physical principle. In addition to the association of two existence symbols to make one dicotomous variable, we have encountered the association of two identical existence symbols in two rows to make an effective single existence symbol—a development that was forced by the necessary occurrence of "doubled descriptors." If we were to exploit, at level II, the full possibilities of the increased scope in our descriptive language offered by treating each row as independent, we would get $16-1=15$ possible systems. The mapping construction allows only 7 of these, consisting of one doubled existence symbol and one dichotomic variable. We see this more clearly if we enumerate four cases:

(I) Triple existence symbol plus single existence symbol. This is isomorphic to the basis for level I and gives nothing new.

(II) Triplet system exhibited in Table II. Since we are considering a system of four rows, the singlet possibility effectively represents nothing and is excluded. Further, we see that triplet system is simply a doubled representation of level I and again gives us nothing new.

(III) The doubled existence symbols together with the two-row dichotomous variables already exhibited in (2.3) is the unique MDCS forced by the hierarchy construction.

(IV) The maximum set, obtained by treating each descriptor independently, is excluded by the hierarchy construction. We are thus limited to case III, which exhibits the necessity of the interpretation.

We have used conservation as the basic interpretive principle. We have yet to display this in the context of the sequential dynamics of step-by-step discrimination which is implied in speaking of conservation. We approach this problem for the first three levels of the hierarchy by interpreting sequences of discriminations as the flow of quantum numbers through sequentially ordered "Feynman diagrams." As we will see below, the direction of the sequence has to be established *external* to the hierarchy as part of our construction of a finite representation of "space–time" which could, sometimes, approach conventional space–time in a large number regime.

The basic postulate by which we convert the symmetric discrimination operation $x + y = z = y + x$ into a partial ordering is to assume that when the discrimination occurs between two identical columns, i.e., when $x + x = 0$, there is some externally established criterion, which eventually is to be established recursively, by which the two x's are assigned to *different* sets. Our justification for this assumption is our equally basic postulate that the nonnull descriptors in a column refer to *conserved* quantum numbers. This is clearly impossible in the case at hand if both columns are on an identical footing, since then the symmetric operation would destroy quantum numbers. Abstracting from the empirical structure of elementary particle physics, we assume that $x + x = 0$ refers to a particle and an antiparticle which, so far as quantum numbers go, can indeed annihilate each other if they have opposite charge, opposite baryon number, opposite lepton number, and equal but opposite helicity ("z component of spin"), and *no* other distinguishing characteristics. This idea has yet to be worked out in deductive mathematical terms. Here we work it out, level by level through the first three levels of the hierarchy, using a diagrammatic technique abstracted from the familiar rules for Feynman diagrams.

Consider first a "universe" consisting only of identical columns x. This we call "level 0" of the hierarchy, since it clearly can be modeled by sets of "columns of height one" consisting of sets of the existence symbol 1, or the null 0. Notationally we represent the basic discrimination $1 + 1 = 0$ by Figure 1a, where the first 1 stands for a "particle" represented by the solid line and the second 1 stands for an "antiparticle" represented by the

321

Combinatorial Hierarchy   465

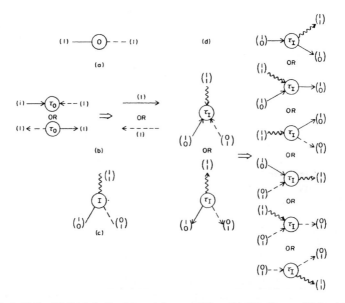

Fig. 1. (a) Level-0 discrimination interpreted as a particle–antiparticle diagram. (b) Level-0 sequentially ordered discrimination as particle or antiparticle. (c) Unique level-I DCsS as a particle–antiparticle–quantum vertex. (d) Sequential ordering of the level-I vertex.

dashed line. To make this into an ordered relation we assume each line has a "direction" relative to some externally established sequence of discriminations, which we indicate by placing an arrowhead on the line. The interpretation that conserves the (single type of) quantum number is then that both lines are "incoming" or "outgoing" as in the left side of Figure 1b. We now adopt the Feynman rule that a particle moving "forward" is the same as an antiparticle moving "backward." Since there is only one type in our level-0 "universe" we reverse one arrow. Then the discrimination has no effect and the universe consists only of particles moving forward (or of antiparticles moving backward). This is truly a Parmenidean universe in which there are no scatterings and nothing happens. In a broader context with higher columns, our (now ordered) discrimination makes a partial ordering selecting sets of "identical" columns with an "orthogonality" relation. So far as we can see, if this were all we had, we would have precisely the model discussed by Finkelstein (1977, 1979)—an "emission" followed by an "admission" which taken together form a detection which, when null, corresponds to the failure to detect—a partial ordering in which the "particles" continue to "move" undisturbed. But our structure is more complicated, as we will see shortly. An alternative to introducing an ordering relation might be to develop a metalanguage in which we can retain the nonordered discrimination operation; as we understand it, this is what Parker-Rhodes (1978) has done in his theory of indistinguishables, which allows the discussion of "twins" that are individually indistinguishable, and that cannot be ordered, but which allows the assignment of cardinal numbers to sets composed of them. We believe the route followed here is more consistent with our basic process philosophy.

We now proceed to level I, where we have three nonnull columns that can be symbolized as follows: $\binom{1}{0}$ by ————, $\binom{0}{1}$ by ----, and $\binom{1}{1}$ by $\sim\!\!\sim\!\!\sim$. We can symbolize the unique MDCS by the discrimination diagram given in Figure 1c. As a nonordered discrimination diagram this is to be interpreted as representing the fact that discrimination between any two of the columns yields the third. As a Feynman diagram with all three lines either incoming or outgoing (Figure 1d) there is still no internal way to assign order. If, however, we assign a sequential direction externally, and use the Feynman rule, we obtain six possibilities also given in Figure 1d. There is now a structural difference compared to "level 0," because we now need a rule to say what happens to the two rows when we reverse the direction of the arrow. We see that to conserve quantum numbers we must interchange the two rows.

Now physical interpretation becomes possible. Row one represents one dichotomic variable, or conserved quantum number, whose presence or absence is indicated by the exitence symbols 1 or 0, respectively. The second row represents a second distinct dichotomic variable. In order that both quantum numbers be conserved, they must be conjugate in the sense that reversing sequence interchanges rows. The simplest choice for interpretation, following Eddington's insight that the basic quantization is that of charge, is that the two quantum numbers are simply positive and negative unit electric charge. Then our rule that reversal of sequence must be coupled to interchange of rows translates to the usual Feynman rule that a positive particle moving forward "in time" is equivalent to a negative particle (antiparticle) moving backward "in time." Note that in contrast to $\binom{1}{0}$ and $\binom{0}{1}$ the column $\binom{1}{1}$ is self-conjugate, and we are free to assign it either direction until we have sufficient *external* structural information to specify that direction in another way.

High-energy physics allows us to provide an experimental model isomorphic to this lowest level of the hierarchy—a hydrogen bubble chamber in a magnetic field with a beam of antiprotons incident. Protons curve one way and antiprotons the other way, distinguishing the two quantum numbers. Annihilation produces electrically neutral quanta that leave no tracks in the chamber but whose presence can be inferred by the appearance of proton–antiproton pairs that can be spacially correlated with kinks in the tracks. A more detailed working out of this operational definition of quantized particles has been given elsewhere (Noyes, 1957). Such experiments provide direct empirical evidence for the quantization and conservation of unit electric charge. Note that the direction of the tracks must be inferred from external information on which side of the chamber the beam enters, or internally by the relation between density of bubbles along the track and velocity or energy. Relativistic kinematics allows the specific case when particle, antiparticle, and neutral quantum all have the same mass to be made into a model in which the three bind ("bootstrap") to form a single particle of the same mass and charge as one of the three, as has been discussed elsewhere (Noyes, 1979).

By such external considerations, we can talk about the ordered vertices of level I, symbolized in the figure by (T$_I$) since they will eventually become time ordered scattering vertices, and the nonordered (I), which represents the unique DCsS of level I. But it is easy to see that if we start with an arbitrary statistical assemblage of all three possible columns and all "directions," on the average nothing will happen. There will be the (unobservable and ignorable) discriminations of "level 0," and level I vertices with as many incoming as outgoing lines. Charge is conserved in the microscopic processes, and hence for the system as a whole. Any asymmetries would have to be established externally. This "universe" is still Parmenidean so far as observable consequences go.

When we go to level II the situation changes. If we represent columns $(11xy)$ by ═══, and columns $(00xy)$ by ∿∿ the seven DCsSs of Equation (2.4) can be pictured by the seven discrimination diagrams given in Figure 2. To convert these to ordered diagrams that conserve quantum numbers, we see that rows 3 and 4 are isomorphic to level I, and that we must interchange these two rows when we reverse the direction of an arrow. But rows 1 and 2 are self-conjugate and act within this group of seven columns like a single new dichotomic variable which is either present or absent. But now we have eight additional columns $(10xy)$ and $(01xy)$ *outside* the hierarchy. Under our basic statistical assumption that initially all columns have equal probability, and that all rows are to be interpreted in terms of conserved quantum numbers, we see that we have added not one but two new dichotomic variables. Further, they also can form DCsSs, as we can see for example in Figure 3, ignoring for the moment the arrows. If, as we did within the hierarchy, we assigned all lines as incoming (or outgoing) the quantum number in the first row would be annihilated, contrary to our basic interpretive postulate. Hence, for these new vertices we *must*, in order

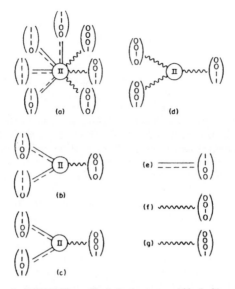

Fig. 2. (a) Unique level-II MDCS as a discrimination vertex within the hierarchy. (b)–(g) Six DCsS of level II in a particular representation as discrimination vertices within the hierarchy.

to conserve quantum numbers, assume that we have one incoming and two outgoing arrows. Then for any sequence of processes involving all 15 nonnull columns, *and* ordered vertices when $(10xy)$ or $(01xy)$ are involved, all four dichotomic quantum numbers will be conserved, provided (in our specific representation) we interchange both row 1 with row 2 *and* row 3 with row 4 when we change the direction of an arrow.

How are we to interpret this situation physically? We claim that the structural characteristic of the hierarchy—which, as proved in the last

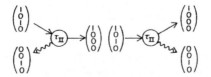

Fig. 3. Two level-II vertices outside the hierarchy sequentially ordered to conserve quantum numbers; the two shown can be interpreted as the emission or absorption of a charged quantum by a baryon.

section, necessarily doubles one descriptor in the basis used for constructing level II—implies two different types of dichotomic quantum numbers at level II. Since one pair is isomorphic to level I, we retain the identification of this with electric charge. The second we propose to interpret as baryon number in row 1 and antibaryon number in row 2. The seven columns within the hierarchy can then be interpreted as four baryon–antibaryon pairs $B^+\bar{B}^0, B^+B^-, B^0B^-, B^0\bar{B}^0$, and three quanta $Q^+, Q^\pm, Q^-$. We also have the start of a sequential dynamics because of the necessity of ordered vertices once we deal with single baryons. If we identify these with nucleons and antinucleons, and the quanta with charged and neutral mesons, we have a crude model for nuclear physics. We will not develop this here, as we have a more specific calculation closer to reality to present in level III. Note also that, again by use of the bubble chamber, it is possible to distinguish baryons from mesons since, empirically, the number of baryons minus the number of antibaryons is conserved, while the number of mesons is not; charge is, of course, still conserved. A little thought should convince the reader that our rules guarantee this contact with experiment.

We wish to emphasize here the structural features of the hierarchy which allow this comparison with experiment. Suppose we ignored the doubling of one of the descriptors in going from level I to level II. Then we could model the $2^3 - 1 = 7$ DCsSs with columns of height 3, e.g., the basis $(100), (010), (001)$ which would put all three rows on the same footing. Quantum numbers could be conserved, and the DCsSs mapped by 3×3 matrices, which would then give $2^7 - 1 = 127$ DCsSs of columns of height 9. But these cannot be mapped by the $9 \times 9 = 81$ linearly independent matrices available; this hierarchy terminates too quickly. Another alternative would be to use the $2^4 - 1 = 15$ DCsSs constructed from columns of height 4, e.g., using the symmetric basis $(1000), (0100), (0010), (0001)$, which again makes all rows indistinguishable. These again can be mapped and provide a basis for $2^{15} - 1$ DCsSs of columns of height 16; again these cannot be mapped by the $16 \times 16 = 256$ linearly independent matrices available, so this also terminates too quickly. Only the asymmetric basis obtained from the mapping of level I allows the continuation to both level III and level IV. Further, as we have seen, this asymmetric basis, by distinguishing between columns inside and outside the hierarchy allows us, for the first time, to introduce meaningful sequence along with conservation. Thus, discrimination, conservation, and the existence of DCsSs that can be mapped at a single level are even conjointly not enough. We *must* use the unique hierarchy construction to get a rich enough physics without additional postulates. When we do, we are rewarded by finding a structure that can be interpreted as exhibiting the asymmetry between baryons and mesons that lies at the core of all nuclear theory.

Going now to level III, we have seen in equation (2.5) that we have a representation of the seven basis columns with one quadrupled and six doubled descriptors. Here we are not on so firm ground in interpretation, because this representation is no longer unique, and we have to argue instead that it is the simplest and most symmetric representation we can construct. But we believe, though we have not proved, that *any* level-III representation will have a quadrupled descriptor. Guided by the hypothesis that the third level, being stable, should contain quantum numbers corresponding to the absolute conservation laws of charge, baryon number, lepton number, and helicity ("z component of spin"), and our successful handling of the doubled descriptor as baryon–antibaryon quantum numbers at level II, we assume that the quadrupled quantum number represents a baryon–antibaryon pair in conjunction with a lepton–antilepton pair. Then, following the scheme given in Table II, two of the doubled descriptors represent the four spin states obtained by putting together a spin-1/2 baryon with a spin-1/2 antibaryon to form a singlet–triplet system, two of the doubled descriptors correspond to putting together (the same) baryon antibaryon pair to form a singlet–triplet isospin system, and the last two doubled descriptors to the singlet–triplet spin system obtained from spin-1/2 lepton and a spin-1/2 antilepton. Explicitly, the 16 column of equation (2.6) is then $(B, \bar{B}, l, \bar{l}, s_B^+, s_B^-, s_B^{\pm}, s_{\bar{B}}^-, i_B^+, i_B^-, i_B^{\pm}, i_{\bar{B}}^-, s_l^+, s_l^-, s_{\bar{l}}^+, s_{\bar{l}}^-)$. Anyone familiar with Feynman rules will see immediately that if we interchange rows pairwise when we change the direction of an arrow, we have the usual rule that spins, particle–antiparticle designation, and charge reverse under time reversal, and that we can conserve quantum numbers in the same way we did at lower levels.

The physical interpretation of the individual states in the hierarchy is now straightforward. When we have (1111...) we have 16 spin states×4 isospin states or 64 in all. Note that we now have to talk about conservation of the "z component of isospin," which is equivalent to charge conservation in this context. Note also that we are referring to helicity rather than "spin" in a 3-space or 4-space sense. This is not to carry any implications about "rotations" until we have constructed some discrete approximation to "space–time," which we have yet to do. The (0000...) columns are also easy to interpret. Three of them carry isospin without spin, like pions; nine of them carry both spin and isospin, like the three spin × three charge states of the ρ mesons; three have isospin zero in three spin states like the ω meson. All of these 15 mesons come from rows associated with the baryons. The remaining three spin states associated with the leptons we identify with the two helicity states of the photon (γ) and the Coulomb field. The mesons can be put together with the γ to form $3 \times 15 = 45$ states. Thus the total number of states is $64 + 15 + 3 + 3 \times 15 = 127$ as required.

The presence of the γ is particularly interesting. Empirically the mesons all have finite mass and dimensionally speaking explore "distances" of the order of 10^{-13} cm, where many people agree our ordinary ideas of space–time are suspect. But the γ, being massless, has effects of infinite range, and in the large-number limit goes over, via the correspondence principle, to the classical electromagnetic field. One might think that, prior to the development of an explicit dynamics, we should not be able to get quantitative results from the theory at this stage. But the presence of the γ and the Coulomb field in our interpretation allows us to discuss, at least heuristically, a remarkable calculation.

The calculation was originally achieved by A. F. Parker-Rhodes (1978), who justifies his physical interpretation of the hierarchy, and of more extended structures, on the basis of his theory of indistinguishables. Unfortunately, this theory requires considerable logical development for consistent presentation since objects that can be counted as two when together, but that are truly indistinguishable when separate (called "twins"), cannot be grouped in ordered sets; they can, however, be grouped in such a way as to define a unique cardinal for the group or "sort." Thus a "sort theory" dealing with this possibility has to be developed, based on the three parity relations "identical," "distinguishable," and "twins"—together with their negations. This requires a semantic theory, using two-valued logic, for discussion of the object theory, and an implication language, again using two-valued logic, for the statement and proof of theorems. However important the theory of indistinguishables may be, Parker-Rhodes' ideas of interpretation are inconsistent with those developed in this paper, and we give his deductions in an amended form. We expect that before very long a consistent presentation on our own principles will have been reached, but the form we give below is to some extent a compromise with conventional thinking. Our excuse for (in a sense) premature publication is the astonishing accuracy of the result. We believe that the presentation we give here is believable in terms that are closer to ordinary quantum mechanical usage—once one is willing to make the conceptual leap that allows the discussion of quantum ideas *prior* to any mention of space–time.

We have seen that the three stable levels of the hierarchy can be viewed as systems carrying the quantum numbers of baryon–antibaryon pairs and lepton–antilepton pairs and the associated bosons. Since comparison between any two such systems leads to a third, and all three levels map up or down, it seems appropriate to think of the hierarchy as containing all 137 possibilities with equal *a priori* probability. But to discover the actual structure, we must somehow "break into" this closed system, which necessarily requires a column that is not one of the members of the hierarchy. The example we pick is the electron.

Using the specific choice of row designations already introduced, i.e., $(B, \bar{B}, l, \bar{l}, s_B^+, s_B^-, s_{\bar{B}}^+, s_{\bar{B}}^-, i_B^+, i_B^-, i_{\bar{B}}^+, i_{\bar{B}}^-, s_l^+, s_l^-, s_{\bar{l}}^+, s_{\bar{l}}^-)$, an electron with "spin up" is (0010 0000 0101 1000) and with "spin down" is (0010 0000 0101 0100).

In order to couple this column into the hierarchy, we have to introduce some new sort of vertex that does conserve quantum numbers; just how does not have to be specified for our current purpose. Presumably this can be done in the same way that we introduced an ordered meson–baryon vertex at level II. The only member of the 137 columns in the hierarchy that does not change the electron spin or charge, or refer to irrelevant quantum numbers, is the Coulomb case. So we assume that the electron couples to this with a probability of $1/137$. This member of the hierarchy then communicates with all the others in a random fashion, eventually ending up again with the Coulomb case and back to the electron. In this respect we view the hierarchy as resembling something like the "vacuum fluctuations" of quantum field theory. The reason that this can lead to a result is that the electron cannot coincide with those members of the hierarchy that contain electron–positron pairs while this process is taking place, thanks to the exclusion principle. Particularly since we have as yet not made use of the exclusion principle, an assumption more in keeping with our basic statistical approach (which has the same effect on the calculation) is that the statistical uncertainties in the concept of "length" at nuclear dimensions do not allow us to discuss Coulomb energy separations for lengths smaller than some distance d. Thus the process necessarily involves some space–time separation or interval between the electron and the hierarchy, which we will estimate statistically. Further, since we have no reference frame to refer this distance to, the resulting charge distribution relative to this space–time interval must also be distributed statistically, subject only to charge conservation. The calculation we present is of the ratio of the square of this statistically smeared-out charge to the statistically estimated distance of separation, equated, as is often assumed, to the electron rest energy $m_e c^2$. Schematically, the process we are computing is shown in Figure 4.

Our first step is to take out the dimensional factors and thus reduce the statistical part of the calculation to dimensionless form. The square of the charge is e^2; it is smeared out into two (or more) parts over some

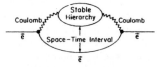

Fig. 4. Schematic representation of the electron self-energy.

distance r. We introduce a random variable x to represent the charge in one part, and, in order to conserve charge between two parts, write the square of the charge as $e^2x(1-x)$. As we have already argued, the coupling we should use at this stage in the development of the theory is $1/137$, not the empirical value of the fine-structure constant α, so $e^2 = \hbar c/137$.

Because of the statistical uncertainty in the concept of length at nuclear dimensions, or because of the exclusion principle, there is some distance of closest approach d, which acts as a cutoff in the distance r. Since the only stable mass other than the m_e we are computing is the proton mass m_p, and proton–antiproton pairs occur in the levels of the hierarchy, it seems reasonable to take this shortest distance we can define to be the Compton wavelength of a proton–antiproton pair $d = h/2m_pc$; our second random variable y is then defined by $r = yd$, with $y \geqslant 1$. We like the idea of introducing Planck's constant into the theory as a basic measure of the breakdown of the concept of macroscopic length.

The random variable x represents the charge in a system with three degrees of freedom smeared out statistically and interacting with the remaining charge $1-x$. If we could cut the charge into two pieces, like a hunk of butter, x would vary between 0 and 1. But in our interpretation the hierarchy contains pieces with both positive charge $(p\bar{n}, \pi^+, \rho^+, \dots)$ and negative charge $(\bar{p}n, \pi^-, \rho^-, \dots)$ as well as neutral and internally neutralized systems, all of which communicate with each other in the stabilization process. Hence, if we look at all the possibilities, and maintain overall charge conservation, x can have any value between $-\infty$ and $+\infty$. Once we have gone beyond the first separation, we have no way of knowing whether the Coulomb energy we are evaluating is attractive (unlike charges) or repulsive (like charges) outside of the interval $0 < x < 1$. Statistically the positive and negative effects outside this interval must cancel. This statement is not obvious, as has been pointed out to us by F. Levin. To explain it, we note first that if Figure 4 represented a single process the charge would have to follow the electron line and there would be no charge smearing. But in fact we are computing a statistical average of such processes in which we assign the charge to two pieces according to the random variable x as ex and $e(1-x)$. The probability of this separation taking place at one vertex is proportional to the dipole $e^2x(1-x)$. Once we have two smeared out charge distributions further smearing will come from the virtual appearance of charged particle-antiparticle pairs; thanks to our diagrammatic rules, charge is conserved at each vertex in such processes and the overall electric neutrality guarantees that for the first distribution the charge remains ex or $e(1-x)$. Thus although this further smearing can lead to regions with any positive or negative value for the charge, these effects cancel outside the interval $0 \leq x \leq 1$. Further, after the initial smearing, the effective squared charge of each piece is e^2x^2 or $e^2(1-x)^2$, a fact we will need below. As we can see from Figure 4, in order to reform the electron from these smeared out distributions, we need a second vertex. By microscopic time reversal invariance, which is guaranteed by our equal *a-priori* probabilities, the probability of this closure is again proportional to the dipole $e^2x(1-x)$. We conclude that the overall weighting factor $P(x(1-x))$ to be used in computing $[e^2x(1-x)]$ is proportional to $[x(1-x)]^2$, and is to be normed on the interval $0 \le x \le 1$.

Putting this together, we see that

$$m_e c^2 = \langle q^2 \rangle \left\langle \frac{1}{r} \right\rangle = \frac{\hbar c}{137} \langle x(1-x) \rangle \frac{2m_p c}{h} \left\langle \frac{1}{y} \right\rangle$$

or

$$\frac{m_p}{m_e} = \frac{137\pi}{\langle x(1-x) \rangle \langle 1/y \rangle} \qquad (3.1)$$

To calculate the expectation value of $1/y$ we need some probability weighting factor $P(1/y)$. We have seen above that the hierarchy has three distinct levels with different interpretations, each carrying charge, so we assume that the distribution of charge in the statistical system has three degrees of freedom, each of which brings in its own random $1/y$. Thus we assume $P(1/y)=(1/y)\cdot(1/y)\cdot(1/y)$ and find that

$$\left\langle \frac{1}{y} \right\rangle = \int_1^\infty \left(\frac{1}{y} \right) P\left(\frac{1}{y} \right) \frac{dy}{y^2} \Big/ \int_1^\infty P\left(\frac{1}{y} \right) \frac{dy}{y^2} = \frac{4}{5} \qquad (3.2)$$

If the charge splitting x had only one degree of freedom, the expectation value of $x(1-x)$ using the weighting $P(x(1-x))=x^2(1-x)^2$ would be

$$K_1 = \langle x(1-x) \rangle_1 = \int_0^1 x(1-x) P(x(1-x)) \, dx \Big/ \int_0^1 P(x(1-x)) \, dx = \frac{3}{14} \qquad (3.3)$$

Actually, as already noted, we have three degrees of freedom coming from the three levels of the hierarchy. Once the distribution has separated into x and $1-x$ the effective squared charge of each piece is x^2 or $(1-x)^2$, so we can write the recursion relation

$$K_n = \int_0^1 \left[x^3(1-x)^3 + K_{n-1} x^2(1-x)^4 \right] \Big/ \int_0^1 x^2(1-x)^2 \, dx$$

$$= \int_0^1 \left[x^3(1-x)^3 + K_{n-1} x^4(1-x)^2 \right] \Big/ \int_0^1 x^2(1-x)^2 \, dx$$

331

Combinatorial Hierarchy   475

$$= \frac{3}{14} + \frac{2}{7} K_{n-1} = \frac{3}{14} \sum_{i=0}^{n-1} \left(\frac{2}{7}\right)^i \tag{3.4}$$

Putting this back into formula, using K_3, because of the three degrees of freedom of the hierarchy, we have

$$\frac{m_p}{m_e} = \frac{137\pi}{\frac{3}{14} \times \left[1 + \left(\frac{2}{7}\right) + \left(\frac{2}{7}\right)^2\right] \times \frac{4}{5}} = 1836.151497\cdots \tag{3.5}$$

as compared with the latest empirical result 1836.15152 ± 0.00070 (Barash-Schmidt et al., 1978).

Clearly, in presenting our calculation in this way, we have leaped ahead of what we are justified in doing as an explicit dynamical calculation. But the calculation illustrates one way in which two algebraic quantities can be introduced into the theory in the form of the square of one divided by the other. The specific interpretation is compelling because of the high quality of the numerical result; the critical integer 3 which enters both the charge distribution and the separation as three degrees of freedom is, we are confident, correctly identified as the three levels of the hierarchy. That we should be able to interpret this calculation within our framework is evident. This fact alone puts us in a strong position.

The quality of the result makes it important to discuss corrections which might destroy it. To begin with, we have used the value 137 for $1/\alpha$ rather than the empirical value. As discussed below, because of coupling to level IV, we can anticipate corrections to $1/\alpha$ of order $1/256^2$, which is of the correct order of magnitude. The second correction we can anticipate is in the cutoff parameter d. Our first estimate is almost certainly approximately correct, but does not account for the fact that electrons in the hierarchy are sometimes present and sometimes absent. Hence, we can anticipate a correction to d of order $m_e/2m_p$ as well as in the calculation of the correction to $1/\alpha$. Thus we anticipate something like the empirical result for $1/\alpha$ and must hope that the correction to d will almost exactly compensate for it in our formula. Looked at this way, the calculation can be viewed as a guide to *how* to construct the dynamics, rather than as a prediction of our theory. It has already proved of great value in setting up the classification scheme given in the last section, and in obtaining the kinematic bootstrap (Noyes, 1979) at level I.

Since the language we use for justifying the calculation when exhibited pictorially as in Figure 4 makes the stable hierarchy look like a photon, we can try to extend this analogy. To begin with, if we look at coupling into the hierarchy through transverse photons, these will flip the spin of the electron. But again, for a specified spin of the electron, this can happen in only 1 of the 137 possible cases, so the coupling constant is the

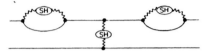

Fig. 5. Single-"photon" exchange between electron and proton.

same as we used in the Coulomb calculation (and including this in our "self-energy" calculation does not alter the result), which is encouraging. So consider an electron and a proton which exchange a "photon" so described. Making the static, nonrelativistic assumption that the mass of the proton does not change with velocity and that its motion does not affect the energy of the system, the additional effect we must consider is that the electron must acquire its own mass both before and after the exchange by the process already considered. This leads to the diagram given in Figure 5.

If the "photon" exchanged in the figure carries any momentum, the diagram cannot represent the whole story, since there will also be the emission of "bremsstrahlung" in the final state. So we consider the diagram only for the case when both electron and proton are at rest, but as far apart as we like. This is to be interpreted as an electron and proton bound in the ground state of hydrogen, and contrasted with a free electron and proton with the Coulomb effect shielded out. The second case then is the one already considered except that an inert proton has been added, and the first can be calculated as before, provided we multiply the coupling by the two additional powers of α shown in Figure 5; the statistical calculation remains unaltered. We conclude that the binding energy of the ground state of hydrogen is given by $\alpha^2 m_e c^2 = m_e e^4 / \hbar^2$, which is indeed the correct result, in the static case. To obtain the center-of-mass correction we must allow for the motion of the proton, which requires more dynamics than we have developed. Further, to get the excited states, we must be able to describe unstable systems that decay via photon emission, for which we are as yet unready.

We summarize the results of this section by pointing out that we already have in hand the basic ingredients from which atomic theory could be built—stable electrons in correct mass ratio to the proton, photons, and time-ordered Feynman vertices, together with a hint as to how the statistical smearing out of the (not time ordered internally) three levels of the hierarchy's DCsS can stabilize dynamical systems with finite "self-energies." Calculation of genuine dynamical processes such as $\pi^0 \rightarrow 2\gamma$ will provide a critical test of whether we are on the right track. We also have the basic ingredients for an approximate nuclear physics—nucleons and antinucleons coupled to pions and the vector mesons. What is still missing are processes involving beta decay and neutrinos. For these we must go on to level IV.

4. LEVEL IV: WEAK INTERACTIONS AND COSMOLOGY

Returning to the basic mapping matrix from which level IV can be constructed as given in equation (2.6), we see that it will lead, rearranged as a column, to an 18-fold descriptor. The specific mapping actually constructed leads in addition to 126 single descriptors, so it leaves 112 of the 256 available rows unaccounted for. We are confident that mappings that fill all rows can be constructed, and that the multiple descriptor can be 20, 22, ... in other representations, still using our preferred basis. This enormous ambiguity is actually what we expect from elementary particle experiments at high energy. For a while it was thought that there were only three "quark" quantum numbers (up, down, and strange) and two types of leptons (muon and electron with associated neutrinos). But now the "charm" quantum number has been observed, the "upsilon," the heavy lepton called "tau," and most experimental physicists believe that is unlikely to be the end of the story. The important point for us is that none of these new quantum numbers (in contrast to charge, baryon number, lepton number, and helicity) are reliably known to be exactly conserved. Many (e.g., strangeness) are violated in weak decays. But this is what we expect from our combinatorial hierarchy. From our basis of 127 linearly independent columns, we can construct $2^{127} - 1$ DCsSs. But only $(256)^2$ linearly independent matrices are available to map, and hence stabilize, them. Thus, even if we happen to start with a particular DCsS, because of our basic statistical assumption that all possible columns are randomly available, after roughly $(256)^2$ discriminations we can expect this set to encounter some column from outside. This will destabilize the system and lead to a "weak decay." Our rough estimate of the coupling constant as $1/(256)^2$ is close to the "weak decay constant" of $10^{-5}m_p$, where, as we saw in our last section, we are constrained to use m_p as our unit of mass. Thus, qualitatively, the scheme predicts weak decays, as was already noted in the first presentation of the hierarchy (Bastin, 1966). We will not even attempt to sketch how this dynamics might work in this paper.

However, we can proceed a little way with the implications of our structure as a classification scheme. The number 18 that occurs in the simplest possible construction of a mapping is already suggestive of quark–antiquark pairs with three colors and three flavors. The 18-fold descriptor then corresponds to conservation of baryon (or quark) number for this system. Doubling 18 of the single descriptors will give us 36 spin states. We can use $9 \times 18 = 162$ rows to assign color and flavor, leaving $256 - 18 - 36 - 162 = 40$ rows to describe various types of leptons. Working out the details of all this will be a fascinating puzzle. We will certainly want to be intimately in touch with high-energy experiments and current quantum chromodynamics and lepton theories in order to obtain empirical guidance. But, since we can count on destabilization of these "partially conserved quantum numbers," we know that, qualitatively at least, we are dealing with the right structure. We believe it will be more profitable to tackle this problem after we have worked out a firmer hold on atomic and nuclear physics at level III than to plunge into it now.

Before leaving the subject of "weak interactions" we note that we may have been too hasty in placing all of them in level IV. Just as we were able to interpret two columns at level III as a charged lepton (electron) with two spin states, we could leave off the charge descriptors and interpret the resulting columns as an electron-type neutrino. Then, if we can find a way to couple this to the baryons—which we have not yet succeeded in doing —we might be able to include ordinary beta decay at level III. This would not only complete our picture of low-energy nuclear physics, but also could lead to a Weinberg–Salam-type of weak-electromagnetic unification with the same coupling constant of $1/137$. The difficulty will be to show that the coupling to baryons generates a sufficiently large mass for the "W boson" so that the fact that it has yet to be observed experimentally can be accounted for. Then only the more exotic leptons, like the quark quantum numbers, would come in at level IV. We suspect this is the correct route to follow. The check will be whether the extension to level IV gives the quantitatively correct modification of α in accord with experiment. The correction will clearly be of order $1/(256)^2$, which is the right order of magnitude.

But this "high-energy physics" aspect of level IV only deals with the lower levels of its potential complexity—the $2^{127} - 1 \approx 10^{38}$ DCsSs, each of which is a distinct and discriminable entity. Just as we interpret $1/137$ as an approximation to α, we interpret 10^{-38} as an estimate of the gravitational coupling constant between two protons—protons rather than electrons, since we have already accounted for the rest mass of the electron in terms of this unit. At this point a more conventional argument, adapted from a remark of Dyson's (1952), becomes relevant. If we try to count N_e charged particle–antiparticle pairs within a volume whose radius is their compton wavelength, their electrostatic energy is

$$N_e e^2/(\hbar/2mc) = N_e(e^2/\hbar c)2mc^2 \tag{4.1}$$

We interpret this result as saying that if we try to determine the number N_e

for a system with more than 137 pairs by electromagnetic means, we are unable to do so because the energy has become so large that additional pairs could be present, and the counting breaks down. Hence, $N_e = 137$ is the maximum meaningful number of charged particle pairs we can discuss electromagnetically in such a volume (Noyes, 1974).

Extending the argument to gravitation, we see that, since

$$N_G Gm_p^2/(\hbar/m_p c) = N_G \left(Gm_p^2/\hbar c \right) m_p c^2 \qquad (4.2)$$

the maximum number of gravitating protons we can discuss within the compton wavelength of any one of them is $N_G \cong 10^{38}$. In this case, the gravitational field at the surface is so intense that light cannot escape, so this system forms a Laplacian "black hole" (Laplace, 1795). Hence, just as failure of the "fourth level" of the hierarchy to possess linearly independent mappings gives us an estimate of instability to weak decay, the upper limit $2^{127} - 1 \approx 10^{38}$ represents a gravitational instability for systems with large numbers of particles.

Since we have $\sim 10^{38}$ discriminate entities in the scheme, we are logically justified in starting our discussion with the $(10^{38})^2$ possible discriminations between them. For stability, these systems should contain lepton number and baryon number $(10^{38})^2$, although we cannot as yet prove such a conjecture. Given it, the initial discriminations will create all sorts of ephemeral forms of the type already discussed, and a historical system of loci that provides an initial space–time mesh. Once the decays and scattering have proceeded a while, these will settle down to protons, electrons, photons, hydrogen atoms,... and we have started the "big bang." The radiation soon breaks away from the matter, and provides a unique discrete approximation to a space–time framework, locally defined in terms of the cosmic background radiation. Since this "black body spectrum" can be measured locally, it provides us both a cosmic time scale from the temperature, and an absolute frame for measuring particle velocities. Our hope is that we can use this idea to define space–time frameworks more easily connected to laboratory observation than abstract definitions. In particular, since our W boson–photon coupling is discrete, and defined at proto-space–time loci, we should be able to use our dynamic scheme to explain what we mean by a local discrete coordinate system for physical measurement. Only when this task is complete can we tackle the question of what we might mean by a "wave function," and how we are to relate our particular formalism to the successful results obtained by conventional quantum mechanics.

Bastin et al.

5. CONCLUSION

In this paper we have sketched a physical interpretation of the combinatorial hierarchy, which, if the program can be carried through, should provide a finitist conceptual frame for that fundamental revision of physics which we seek. Our philosophical reasons for adapting this approach are discussed in detail in the opening section. Here we stress that the contact with experiment already established in this paper, together with the indications of structural contact with the classification schemes used in elementary particle physics, and conceptual contact with the fundamental ideas underlying current cosmology, make it clear that no field of physics need be omitted in this synthesis. The original coincidence between the cardinals of the hierarchy and the inverse boson field coupling constants allows us to believe that we have indeed unified strong, electromagnetic and gravitational phenomena in one framework. The weak decay instability is also indicated. Our proposed classification scheme brings in the absolute conservation laws at the correct level, and points toward a weak-electromagnetic unification at that or the next level. Structural contact exists between SU_2, SU_3, and SU_6 (quark) classifications, including an appropriate three-color–three-flavor option flexible enough to allow for new flavors and new heavy leptons. The cosmology should yield the conserved quantum numbers of the universe, some sort of "big bang," and hence the cosmic background radiation as a unique reference system. Since this background is not time reversal invariant, it might even lead ultimately to the explanation of the $K_L - K_S$ decay. So far as we see, no major area of physics has been omitted as potentially outside the reach of a scheme of this structure.

APPENDIX: MATHEMATICAL STRUCTURE OF THE HIERARCHY

This appendix contains a short formal account of the essential mathematical features of a "discrimination system." Throughout, S will denote a nonempty finite set, and $C = \{0, 1\}$ will denote either the cyclic group of order 2 (with addition mod 2, or equivalently, Boolean Exclusive-Or as group operation) or the field of two elements (with addition as before, and integer multiplication, or equivalently, Boolean And as field multiplication operation); the context makes clear which usage is intended. The empty set is $\varnothing$; $\mathbb{N} = \{1, 2, 3, \dots\}$, $\mathbb{N}_0 = \{0, 1, 2, 3, \dots\}$; $|X|$ is the cardinality of a set X.

337

A.1. Discrimination System

A.1.1. Definition. A *discrimination system of type* N ($N \in \mathbb{N}$) is a group S isomorphic to the Abelian group $C^N = C \oplus \cdots \oplus C$, direct sum of N copies of C, together with additional structure as detailed later; its order is $|S| = 2^N$. Thus $x \in S$ iff $x = (x_1, \ldots, x_N)$ ($x_i = 0, 1$), the group operation (written $+$) on S is termwise addition mod 2 (or equivalently, Boolean Exclusive-Or applied to strings of length N), and the group neutral is $e = (0, \ldots, 0)$.

A.1.2. Fact. Besides being symmetric (Abelian) and associative, the group operation $+$ on S is also *discriminative*:

$$(\forall x, y, z \in S) \qquad x + x = e \quad \text{and} \quad y \neq z \Rightarrow y + z \neq e$$

i.e., $+$ can "discriminate" between a pair of equal elements and a pair of unequal elements; the (unique) group neutral e is called the "(discrimination) neutral for S."

A.1.3. Theorem. Any set S equipped with a binary operation that is symmetric, associative, and discriminative (with respect to a unique discrimination neutral e) is isomorphic to an Abelian group C^N for some $N \in \mathbb{N}$; the discrimination neutral e is then (identified with) the neutral element in the group C^N.

A.1.4. Remarks. (1) The Boolean dual $u = (1, \ldots, 1)$ of the discrimination neutral $e = (0, \ldots, 0)$ in a discrimination system S is referred to as the "antineutral" for S. (2) The group C^N, $+$ can always be given a multiplication $*$ so that $C^N, +, *$ becomes a field F of prime power 2^N isomorphic to the Galois field $GF(2^N)$; its neutral-free part $C^N \setminus \{e\}$ forms a multiplicative cyclic group of order $2^N - 1$ with identity element which can be chosen to be the antineutral $u = (1, \ldots, 1)$.

A.2. Discriminately Closed Subsets

A.2.0. Remark. To avoid repetition, the abbreviation "d" or "d-" will be used for the words "discrimination, discriminate, discriminately" as appropriate throughout this and later sections.

A.2.1. Definition. Let S be a d-system with neutral e and let $T \subseteq S$ be a subset. Then T is a *dc-subset* (discriminately closed subset) (alias, subset T is *dc*) iff (a) T is *neutral-free* (i.e., $T \subseteq S \setminus \{e\}$), (b) the *e-join* $T \cup \{e\}$ of T is a subgroup in S.

A.2.2. Facts. (1) Conditions (i) and (ii) are equivalent: (i) T is a dc-subset of S; (ii) $(\forall x, y \in T)$ $x \neq y \Leftrightarrow x + y \in T$. (2) $S \setminus \{e\}$ is a dc-subset of S. (3) $\emptyset$ is a dc-subset of S. (4) Singleton $\{x\}$ is a dc-subset of $S \Leftrightarrow x \neq e$. (5) T is a subgroup of $S \Leftrightarrow T \setminus \{e\}$ is a dc-subset of S. (6) $R \cap T$ is a dc-subset of S whenever R and T are dc-subsets of S.

A.2.3. Definition. The *d-closure* T^{dc} of a neutral-free subset $T \subseteq S$ is the smallest dc-subset of S containing T; T^{dc} is *d-generated* by T. The *d-union* $R \cup^{dc} T$ of two neutral-free subsets $R, T \subseteq S$ is the dc-subset $(R \cup T)^{dc}$. The latter definition extends in an obvious way to families $(T_i)_{i \in I}$ of neutral-free subsets of S.

A.2.4. Facts. Let R, T be dc-subsets of S; then (1) T is $dc \Leftrightarrow T = T^{dc}$. (2) $(T^{dc})^{dc} = T^{dc}$, hence T^{dc} is dc. (3) $R \subseteq T \Rightarrow R^{dc} \subseteq T^{dc}$. (4) $R^{dc} \cup T^{dc} \subseteq (R \cup T)^{dc}$. (5) $(R^{dc} \cup T^{dc})^{dc} \subseteq (R \cup T)^{dc}$. (6) $R^{dc} \cup^{dc} T^{dc} = (R^{dc} \cup T^{dc})^{dc} = (R \cup T)^{dc} = R \cup^{dc} T$.

A.2.5. Fact. If $\langle T \rangle$ denotes the subgroup generated in S by a subset $T \subseteq S$ and T is neutral-free then $T^{dc} = \langle T \rangle \setminus \{e\}$ and $\langle T \rangle = T^{dc} \cup \{e\}$.

A.2.6. Definition. A subset T of a d-system S is a *d-subsystem* of S iff T is a subgroup of the group S and $T \neq \{e\}$.

A.2.7. Fact. If T is a d-subsystem of a d-system S of type N then T is isomorphic to a nontrivial subgroup $C^M \subseteq C^N$ with $1 \leqslant M \leqslant N$, and $1 < |T| = 2^M \leqslant |S| = 2^N$, and the neutral elements of T and S coincide.

A.2.8. Definition. The *d-complement* of a dc-subset T in a d-system S is the unique dc-subset R such that the subgroup $R \cup \{e\}$ is the direct complement of the subgroup $T \cup \{e\}$ in the group S.
Notation: $R = S \ominus^{dc} T$ and $S = R \oplus^{dc} T$.

Remark. Since $R = S \ominus^{dc} T \Leftrightarrow T = S \ominus^{dc} R$, so s is said to be *d-decomposed* by the *d-complementary* subsets R and T.

A.2.9. Fact. R and T are d-complements in $S \Leftrightarrow R \cap T = \emptyset$ and $R \cup^{dc} T = S \setminus \{e\}$.

A.2.10. Definition. Subset T is *d-independent* in S iff T is neutral-free and $(\forall t \in T) \; \{t\}^{dc} \cap (T \setminus \{t\})^{dc} = \emptyset$; otherwise T is *d-dependent* in S.

Remark. A neutral-free subset T is d-independent in d-system $S \Leftrightarrow T$ is an independent subset in the group S. The definition extends in an obvious way to families $(T_i)_{i \in I}$ of neutral-free subsets of S, thus $(T_i)_{i \in I}$ is a d-independent family iff $(\forall k \in I) \; T_k^{dc} \cap [\cup_{i \in I, i \neq k} T_i]^{dc} = \emptyset$.

A.2.11. Fact. These four conditions are equivalent: (a) Neutral-free family $(T_i)_{i \in I}$ is d-independent in d-system S. (b) Subgroup family $(\langle T_i \rangle)_{i \in I}$ is independent in group S. (c) Subgroup $\langle \cup_{i \in I} T_i \rangle =$

group direct sum $\oplus_{i\in I}\langle T_i\rangle$. (d) Each $x\in\cup_{i\in I}^{dc}T_i$ has a unique representation $x=\oplus_{i\in I}x_i$ with each component $x_i\in T_i^{dc}\cup\{e\}=\langle T_i\rangle$ and $x_j\neq e$ for at least one index $j\in I$.

A.3. Discriminate Morphisms

A.3.1. Definition. A morphism $f:S\to T$ between two d-systems S and T is a *d-morphism* iff f is an injective group homomorphism between the groups S and T. (Thus every automorphism $f:S\to S$ is a d-morphism on the d-system S.)

A.3.2. Remark. An automorphism $f:S\to S$ on a d-system S leaves fixed the neutral e [$f(e)=e$] and permutes some or all of the members of the maximal neutral-free subset $S\setminus\{e\}$ in S.

A.3.3. Facts. Let $f:S\to T$ be a d-morphism; then (1) $R\subseteq S\Rightarrow f(\langle R\rangle)=\langle f(r)\rangle$; (2) $R\subseteq S\setminus\{e\}\Rightarrow f(R^{dc})=[f(r)]^{dc}$; (3) $R=R^{dc}\Leftrightarrow f(R)=f(R)^{dc}$; (4) $(S_i)_{i\in I}$ is independent (or, respectively, d-independent) in $S\Leftrightarrow[f(S_i)]_{i\in I}$ is independent (or, respectively, d-independent) in T.

A.3.4. Remark. Recall the following: Let G be a group with neutral e; let $E(G)$ be the group of endomorphisms of G with respect to the composition operation $\circ$, $[(f\circ h)(g)=f(h(g))\ \forall g\in G]$; let $A(G)\subset E(G)$ be the subgroup of automorphisms of G. Introducing a second group operation $(+)$ on $E(G)$, namely, pointwise addition $[(f+h)(g)=f(g)+h(g)\ \forall g\in G]$, makes $E(G),+$ Abelian when G is Abelian, and $E(G),+,\circ$ becomes a ring with neutral endomorphism $e(g)=e\ (\forall g\in G)$ and identity automorphism $u(g)=g\ (\forall g\in G)$. The case where G is a d-system is of special interest.

A.3.5. Theorem. Let S be a d-system of type N with neutral e. Let $E(S)$ be the Abelian group of endomorphisms of S under pointwise addition, with neutral endomorphism e. Then $E(S)$ is a d-system of type $M=N^2$ and order $2^{(N^2)}$, with neutral e and antineutral u. [Hence pointwise addition is discriminative on $E(S)$.]

A.3.6. Theorem. The ring $E(S),+,\circ$ of endomorphisms of a d-system S of type N is isomorphic to the ring of square $N\times N$-matrices over C.

A.3.7. Theorem. Let $A(S)\subset E(S)$ be the subset of automorphisms of S; then $A(S)\subseteq E(S)\setminus\{e\}$, i.e., is a neutral-free subset in the d-system $E(S)$, but is not a dc-subset in $E(S)$. Indeed, $A(S)^{dc}=E(S)\setminus\{e\}$.

Corollary. Every nonneutral endomorphism of S is a finite sum of distinct automorphisms of S.

A.3.8. Remarks. Let S be a d-system of type $N = t$; then $|S| = 2^t$, $|E(S)| = 2^{(2^t)}$, $|A(S)| = (2^t - 1)(2^t - 2)(2^t - 4) \cdots (2^t - 2^{t-1})$; let $r_t = |A(S)|/|E(S)|$, then $r_1 = 0.5$ and r_t decreases monotonically, and $\lim_{t \to \infty} r_t = 0.288788\ldots$ (i.e., for large t about 29% of all endomorphisms on S are automorphisms). For example:

t	1	2	3	4	5	16
$|S|$	2	4	8	16	32	65,536
$|A(S)|$	1	6	168	20,160	9,999,360	$3.34\ldots(10^{76})$
$|E(S)|$	2	16	512	65,536	33,554,432	$2^{256} = 1.1579\ldots(10^{77})$

A.3.9. Remark. Recall the following: If $\mathbf{a} \in A(S)$ then we may define an equivalence relation $[\mathbf{a}]$ on S by $x[\mathbf{a}]y \Leftrightarrow x = \mathbf{a}^k y$ for some $k \in \mathbb{N}_0$. Let $s \in \mathbb{N}$ be the least integer such that $\mathbf{a}^s = \mathbf{u}$ (the identity automorphism on S). Then an equivalence class $\bmod[\mathbf{a}]$ is called an $\mathbf{a}$-cycle of size r where r is its cardinality. Each $\mathbf{a}$-cycle is an orbit of the subgroup $\langle \mathbf{a} \rangle = \{\mathbf{u}, \mathbf{a}, \mathbf{a}^2, \ldots, \mathbf{a}^{s-1}\}$ in $A(S), \circ$, and vice versa. Its size $r = \min\{0 < k \leqslant s | x = \mathbf{a}^k x\} = \mathrm{index}|\langle \mathbf{a} \rangle : A_x|$ where A_x is the stabilizer subgroup $\{\mathbf{b} \in A(S) | x = \mathbf{b}x\}$ of an arbitrary element x in the $\mathbf{a}$-cycle.

A.3.10. Definition. An automorphism $\mathbf{a} \in A(S)$ is *maximal* iff there exists an $\mathbf{a}$-cycle equal to $S \setminus \{e\}$ (i.e., of maximum size $r = 2^N - 1$); $\mathbf{a}$ is *minimal* iff there exists an $\mathbf{a}$-cycle equal to $\{x\}$ for some $x \neq e$ (i.e., a nonneutral $\mathbf{a}$-cycle of minimum size $r = 1$).

A.3.11. Theorem. Each d-system S of type N has (a) at least $2^N - 2$ distinct maximal automorphisms, and (b) at least $2^N - 1$ distinct minimal automorphisms.

A.3.12. Remark. The proof of the above theorem requires the construction of some not immediately obvious automorphisms:

(a) Let F be the (Galois) field associated with S [Remark A.1.4(2)], $F_0 = F \setminus \{e\}$ its neutral-free multiplicative group, cyclic of order $n = 2^N - 1$. Choose any one of the $n - 1$ generators $b \in F_0$ (thus $b^n = u \neq b$, and $u, b, b^2, \ldots, b^{n-1}$ are all the distinct elements of F_0). Let $\mathbf{a} : S \to S$, $\mathbf{a}(x) = bx$ (if $x \neq e$), $\mathbf{a}(e) = e$; then $\mathbf{a} \in A(S)$ and for a fixed element $x \in S \setminus \{e\}$ the images $\mathbf{a}^k(x) = b^k x$ $(k = 1, \ldots, n)$ are all distinct and exhaust $S \setminus \{e\}$. Thus each such $\mathbf{a}$ is a maximal automorphism on S, one for each of the $2^N - 2$ generators $b \in F_0$.

(b) Given a dc-subset T in S, let R be its d-complement (Definition A.2.8). Define $f = u' \oplus m' : S \to S$ by $f(x) = u'(x)$, $(\forall x \in T \setminus \{e\})$, where u' is the identity automorphism on the d-subsystem $T \setminus \{e\}$, and $f(y) = m'(y)$, $(\forall y \in R \setminus \{e\})$, where m' is a maximal automorphism [by (a) above] on the

d-subsystem $R \setminus \{e\}$. Then $\forall x = t \oplus r \in S = (T \setminus \{e\}) \oplus (R \setminus \{e\})$, we have $f(x) = (u' \oplus m')(t \oplus r) = u'(t) + m'(r)$. Thus $f \in A(S)$ and f fixes the dc-subset T. Taking $T = \{x\}$ ($x \neq e$) makes f minimal, and T is one of its cycles of size 1 (the only nonneutral one).

A.3.13. Definition. The *df-set* (discrimination fixed set) of an automorphism $\mathbf{a} \in A(S)$ is the subset $DF(\mathbf{a}) = \{x \in S \setminus \{e\} \mid x = \mathbf{a}(x)\}$.

Remark. Each $DF(\mathbf{a})$ is a dc-subset; it may be empty [e.g., if $\mathbf{a}(x) = x$ only if $x = e$, i.e., if $\mathbf{a}$ "unfixes" every nonneutral member of S].

A.3.14. Theorem. Each dc-subset T in a d-system S is the df-set of some automorphism $\mathbf{a} \in A(S)$.

A.4. Discrimination Hierarchies

A.4.1. Definition. A d-system S of type N *determines* iteratively a sequence $E^0, E^1, E^2, \ldots, E^m, \ldots$ of d-systems where $E^0 = S$ and $(\forall m \in \mathbb{N})$ $E^m = E(E^{m-1})$ is the group of endomorphisms of the d-system E^{m-1} under pointwise addition. Then E^m is the *d-system of level m determined by the base d-system* $E^0 = S$; it is of type $t(m)$ and order $|E^m| = 2^{t(m)}$; A^m denotes the subset of automorphisms in E^m; the neutral (or, respectively, identity) morphisms in E^m are denoted by $\mathbf{e}^m$ (respectively, $\mathbf{u}^m$).

Remark. Where need be, the previous single-level notations such as $S, e, u, E(S), A(S), \mathbf{e}, \mathbf{u}$ may now be replaced by $E^0, \mathbf{e}^0, \mathbf{u}^0, E^1, A^1, \mathbf{e}^1, \mathbf{u}^1$.

A.4.2. Fact. Since $t(0) = N$ and $t(m) = t(m-1)^2$, so $t(m) = N^{(2^m)}$ and $|E^m| = 2^{t(m)}$ $(\forall m \in \mathbb{N}_0)$.

A.4.3. Remark. Plainly, each E^m is isomorphic to E^0 if E^0 is of type $N = 1$. More generally, if $N \geq 2$, we have an injective mapping f^m of E^m strictly into E^{m+1} given $(\forall m \in \mathbb{N}_0)$ by $f^m(\mathbf{e}^m) = \mathbf{e}^{m+1}$ and $f^m(x) = \mathbf{a}_x \in E^{m+1}$ $(\forall x \neq \mathbf{e}^m$ in $E^m)$ where $\mathbf{a}_x$ is an automorphism with singleton dc-subset $\{x\}$ as its df-set (Definition A.3.13). This mapping can be extended, in certain circumstances, to one that maps many more df-sets in one level injectively into an independent set of automorphisms in the next level, in a way now to be made precise.

A.4.4. Construction. Let $N \geq 2$; let $m \in \mathbb{N}_0$; let $K^m \subset E^m$ be an independent subset with $|K^m| = k(m)$ $[\leq t(m)]$ (Fact A.4.2). Let $K \subseteq K^m$ be any one of the $2^{k(m)} - 1$ nonempty subsets of K^m; and define $W_K = \{\mathbf{a} \in A^{m+1} \mid K^{dc} = DF(\mathbf{a})\}$. (Note that distinct subsets K of K^m have distinct d-closures K^{dc} because K^m is an independent set of elements.) Simple examples with $N = 3$, $m = 1$, show that we may have $|W_K| > 1$. In such a case, choose precisely one automorphism $\mathbf{a}_K$, say, in W_K and let C^{m+1} be the set of all such choices; thus

$$C^{m+1} = \left\{ \mathbf{a}_K \in A^{m+1} \mid K \subseteq K^m, K \neq \varnothing, DF(\mathbf{a}_K) = K^{dc} \right\}$$

$[= C^{m+1}(K^m)$, if we need to refer to the particular set K^m in use]. Hence $C^{m+1} \subset A^{m+1} \subset E^{m+1}$, and $|C^{m+1}| = 2^{k(m)} - 1$ $[= c(m+1)$, say, by way of definition]. To initialize this construction we define C^0 to be a basis (i.e., a maximal independent subset) for E^0 $(=S)$, so that $c(0) = |S| = N$.

A.4.5. Question. Is it possible to construct iteratively the sequence $K^0 = C^0, K^1 = C^1(K^0), \dots, K^{m+1} = C^{m+1}(K^m), \dots$ with each K^m an independent subset (as required by Construction A.4.4)? An obviously necessary condition for this to be possible is this inequality:

$$k(m+1) = c(m+1) = 2^{k(m)} - 1 \leqslant t(m)^2 \qquad [\,*\,]$$

since $K^{m+1} \subset E^{m+1}$. A sufficient condition will be given below (A.4.8).

A.4.6. Definition. Let $S = E^0$ be a base d-system of type $N \geqslant 2$.

(A) For $m \in \mathbb{N}_0$, E^m is *d-injectable* into E^{m+1} *via* an independent subset $K^m \subset E^m$ iff there exists at least one choice of automorphisms for the set $C^{m+1}(K^m)$ which makes the latter set independent in E^{m+1}.

(B) A finite sequence $(E^0, E^1, \dots, E^H)$ of d-systems determined by E^0 is a *d-hierarchy* (*discrimination hierarchy*) of *height* $H + 1$ iff these three conditions hold: (1) $H \geqslant 1$. (2) Independent subset K^0 is maximal in E^0. (3) For each $m = 0, 1, \dots, H - 1$, but not for $m = H$, E^m is d-injectable into E^{m+1} via the independent subset $K^m \subset E^m$, where $K^m = C^m(K^{m-1})$ for each $m = 1, \dots, H - 1$.

(C) A d-hierarchy is *trivial* if $H \leqslant 1$, otherwise *nontrivial*.

A.4.7. Remark. The sequence of independent subsets $(K^0, \dots, K^H)$ in a d-hierarchy $(E^0, \dots, E^H)$ is a "discriminate spine"; examples show that it need not be unique. If for some m the choice of C^{m+1} is not unique, each possible choice of C^{m+1} gives rise to a different "branch" of the spine.

A.4.8. Main Theorem. A necessary and sufficient condition for the existence of a nontrivial discrimination hierarchy is that the base discrimination system $S = E^0$ be of type $N = 2$; and then the discrimination hierarchy is of height $H + 1 = 4$.

A.4.9. Remarks. (1) The necessity follows from the condition $[\,*\,]$ in (A.4.5): Since $H \geqslant 2$ and E^m is d-injectable into E^{m+1} for $m = 0, 1, \dots, H - 1$, condition $[\,*\,]$ holds in particular for $m = 0, 1$. Thus, $k(0) = N$ and $2^N - 1 \leqslant t(0)^2 = N^2$ so that $2 \leqslant N \leqslant 4$; and $k(1) = 2^{k(0)} - 1 = 2^N - 1$, hence

$2^{k(1)} - 1 = 2^{(2^N - 1)} - 1 \leqslant t(1)^2 = [t(0)^2]^2 = N^4$ so that $N = 2$ as asserted. But then [*] can be satisfied for $m = 0$, 1 or 2 but not for $m \geqslant 3$; in particular E^3 is not then d-injectable into E^4 so that $2 \leqslant H \leqslant 3$; i.e., the discrimination hierarchy must have height 3 or 4. (2) A theoretical proof of the existence of a discrimination hierarchy with $N = 2$ and height $H + 1 = 4$ has been provided by C. W. Kilmister (1978) and will be reported elsewhere; an empirical representation using matrices over the field $\{0, 1\}$ has been constructed by H. P. Noyes and described in the main body of the paper to which this Appendix is attached.

A.4.10. Remark. The connections between the notations used in this Appendix and those used in the main text (e.g., in Table I) are as follows:

Table I	Appendix
Index of level $= 1, 2, 3, 4$	$m = l - 1 = 0, 1, 2, 3$
"Dimension" of level $= n(l)$	"Type" of level $= t(m) = n(l - 1)$
Number of independent columns is $j(l)$	Number of independent elements in subset K^m is $k(m) = j(l - 1)$
Number of discriminately closed subsets used in level is $d(l) = 2^{j(l)} - 1$	Number of automorphisms chosen for the subset C^{m+1}, corresponding one-to-one with dc-subsets used in previous level is $c(m + 1) = 2^{k(m)} - 1 = d(l)$

ACKNOWLEDGMENTS

We are deeply indebted to A. F. Parker-Rhodes, who first formulated the necessary condition for the existence of a discrimination hierarchy, for permission to present the calculation of m_p/m_e drawn from his unpublished manuscript, "The Theory of Indistinguishables," the more particularly since his interpretation of the hierarchy as it occurs in his theory, and his justification for the calculation itself, differ in significant ways from our own views. The crucial notion of a discriminately closed subset arose out of discussions with Ted Bastin. The characterization of a discrimination system (Section 1), together with the proofs of many of the main results quoted here, are due to C. W. Kilmister. The verification of the conjecture that a discrimination hierarchy of height 4 existed owes a great deal to the patience and persistence of C. W. Kilmister and H. Pierre Noyes. One of us (H.P.N.) wishes to thank the Research Institute for Theoretical Physics of the University of Helsinki and K. V. Laurikainen, for generous hospitality, support, and active collaboration during the month after the 1978 Tutzing Conference, in which the existence proof for the hierarchy and one connection with SU_3 were hammered out. T.B. and H.P.N. are both indebted to the Max-Planck-Institüt zur Erforschung der Lebensbedingungen der Wissenschaftlich-Technischen Welt for travel support and living expenses at the 1978 Tutzing Conference, where a preliminary version of this work was presented.

344

REFERENCES

Amson, J. (1976). "Discrimination Systems," 20 pp. (unpublished).

Barasch-Schmidt, N. et al. (1978). "Particle Properties Data Booklet April 1978," p. 2, from *Physics Letters*, **75B**, 1–250.

Bastin, T. (1966). "On the Origin of the Scale Constants of Physics," *Studia Philosophica Gandensia*, **4**, 77–101.

Bastin, T. (1976a). "A Combinatorial Model for Scattering," Report to the Science Research Council (U.K.), 57 pp. (unpublished).

Bastin, T. (1976b). "An Operational Model for Particle Scattering Using a Discrete Approach," Report to the Conference on "Quantum Theory and the Structures of Time and Space 2," Tutzing, 6 pp. (unpublished).

Dyson, F. J. (1952). "Divergence of Perturbation Theory in Quantum Electrodynamics," *Physical Review*, **85**, 631–632.

Finkelstein, D. (1969). "Space–Time Code," *Physical Review*, **184**, 1261–1271.

Finkelstein, D. (1979). "Holistic Methods," submitted to *International Journal of Theoretical Physics*.

Kilmister, C. W. (1978). private communication.

Laplace, P. S. (1795). *Exposition du Monde*, Vol. II, p. 305, Paris.

Noyes, H. P. (1957). "The Physical Description of Elementary Particles," *American Scientist*, Vol. 45, 431–448.

Noyes, H. P. (1974). "Non-Locality in Particle Physics," 55 pp., SLAC-PUB-1405.

Noyes, H. P. (1975). "Fixed Past and Uncertain Future: A Single-time Covariant Quantum Particle Mechanics," *Foundations of Physics*, **5**, 37–43 (Erratum **6**, 125, 1976).

Noyes, H. P. (1976). "A Democritean Phenomenology for Quantum Scattering Theory," *Foundations of Physics*, **6**, 83–100.

Noyes, H. P. (1976). "A Democritean Approach to Elementary Particle Physics," from *Proceedings of the Summer Institute on Particle Physics*, Martha Zipf, ed., pp. 239–259, SLAC Report No. 198 (issued as a separate document as SLAC-PUB-1956, 1977).

Noyes, H. P. (1978). Private communication.

Noyes, H. P. (1979). "The Lowest Level of the Combinatorial Hierarchy as a Particle Antiparticle Quantum Bootstrap," SLAC-PUB-2277.

Parker-Rhodes, A. F. (1978). "The Theory of Indistinguishables," 208 pp., (unpublished).

Weizsäcker, C. F. von. (1978). "Temporal Logic and a Reconstruction of Quantum Theory," 88 pp., presented at the Conference on "Quantum Theory and the Structures of Time and Space 3," Tutzing (unpublished).

Wheeler, J. A., and Patton, C. M. (1977). "Is Physics Legislated by Cosmogony?" pp. 19–35, in *The Encyclopedia of Ignorance*, R. Duncan and M. Weston-Smith, eds., Pergamon, Oxford.

Whiteman, J. H. M. (1971). "The Phenomenology of Observations and Explanation in Quantum Theory," in *Quantum Theory and Beyond*, T. Bastin, ed., pp. 71–84, Cambridge.

Alternative Natural Philosophy Association

Statement of Purpose

1. The primary purpose of the Association is to consider coherent models based on a minimal number of assumptions, so as to bring together major areas of thought and experience within a natural philosophy alternative to the prevailing scientific attitude. The Combinatorial Hierarchy, as such a model, will form an initial focus of our discussions.

2. This purpose will be pursued by research, publications and any other appropriate means including the foundation of subsidiary organisations and the support of individuals and groups with the same objective.

3. The Association will remain open to new ideas and modes of action, however suggested, which might serve the primary purpose.

4. The Association will seek ways to use its knowledge and facilities for the benefit of humanity and will try to prevent such knowledge and facilities being used to the detriment of humanity.

Organisation

1. The Executive Council is the governing body of the Association. It consists of:

   (a) All past presidents of the Association.

   (b) Officers (acting president, vice president, treasurer, secretary and co-ordinator if one is appointed).

   (c) Ordinary members nominated by classes (a) and (b), who serve for three years, with the possibility of re-nomination.

2. Members of the Association are (a) members of the Executive Council and (b) others nominated by the members and approved by the Executive Council.

3. This section (relating to the President and Vice-President) is currently being redrafted.

4. The President is the official representative of the Association in external affairs, and has the responsibility for calling meetings of the Membership, at least annually, for the determination of overall policy.

5. The Treasurer is the responsible financial officer of the Association for the receipt and disbursement of funds and shall maintain appropriate records of the Association Activities, membership, mailing-lists, etc.

6. The Secretary is responsible for keeping minutes of the Membership and Executive Council meetings, production of a newsletter to keep members of the Association informed of its activities, and such other duties as may be assigned.

7. President, Secretary and Treasurer will not be paid for their services but may, as appropriate, receive funds for travel expenses, secretarial help, etc.

8, The Co-ordinator, if one is appointed, may be paid an appropriate salary for his services, funds permitting. These services will include the organisation of meetings and the editing of the Proceedings of such meetings for publication, co-ordination of and participation in the research activities of the Association, preparation when appropriate of research reports and publication of such reports, and other such duties as may be assigned.

9. The Executive Council has selected an independent Advisory Board. It may adopt its own rules for the operation and replacement of members. The Executive Council may nominate candidates to the Board. Any member of the Board, or the Board collectively, may make recommendations to the Executive Council, or directly to the Membership. Action taken on such recommendations must be promptly reported by the Executive Council to the Board in writing.

10. Dues are currently £20.00 per annum.

Executive Council: Dr. John Amson, Dr. Ted Bastin, Mr. Anthony M. Deakin, Dr. Tom Etter, Ms. Arleta Griffor, Prof. Louis Kauffman, Dr. Michael Manthey, Prof. H. Pierre Noyes, Dr. David Roscoe, Dr. Fredric S. Young, Prof. Rainer Zimmerman.

President: Dr. Keith Bowden, 139 Sandringham Road, Barking, Essex, IG11 9AH, UK. [Tel: 0208 594 5064, Email: k.bowden@physics.bbk.ac.uk].

Co-ordinator and Secretary: At present no co-ordinator or secretary is appointed.

Treasurer: David Roscoe, Department of Applied Mathematics, Sheffield University, Sheffield S3 7RH. [Tel: 01142 235 2785, Email: d.roscoe@sheffield.ac.uk]

Proceedings Editors:

Philosophical Aspects: Arleta Griffor, 1 Venetia Rd, London N4 1EJ. [Tel: 0208 340 7985, Email: a.griffor@physics.bbk.ac.uk]

Scientific Aspects: Keith Bowden.

Advisory Board: M. Horner (Chairman), Profs. G.F. Chew (Berkeley), C. Isham (Imperial College), M. Redhead (Cambridge), N. Cartwright (LSE), C. W. Kilmister (London, retired), H. Pierre Noyes (Stanford, retired).